THEORY OF X-RAY DIFFRACTION IN CRYSTALS

THEORY OF X-RAY DIFFRACTION IN CRYSTALS

William H. Zachariasen

Ernest DeWitt Burton Professor of Physics
University of Chicago

DOVER PUBLICATIONS, INC.
NEW YORK

Copyright

Published in Canada by General Publishing Company, Ltd., 30 Lesmill Road, Don Mills, Toronto, Ontario.
Published in the United Kingdom by Constable and Company, Ltd., 3 The Lanchesters, 162–164 Fulham Palace Road, London W6 9ER.

Bibliographical Note

This Dover edition, published in 1994, reprints the 1967 Dover edition, which was an unabridged and unaltered republication of the work originally published by John Wiley and Sons, Inc., in 1945.

Library of Congress Cataloging-in-Publication Data

Zachariasen, William H.
Theory of x-ray diffraction in crystals / William H. Zachariasen.
p. cm.
"This Dover edition published in 1994, reprints the 1967 Dover edition, which was an unabridged and unaltered republication of the work originally published by John Wiley and Sons, Inc., in 1945"—T.p. verso.
Includes index.
ISBN 0-486-68363-X (pbk.)
1. Crystals. 2. X-rays—Diffraction. I. Title.
QD945.Z3 1994
548′.83—dc20 94-34490
CIP

Manufactured in the United States of America
Dover Publications, Inc., 31 East 2nd Street, Mineola, N.Y. 11501

PREFACE

The theory of space lattices and their symmetry properties and the theory of x-ray diffraction in crystals form the subject matter of this book. These are the fundamental theories of crystal structure with which the serious student of the field must be thoroughly familiar. I undertook to write this book because, in my opinion, none of the available books on crystal structure gives an adequate treatment of these basic theories.

This book is to a considerable extent based upon the notes for a lecture course on crystal structure which I have given periodically for graduate students of physics and chemistry at this University. I have tried to give a logical presentation of both the theory of crystal symmetry and the theory of x-ray diffraction in crystals. The treatment of some topics is as a consequence radically different from that used elsewhere, and a considerable fraction of the material presented in this book represents the results of original researches. Indeed, the modest size of the book is not a fair measure of the time I have spent on it.

Dr. R. E. Platzman kindly volunteered to read the entire manuscript and made many helpful suggestions for improvements in style.

W. H. Zachariasen

University of Chicago
September 8, 1944

CONTENTS

CHAPTER I: THE NATURE OF CRYSTALS

CHAPTER II: THE SYMMETRY OF CRYSTALS

CHAPTER III: THEORY OF X-RAY DIFFRACTION IN IDEAL CRYSTALS

CHAPTER IV: X-RAY INTERFERENCE IN REAL CRYSTALS

APPENDIX A: DYADICS

APPENDIX B: ELEMENTS OF GROUP THEORY

EXPLANATION OF SYMBOLS

The scheme of notation used in this book is briefly the following:

Dyadics (Tensors)

Symbols for dyadics are printed in bold-face type. Examples: $\mathbf{n}$, $\mathbf{\Phi}$, $\mathbf{3}$.

A heavy bar printed over a bold-face character represents a negative dyadic. Example: $\bar{\mathbf{n}} = -\mathbf{n}$.

Vectors

The symbol for a vector is a heavy bar over a character which is not printed in bold-face type. Examples: $\bar{A}$, $\bar{a}$, $\bar{\varphi}$.

Scalars

A symbol which is printed neither in bold-face type nor with a heavy bar over the character represents a scalar quantity.

Because of war restrictions it has not proved possible to attain complete uniformity in the weight and length of the " vector " bars. However, there is a marked difference between the " vector " bars and the much lighter " average " bars which are used to represent mean values.

THEORY OF X-RAY DIFFRACTION IN CRYSTALS

CHAPTER I

THE NATURE OF CRYSTALS

1. THE MACROSCOPIC CONCEPT OF A CRYSTAL

The term crystal is used to designate a class of solids exhibiting certain characteristic properties; its meaning has been subject to revision and augmentation from time to time as new experimental methods have been developed and further properties made observable. The submicroscopic domain became accessible to physical observations in 1912 through von Laue's discovery, and the modern concept of a crystal is based directly upon the characteristic internal structure as it is revealed by x-ray diffraction experiments, whereas in earlier days the classification of solids into crystalline and non-crystalline matter rested upon properties which we now consider less fundamental. The development of crystal structure theory prior to the Laue experiment forms the subject of the first two chapters, and it is accordingly proper to start with an older concept of a crystal rather than with the one now commonly accepted. A hundred years ago a crystal was characterized in terms of its external geometrical form. Towards the end of the last century this geometrical picture of a crystal was replaced by another based upon physical properties, and we may conveniently begin with this late nineteenth century concept.

The experimental physicist of the nineteenth century had to rely on observations of comparatively limited resolving power. Thus, if $\Omega(\bar{r})$ represents a physical property of a material medium as a function of position, only average values $\Omega = \dfrac{\int \Omega \, dv}{\Delta V}$ over volumes ΔV containing thousands of atoms can be directly measured. We shall call observations of this type macroscopic observations, and the corresponding crystal will be referred to as the macroscopic crystal.

The macroscopic crystal may be described as a homogeneous and anisotropic solid medium. Homogeneity implies that the physical properties are the same for every volume element in the solid. In a real crystal there will certainly be some change in the physical properties as the surface is approached, and in order to avoid difficulties of this sort it is useful to imagine the crystal medium to have unlimited extension in space. This formal procedure merely implies that only properties independent of the actual size of the crystal are to be considered, and homogeneity may then be conveniently defined as the invariance of all physical properties under any translation, i.e.,

$$\bar{\Omega}(\bar{r}) = \bar{\Omega}(\bar{r} + \bar{t}) \qquad [1\cdot1]$$

for any translation $\bar{t}$. It is clear that the quantities $\bar{\Omega}$ must reduce to constants if they are to be independent of position; but it is important to note that the functions Ω are not necessarily scalar functions, so that a quantity $\bar{\Omega}$ may be a constant scalar, a constant vector, or a constant tensor of second or higher order, depending upon the nature of the physical property which the function Ω represents.

Just as homogeneity is defined as invariance under any translation, so isotropy may be defined as invariance under any rotation. The anisotropic nature of the macroscopic crystal is not to be interpreted as a purely negative statement that the properties are not invariant under any rotation. Measurements show, rather, that the variation of the physical properties with direction is of orderly nature and may be expressed by means of analytic functions which involve a small number of constants. Examples of properties which may depend upon direction are the dielectric constant, the coefficient of thermal expansion, and the thermal and electrical conductivities. Certain properties, like density and temperature, are always independent of orientation by virtue of their scalar nature.

In contrast with vitreous substances a crystal has a sharp melting point, and the chemical composition may as a rule be expressed in the form of a definite chemical formula. These are additional important features which in no way follow directly from the homogeneous and anisotropic character of macroscopic crystals.

2. CRYSTAL FACES

Crystals are usually formed from the molten or vapor state or from solutions. When formed in an unconfined space, they usually are bounded by plane surfaces which are called crystal faces. It is to be clearly understood that the actual presence or absence of crystal faces need not be regarded as essential. The faces may be accidentally or intentionally destroyed, but the substance does not thereby cease to be a crystal, since we have adopted the viewpoint that the term crystal applies to the physical properties of volume elements rather than to the geometrical properties of the surface. The potential ability of all crystals to develop crystal faces under proper conditions of growth is, however, a characteristic and important property, and the study of the relative orientation of the crystal faces has played a decisive role in the development of crystallography.

The appearance of different individuals of the same kind of crystals may vary considerably with the conditions of growth, but it is found that the angle between corresponding faces remains constant. (The interfacial angles may vary with the temperature since the thermal expansion is anisotropic.) Accordingly the relative orientations of the crystal faces are characteristic properties while the external form as such is not. The orientations of the crystal faces may be represented by the collection of their unit normals. These may be drawn from any point in the interior. After the unit normals have been obtained, we are no longer concerned with the boundary of the finite crystal and may conveniently imagine the surface receding to infinity.

The crystal faces will be expressed analytically in terms of a suitably chosen coordinate system. Let the coordinate axes, X_1, X_2, X_3, be chosen parallel to three prominent crystal edges not all lying in a plane. In the general case three mutually orthogonal edges do not occur so that the coordinate system is oblique, i.e., the three axial angles, $\alpha_1(\measuredangle\ X_2X_3)$, $\alpha_2(\measuredangle\ X_3X_1)$, $\alpha_3(\measuredangle\ X_1X_2)$, are in general different from $\pi/2$ and from one another. It is convenient to operate with different unit lengths along the three coordinate axes. The unit lengths will be denoted by a_1, a_2, a_3, or by $\bar{a}_1$, $\bar{a}_2$, $\bar{a}_3$ when their directions are also to be indicated.

The equation of a crystal face in such a coordinate system is

$$h_1x_1 + h_2x_2 + h_3x_3 - k = 0 \qquad [1\cdot 2]$$

where x_1 is measured in units a_1, x_2 in units a_2, and x_3 in units a_3. As long as we are interested only in the orientation of the crystal face, the constant k is of no consequence, and only the ratios $h_1 : h_2 : h_3$ and $a_1 : a_2 : a_3$ need be considered. The triplet $h_1h_2h_3$, or rather the ratios $h_1 : h_2 : h_3$, are called the indices of the face. From Equation 1·2 it is seen that the indices are proportional to the reciprocal intercepts of the crystal face on the three coordinate axes, the intercepts being measured in their respective units a_1, a_2, a_3.

It was agreed to choose the coordinate axes along three edges not all lying in a plane, but to specify the coordinate system, the units a_1, a_2, a_3, or rather their ratios, must also be known. These units may be chosen in the following manner. A prominent crystal face is selected which cuts all three of the previously chosen coordinate axes. None of the three indices of the plane may then be zero, and we shall arbitrarily assume that the three indices of this crystal face are all equal, i.e., $h_1 : h_2 : h_3 = 1 : 1 : 1$. The lengths of the intercepts of this face on the three coordinate axes are then proportional to the units a_1, a_2, a_3. Once a coordinate system has been chosen in this manner the equations of all other faces which occur on the crystal may be found from angle measurements, and the orientations of these faces may be uniquely specified by giving the ratios $h_1 : h_2 : h_3$.

3. THE LAW OF RATIONAL INDICES

When the procedure outlined in the preceding section is followed, it is found that the indices h_1, h_2, h_3 of any crystal face are proportional to three small integers. This remarkable empirical law is referred to as the law of rational indices, and it is supported by accurate measurements made upon thousands of crystals. The law was first properly formulated by F. Neumann in 1823,[1] but Renée Haüy probably discovered it some forty years earlier.

It needs to be pointed out that the law of rational indices does not hold if the coordinate system is chosen in an arbitrary way. On the other hand, one must not be misled to believe that the law is valid only in a reference frame which is selected in accordance with the rules suggested in section 2. The important point to be emphasized at this stage is simply that we have at our disposal a method of choosing at least one coordinate system in which the indices of any crystal face are represented by small integers. A more detailed discussion will be found in section 6 of this chapter.

As a consequence of the law of rational indices there arises the possibility of expressing the orientations of the various faces of a crystal by sets of three integers, called Miller indices. It is customary to enclose the Miller indices in parentheses to avoid possible confusion, while negative signs are indicated by bars over the indices, e.g., (403), $(6 \cdot 1 \cdot \overline{10})$. It may, of course, be assumed that the three Miller indices have no common integral factor.

4. RECIPROCAL VECTORS

Since we are concerned only with the orientation of the crystal faces, it is useful to operate directly with the face normals. The coordinate system may be described by means of the three vectors $\bar{a}_1$, $\bar{a}_2$, $\bar{a}_3$ which are parallel to the three coordinate axes; we wish to express the unit normals in this reference frame.

Imagine the plane in Fig. 1·1 to represent a crystal face with Miller indices $(h_1h_2h_3)$. The unit normal, which is to be drawn from an interior point towards the face, is denoted by $\bar{u}_{h_1h_2h_3}$ or, in abbreviated

[1] F. Neumann, *Beiträge zur Kristallonomie*, Berlin and Posen, 1823.

form, $\bar{u}_h$. The vector intercepts of the crystal face on the three coordinate axes are proportional to $\bar{a}_1/h_1$, $\bar{a}_2/h_2$, and $\bar{a}_3/h_3$. The normal $\bar{u}_h$ is perpendicular to the two vectors $\bar{a}_2/h_2 - \bar{a}_1/h_1$ and $\bar{a}_3/h_3 - \bar{a}_2/h_2$ and

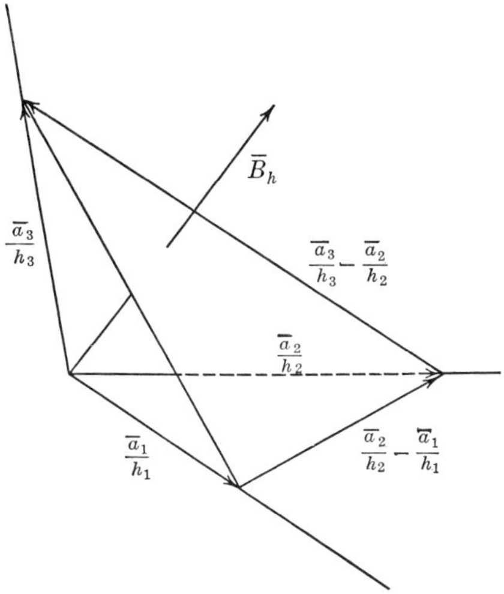

FIG. 1·1.

hence it is parallel to their vector product multiplied with the scalar normalization factor $h_1h_2h_3/(\bar{a}_1\bar{a}_2\bar{a}_3)$. One finds readily

$$\bar{u}_h = \frac{\bar{B}_h}{|\bar{B}_h|}, \quad \bar{B}_h \equiv h_1\bar{b}_1 + h_2\bar{b}_2 + h_3\bar{b}_3 \qquad [1\cdot3]$$

where

$$\bar{b}_1 \equiv \frac{\bar{a}_2 \times \bar{a}_3}{(\bar{a}_1\bar{a}_2\bar{a}_3)}, \quad \bar{b}_2 \equiv \frac{\bar{a}_3 \times \bar{a}_1}{(\bar{a}_1\bar{a}_2\bar{a}_3)}, \quad \bar{b}_3 \equiv \frac{\bar{a}_1 \times \bar{a}_2}{(\bar{a}_1\bar{a}_2\bar{a}_3)} \qquad [1\cdot4]$$

The symbol $(\bar{a}_1\bar{a}_2\bar{a}_3)$ is used for the triple scalar product, which represents the volume of a parallelopiped with edges $\bar{a}_1$, $\bar{a}_2$, and $\bar{a}_3$.

The vectors $\bar{b}_1$, $\bar{b}_2$, $\bar{b}_3$ as defined by the relations (1·4) have interesting properties.[2] They are called the set of vectors reciprocal to $\bar{a}_1$, $\bar{a}_2$, $\bar{a}_3$, since the scalar products $\bar{a}_j \cdot \bar{b}_k$ satisfy the conditions

$$\bar{a}_j \cdot \bar{b}_k = \delta_{jk} \begin{cases} = 0 & \text{if} \quad j \neq k \\ = 1 & \text{if} \quad j = k \end{cases} \qquad [1\cdot5]$$

One verifies readily that

$$(\bar{a}_1\bar{a}_2\bar{a}_3)(\bar{b}_1\bar{b}_2\bar{b}_3) = 1 \qquad [1\cdot6]$$

[2] For a more detailed discussion see p. 81 in Gibbs-Wilson, *Vector Analysis*, Yale University Press, 1901.

It is furthermore easily shown that

$$\bar{a}_1 = \frac{\bar{b}_2 \times \bar{b}_3}{(\bar{b}_1\bar{b}_2\bar{b}_3)}, \quad \bar{a}_2 = \frac{\bar{b}_3 \times \bar{b}_1}{(\bar{b}_1\bar{b}_2\bar{b}_3)}, \quad \bar{a}_3 = \frac{\bar{b}_1 \times \bar{b}_2}{(\bar{b}_1\bar{b}_2\bar{b}_3)}, \qquad [1·7]$$

meaning that the two sets of vectors are mutually reciprocal. The angles between the vectors $\bar{b}_1$, $\bar{b}_2$, $\bar{b}_3$ will be given the symbols $\beta_1(\measuredangle\, \bar{b}_2\bar{b}_3)$, $\beta_2(\measuredangle\, \bar{b}_3\bar{b}_1)$, and $\beta_3(\measuredangle\, \bar{b}_1\bar{b}_2)$. With the aid of the definitions (1·4) the angles α_1, α_2, α_3 may be expressed in terms of the angles β_1, β_2, β_3, and vice versa. These relations are of the form

$$\cos \alpha_1 = \frac{\cos \beta_2 \cos \beta_3 - \cos \beta_1}{\sin \beta_2 \sin \beta_3} \qquad [1·8a]$$

$$\cos \beta_1 = \frac{\cos \alpha_2 \cos \alpha_3 - \cos \alpha_1}{\sin \alpha_2 \sin \alpha_3} \qquad [1·8b]$$

We also list several useful expressions for the volume $V = (\bar{a}_1\bar{a}_2\bar{a}_3)$, namely,

$$V = \begin{vmatrix} \bar{a}_1 \cdot \bar{a}_1 & \bar{a}_1 \cdot \bar{a}_2 & \bar{a}_1 \cdot \bar{a}_3 \\ \bar{a}_2 \cdot \bar{a}_1 & \bar{a}_2 \cdot \bar{a}_2 & \bar{a}_2 \cdot \bar{a}_3 \\ \bar{a}_3 \cdot \bar{a}_1 & \bar{a}_3 \cdot \bar{a}_2 & \bar{a}_3 \cdot \bar{a}_3 \end{vmatrix}^{1/2} \qquad [1·9a]$$

$$V = a_1a_2a_3(1 + 2\cos \alpha_1 \cos \alpha_2 \cos \alpha_3 - \cos^2 \alpha_1 - \cos^2 \alpha_2 - \cos^2 \alpha_3)^{1/2} \qquad [1·9b]$$

$$V^{-1} = b_1b_2b_3(1 + 2\cos \beta_1 \cos \beta_2 \cos \beta_3 - \cos^2 \beta_1 - \cos^2 \beta_2 - \cos^2 \beta_3)^{1/2} \qquad [1·9c]$$

The representation 1·3 of the unit normals is of great convenience in crystallographic calculations as well as for other purposes, and the concept of reciprocal vectors will be used extensively throughout this book.

5. CRYSTAL EDGES. THE ZONE CONCEPT

Let $\bar{u}$ be a unit vector parallel to an edge which is defined as the intersection line of two faces $(h_1h_2h_3)$ and $(h_1'h_2'h_3')$. The vector $\bar{u}$ is then parallel to the vector product $\bar{B}_h \times \bar{B}_{h'}$ multiplied by the scalar factor $V = (\bar{b}_1\bar{b}_2\bar{b}_3)^{-1}$. Using Equations 1·7 one finds

$$\bar{u} = \frac{\bar{A}_l}{|\bar{A}_l|}, \quad \bar{A}_l \equiv l_1\bar{a}_1 + l_2\bar{a}_2 + l_3\bar{a}_3$$

$$l_1 = \begin{vmatrix} h_2 & h_3 \\ h_2' & h_3' \end{vmatrix}, \quad l_2 = \begin{vmatrix} h_3 & h_1 \\ h_3' & h_1' \end{vmatrix}, \quad l_3 = \begin{vmatrix} h_1 & h_2 \\ h_1' & h_2' \end{vmatrix} \qquad [1·10]$$

The quantities l_1, l_2, l_3 may logically be called the indices of the edge. According to the law of rational indices h_1, h_2, h_3 and h_1', h_2', h_3' are integers, and hence l_1, l_2, l_3 are also integers. It is thus immaterial whether the law of rational indices applies to face indices $(h_1h_2h_3)$ or to edge indices $[l_1l_2l_3]$. (We shall adopt the rule of enclosing edge indices in brackets in order to distinguish them from face indices which are given in parentheses.) As shown by the representations 1·3 and 1·10 there is a close analogy between face normals and edges. An expression of the form $\bar{B}_h = h_1\bar{b}_1 + h_2\bar{b}_2 + h_3\bar{b}_3$, where h_1, h_2, h_3 are any three integers, is said to represent a *possible* crystal face, while the analogous expression, $\bar{A}_l = l_1\bar{a}_1 + l_2\bar{a}_2 + l_3\bar{a}_3$ with l_1, l_2, and l_3 integers, represents a *possible* crystal edge.

All crystal faces which are parallel to a given direction are said to lie in the same zone, and the given direction is called the zone axis. The zone axis is obviously given as the intersection line of any two faces in the zone. All faces $\bar{B}_h$ belonging to the zone $\bar{A}_l$ must satisfy the zone relation

$$\bar{A}_l \cdot \bar{B}_h = h_1l_1 + h_2l_2 + h_3l_3 = 0 \qquad [1{\cdot}11]$$

Suppose that $\bar{B}_h$, $\bar{B}_{h'}$, and $\bar{B}_{h''}$ represent three different crystal faces. In general three such faces define three different zones, the zone axes being given by the three vector products $\bar{B}_h \times \bar{B}_{h'}$, $\bar{B}_{h'} \times \bar{B}_{h''}$, and $\bar{B}_{h''} \times \bar{B}_h$. It may happen, however, that the three normals are coplanar, in which case only one zone is defined, namely, the one to which all three faces belong. The condition that the three faces belong to the same zone is evidently

$$(\bar{B}_h\bar{B}_{h'}\bar{B}_{h''}) = 0 \quad \text{or} \quad \begin{vmatrix} h_1 & h_2 & h_3 \\ h_1' & h_2' & h_3' \\ h_1'' & h_2'' & h_3'' \end{vmatrix} = 0 \qquad [1{\cdot}12]$$

6. LINEAR TRANSFORMATIONS OF THE COORDINATE SYSTEM

In order to attain a better understanding of the significance of the law of rational indices it is necessary to investigate the relationship between various coordinate systems. Suppose that a reference frame has been chosen in accordance with the conventions suggested in section 2. This choice is not unique since there is ambiguity both with respect to the edges that are selected as coordinate axes and with respect to the selection of the crystal face defining the ratios $a_1 : a_2 : a_3$. It is, however, an empirical fact, as expressed in the law of rational indices, that the indices of all crystal faces are proportional to integers in any one of the coordinate systems so obtained.

Let the vectors $\bar{a}_1$, $\bar{a}_2$, $\bar{a}_3$ characterize one such reference frame, and consider a new system, $\bar{a}_1'$, $\bar{a}_2'$, $\bar{a}_3'$, which is related to the old one by means of the linear equations

$$\begin{aligned} \bar{a}_1' &= c_{11}\bar{a}_1 + c_{12}\bar{a}_2 + c_{13}\bar{a}_3 \\ \bar{a}_2' &= c_{21}\bar{a}_1 + c_{22}\bar{a}_2 + c_{23}\bar{a}_3 \quad \text{or} \quad \bar{a}_j' = \sum_k c_{jk}\bar{a}_k \\ \bar{a}_3' &= c_{31}\bar{a}_1 + c_{32}\bar{a}_2 + c_{33}\bar{a}_3 \end{aligned} \qquad [1\cdot13]$$

The three new vectors $\bar{a}_1'$, $\bar{a}_2'$, $\bar{a}_3'$ must not be coplanar, and the triple scalar product $(\bar{a}_1'\bar{a}_2'\bar{a}_3')$ must therefore be different from zero, i.e.,

$$V' \equiv (\bar{a}_1'\bar{a}_2'\bar{a}_3') = (\bar{a}_1\bar{a}_2\bar{a}_3)\begin{vmatrix} c_{11} & c_{12} & c_{13} \\ c_{21} & c_{22} & c_{23} \\ c_{31} & c_{32} & c_{33} \end{vmatrix} = V\Delta \neq 0 \qquad [1\cdot14]$$

The converse transformation formulas are readily found to be

$$\bar{a}_j = \frac{1}{\Delta}\sum_k c_{k\,j}^*\bar{a}_k' \qquad [1\cdot15]$$

where $c_{k\,j}^*$ is the cofactor of the element c_{kj} in the determinant Δ. The corresponding transformation equations for the reciprocal vectors become

$$\bar{b}_j' = \frac{1}{\Delta}\sum c_{k\,j}^*\bar{b}_k \quad \text{and} \quad \bar{b}_j = \sum c_{kj}\bar{b}_k' \qquad [1\cdot16]$$

By means of the transformation formulas given above it is easily seen that face indices $(h_1h_2h_3)$ transform as do the vectors $\bar{a}_1$, $\bar{a}_2$, $\bar{a}_3$, while zone indices $[l_1l_2l_3]$ transform as do the reciprocal vectors $\bar{b}_1$, $\bar{b}_2$, $\bar{b}_3$.

The old indices ($(h_1h_2h_3)$ and $[l_1l_2l_3]$) are rational according to the law of rational indices; but our equations show that the new indices will be rational as well if all the transformation coefficients c_{jk} are rational. Hence it becomes possible to find an infinite number of coordinate systems in which the indices are rational. In many of these coordinate systems the indices are proportional to such large integers that it becomes difficult to determine their values from the experimental data. The additional stipulation of the law of rational indices that there are coordinate systems in which the indices are proportional to *small* integers is thus of practical importance since it tells us that there is at least one coordinate system in which the indices can be found with comparative ease.

These considerations show that the fundamental value of the law of rational indices lies in the statement that the indices are rational, while the restriction as regards the proportionality to small integers in some coordinate systems has practical use but it is of no basic importance. All coordinate systems which give rational indices should be considered entirely equivalent. The rules governing the choice of a reference frame are accordingly much more liberal than the discussion of section 2 suggests. Indeed, the coordinate axes may be chosen along any three possible edges of the crystal (not all lying in a plane), while any possible crystal face (cutting all the three coordinate axes) may be given the Miller indices (111). Thus the coordinate directions need not correspond to edges which are actually present on the crystal, nor need the crystal face which defines the ratios $a_1 : a_2 : a_3$ be observed.

7. THE LATTICE POSTULATE

Hitherto we have pictured crystals as homogeneous solids, but the atomic structure of matter makes it clear that they must be treated as inhomogeneous substances in small scale considerations. Homogeneity, defined as invariance under any translation which is large compared with atomic dimensions, is definitely to be associated with the gross properties of crystals. It is convenient to introduce the new concept of a crystal in the form of a postulate.

All physical properties of a crystal medium are invariant under translations $L_1\bar{a}_1 + L_2\bar{a}_2 + L_3\bar{a}_3$, where L_1, L_2, L_3 are any three integers and $\bar{a}_1$, $\bar{a}_2$, $\bar{a}_3$ three (non-coplanar) vectors characteristic of the medium.

Since crystals appear homogeneous in high-power microscopes it may be inferred that the vectors $\bar{a}_j$ are of submicroscopic length. On the other hand, these vectors may be equal to, but certainly not smaller than the smallest interatomic distance.

Let $\Omega(\bar{r})$ be a function (of scalar, vector, or tensor nature), representing any one of the physical properties of a crystal medium. According to the postulate it has the property

$$\Omega(\bar{r}) = \Omega(\bar{r} + L_1\bar{a}_1 + L_2\bar{a}_2 + L_3\bar{a}_3) \qquad [1\cdot17]$$

for any $\bar{r}$ and for any set of three integers L_1, L_2, L_3. All physical properties are, in other words, periodic functions of position, with periods $\bar{a}_1$, $\bar{a}_2$, and $\bar{a}_3$. The position vector $\bar{r}$ may be expressed in terms of the components along the translation vectors $\bar{a}_j$, i.e., $\bar{r} = x_1\bar{a}_1 + x_2\bar{a}_2 + x_3\bar{a}_3$, and it follows from Equation 1·17 that the components x_j may be restricted to the range $0 \leq x_j < 1$.

Two points $\bar{r}$ and $\bar{r}'$ are said to be equivalent if $\Omega(\bar{r}) = \Omega(\bar{r}')$ for any property Ω. The equivalent points generated by the expression $\bar{r} + \sum L_j\bar{a}_j$, where $\bar{r}$ is fixed and L_1, L_2, L_3 assume all possible integral values, form what is termed a simple translation lattice. The operation transforming a point $\bar{r}$ into $\bar{r} + \sum L_j\bar{a}_j$ is called a lattice translation and will be denoted by the symbol

$$\Gamma_{L_1L_2L_3} \quad \text{or} \quad \Gamma_L$$

that is,

$$\bar{r} \cdot \Gamma_{L_1L_2L_3} \equiv \bar{r} + L_1\bar{a}_1 + L_2\bar{a}_2 + L_3\bar{a}_3 \qquad [1\cdot18]$$

The vector $\bar{A}_L \equiv L_1\bar{a}_1 + L_2\bar{a}_2 + L_3\bar{a}_3$ is referred to as a lattice vector. The collection of all operations Γ_L evidently satisfies the group postulates and is called the translation group, (Γ_L). A simple translation lattice may thus be written as $\bar{r} \cdot (\Gamma_L)$. The assembly of all points $\bar{r} = \sum x_j\bar{a}_j$ with $0 \leq x_j < 1$ constitutes the unit cell, which is a parallelopiped with edges $\bar{a}_1$, $\bar{a}_2$, $\bar{a}_3$ and volume $V = (\bar{a}_1\bar{a}_2\bar{a}_3)$. There is a simple translation lattice for every point in the unit cell, and the triple manifold of all these individual translation lattices constitutes the crystal lattice. The crystal lattice is evidently obtained when the unit cell as a whole is subjected to all the operations of the translation group.

The space lattice idea is contained in naive form in a remarkable publication of Haüy[3] (1784), who was the first to seek a correlation between characteristic macroscopic properties and internal structure. The correct formulation of the lattice concept is due to Bravais.[4] We have introduced the lattice structure of crystals in the form of a postulate, and it is both logically and historically proper to do so. Throughout the nineteenth century the lattice idea could not be directly tested since it concerned a submicroscopic world not yet accessible to physical observations. The lattice concept was accepted as correct on the basis of indirect evidence only. The macroscopic consequences of the lattice hypothesis were, indeed, found to be in agreement with experiment. The postulated periodic structure evidently leads to macroscopic homogeneity since the smallest volume elements concerned in macroscopic observations contain a great many unit cells. Similarly the observed anisotropic character of the physical properties is readily understood in terms of the geometrical anisotropy of the lattice. Because of the periodicity, the ratios between the numbers of chemically different atoms which compose the crystal are the same for the unit cell as for the crystal as a whole. The unit cell contains a comparatively small number of atoms. The ratios between the numbers of different atoms are therefore rational and the chemical composition may be expressed by a stoichiometric formula, while the unit cell contains an integral number of stoichiometric molecules. This prediction finds experimen-

[3] R. J. Haüy, *Essai d'une théorie sur la structure des crystaux*, Paris, 1784.

[4] A. Bravais, *J. de l'école polytechnique Paris*, **19**, 1 (1850).

A. L. Cauchy, *Exercices de mathém.*, Paris, 1827.

tal corroboration in most crystals. There are, however, many cases (notably among minerals and metallic crystals) where it is necessary to group chemically different atoms in order to attain rational proportions. It is probably true that the sharp melting point of a crystal is directly associated with the periodicity of the internal structure, but a satisfactory theory of the melting process has yet to be developed.

These are just a few of the many observations which support the lattice postulate, and additional supporting evidence will be brought forth in other chapters.

8. LATTICE ROWS AND LATTICE PLANES

The points of a simple translation lattice $\bar{r} \cdot (\Gamma_L)$ are arranged in straight lines called lattice rows and in planes called lattice planes. For the sake of convenience let $\bar{r} = 0$, so that the lattice points are represented by the lattice vectors $\bar{A}_L = \sum L_j \bar{a}_j$. In the reference frame $\bar{a}_1$, $\bar{a}_2$, $\bar{a}_3$ the coordinates of the lattice points are thus three integers L_1, L_2, L_3. (When it is specifically assumed that three integers have no common integral factor, lower-case letters will be used, i.e., l_1, l_2, l_3 indicate relative primes.)

Two lattice points define a lattice row. If one of the two points is taken to be the origin, the other to be l_1, l_2, l_3, the lattice row may be represented by the vector $\bar{A}_l$. The row contains an infinite number of equidistant lattice points given by $n\bar{A}_l \equiv \bar{A}_L$, where n is any integer. The distance between two consecutive points of the row is the period, which expressed in terms of the quantities a_j and α_j becomes

$$|\bar{A}_l| = (l_1^2a_1^2 + l_2^2a_2^2 + l_3^2a_3^2 + 2l_2l_3a_2a_3 \cos \alpha_1 + 2l_1l_3a_1a_3 \cos \alpha_2 + 2l_1l_2a_1a_2 \cos \alpha_3)^{1/2} \qquad [1\cdot19]$$

Let $\bar{A}_L$, $\bar{A}_{L'}$, and $\bar{A}_{L''}$ be three lattice points not all lying in the same row. These define a lattice plane, the scalar equation of which has the form

$$h_1X_1 + h_2X_2 + h_3X_3 - k = 0 \qquad [1\cdot20]$$

As the three lattice points must satisfy this equation one finds

$$\begin{vmatrix} X_1 & X_2 & X_3 & 1 \\ L_1 & L_2 & L_3 & 1 \\ L_1' & L_2' & L_3' & 1 \\ L_1'' & L_2'' & L_3'' & 1 \end{vmatrix} = 0 \qquad [1\cdot21]$$

Consequently h_1, h_2, h_3, and k assume only integral values and h_1, h_2, h_3 may be considered relatively prime numbers. According to a well-known theorem it is possible to find an infinite set of integral values

X_1, X_2, X_3 which satisfy the relation 1·21; a lattice plane contains therefore an infinite number of lattice points. As the constant k assumes all possible integral values while h_1, h_2, h_3 are held fixed, one obtains an infinite sequence of parallel and equidistant lattice planes which contains all the equivalent points of the simple translation lattice. The sequence may be described by the set of values h_1, h_2, h_3. The distance between two consecutive planes in the sequence, i.e., the distance between two planes for which the k-values differ by one unit, is the spacing, $d_{h_1h_2h_3}$.

A plane having the equation

$$H_1X_1 + H_2X_2 + H_3X_3 - K = 0 \qquad [1\cdot22]$$

with $H_j = nh_j (n, h_j,$ and K integers) is parallel to the sequence $(h_1h_2h_3)$. As K ranges from $-\infty$ to $+\infty$ one gets an infinite sequence of planes $(H_1H_2H_3)$ which includes the sequence $(h_1h_2h_3)$. Equation 1·22 cannot be satisfied by integral values X_1, X_2, X_3 unless K is divisible by n, in which case one obtains a lattice plane of the sequence $(h_1h_2h_3)$. Thus only every nth plane in the set $(H_1H_2H_3)$ is truly a lattice plane, and clearly

$$d_{H_1H_2H_3} = \frac{1}{n} d_{h_1h_2h_3} \qquad [1\cdot23]$$

The considerations given above show that lattice rows and lattice planes have rational indices. By associating crystal faces and edges with lattice planes and rows, we see that the lattice postulate has led to an attractively simple explanation of the law of rational indices.

9. THE RECIPROCAL LATTICE[5]

Consider the sequence of planes $(H_1H_2H_3)$. The spacing $d_{H_1H_2H_3}$ is the distance from the origin to the plane $\sum H_jX_j - 1 = 0$. As shown in section 4 the normal to a plane in a coordinate system $\bar{a}_1$, $\bar{a}_2$, $\bar{a}_3$ may be expressed in convenient form in terms of the reciprocal vectors $\bar{b}_1$, $\bar{b}_2$, $\bar{b}_3$; specifically, the vector $\bar{B}_H \equiv H_1\bar{b}_1 + H_2\bar{b}_2 + H_3\bar{b}_3$ is normal to the sequence $(H_1H_2H_3)$. The projection on this vector of any one of the three vector intercepts $\bar{a}_j/H_j$ of the plane $\sum H_jX_j - 1 = 0$ gives the spacing. Since $\bar{a}_j \cdot \bar{B}_H = H_j$ one finds

$$d_H = \frac{\bar{a}_j}{H_j} \cdot \frac{\bar{B}_H}{|\bar{B}_H|} = \frac{1}{|\bar{B}_H|} \qquad [1\cdot24]$$

[5] P. P. Ewald, *Physik. Zeitschr.*, **14**, 465 (1913).
M. v. Laue, *Jahrb. d. Radioakt. u. Elektr.*, **11**, 308 (1914).

Consequently the vector $\bar{B}_H \equiv H_1\bar{b}_1 + H_2\bar{b}_2 + H_3\bar{b}_3$ is normal to the sequence of planes $(H_1H_2H_3)$ and its length is equal to the reciprocal spacing of the sequence.

The assembly of all sequences $(H_1H_2H_3)$ may accordingly be represented, as regards orientation and spacing, by the assembly of all vectors $\bar{B}_H$, which forms a simple translation lattice. Since this lattice is based upon the vectors $\bar{b}_1$, $\bar{b}_2$, $\bar{b}_3$ rather than upon the vectors $\bar{a}_1$, $\bar{a}_2$, $\bar{a}_3$ it is called the reciprocal lattice. With every lattice point of the reciprocal lattice is thus associated a sequence of planes in the initial lattice. Because of the mutual reciprocity of the vector sets $\bar{a}_1, \bar{a}_2, \bar{a}_3$ and $\bar{b}_1$, $\bar{b}_2$, $\bar{b}_3$, it follows that the reciprocal lattice points are arranged in an analogous manner into sequences of equidistant planes associated with the lattice vectors $\bar{A}_L$ of the initial lattice.

The detailed expression for the spacing d_H is readily obtained from Equation 1·24 and is given below in terms of the constants b_j and β_j, and in terms of the constants a_j and α_j.

$$\frac{1}{d_H^2} = H_1^2b_1^2 + H_2^2b_2^2 + H_3^2b_3^2 + 2H_2H_3b_2b_3 \cos \beta_1 + 2H_1H_3b_1b_3 \cos \beta_2 + 2H_1H_2b_1b_2 \cos \beta_3 \qquad [1·25a]$$

$$\frac{1}{d_H^2} = \frac{1}{(1 + 2 \cos \alpha_1 \cos \alpha_2 \cos \alpha_3 - \cos^2 \alpha_1 - \cos^2 \alpha_2 - \cos^2 \alpha_3)} \times \left\{\frac{H_1^2 \sin^2 \alpha_1}{a_1^2} + \frac{H_2^2 \sin^2 \alpha_2}{a_2^2} + \frac{H_3^2 \sin^2 \alpha_3}{a_3^2} + \frac{2H_2H_3(\cos \alpha_2 \cos \alpha_3 - \cos \alpha_1)}{a_2a_3} + \frac{2H_1H_3(\cos \alpha_1 \cos \alpha_3 - \cos \alpha_2)}{a_1a_3} + \frac{2H_1H_2(\cos \alpha_1 \cos \alpha_2 - \cos \alpha_3)}{a_1a_2}\right\} \qquad [1·25b]$$

10. FOURIER SERIES REPRESENTATIONS OF PHYSICAL PROPERTIES[6]

The variation of a physical property from point to point within a crystal medium is represented by means of a scalar, vector, or tensor function $\Omega(\bar{r})$. According to the lattice postulate any such function satisfies the condition $\Omega(\bar{r}) = \Omega(\bar{r} + \bar{A}_L)$. If all vector quantities are referred to the coordinate system $\bar{a}_1$, $\bar{a}_2$, $\bar{a}_3$ the lattice postulate may be given analytically in the form

$$\Omega(x_1,\ x_2,\ x_3) = \Omega(x_1 + L_1,\ x_2 + L_2,\ x_3 + L_3) \qquad [1·26]$$

where $0 \leq x_j < 1$.

The periodic nature of the lattice functions suggests expansion in Fourier series. The general form of the Fourier series which identically

[6] P. P. Ewald, *Zeitschr. f. Krist.*, **56**, 129 (1921).

satisfies the condition 1·26 is

$$\Omega(x_1, x_2, x_3) = \sum_{-\infty}^{+\infty}\sum\sum \Omega_{H_1H_2H_3}\, e^{-i2\pi(H_1x_1+H_2x_2+H_3x_3)} \qquad [1\cdot27a]$$

The quantities H_1, H_2, H_3 denote any three integers in the entire range from $-\infty$ to $+\infty$. The product sum $\sum H_jx_j$ may therefore be interpreted as the scalar product $\bar{B}_H \cdot \bar{r}$ and permits formal correlations between the different terms in the series and the points of the reciprocal lattice. In a simplified notation the expansion 1·27*a* becomes

$$\Omega(\bar{r}) = \sum \Omega_H\, e^{-i2\pi\bar{B}_H\cdot\bar{r}} \qquad [1\cdot27b]$$

The expression for the expansion coefficients Ω_H is obtained in the usual manner: both sides of the identity 1·27*b* are multiplied by the term $e^{i2\pi\bar{B}_{H'}\cdot\bar{r}}$ and the resulting equation is integrated over the significant range of variation of the variables, which is the unit cell in the present case. One finds

$$\int_0^1\int_0^1\int_0^1 \Omega\, e^{i2\pi\bar{B}_{H'}\cdot\bar{r}}\, dx_1dx_2dx_3 = \sum_H \Omega_H \int_0^1\int_0^1\int_0^1 e^{-i2\pi\bar{B}_{H-H'}\cdot\bar{r}}\, dx_1dx_2dx_3 \qquad [1\cdot28]$$

All except one of the integrals on the right side of Equation 1·28 vanish because of the orthogonality of the exponential functions. The remaining integral corresponds to $H = H'$, i.e., to $H_1 = H_1'$, $H_2 = H_2'$, $H_3 = H_3'$, and it has the value 1, so that the right side of Equation 1·28 reduces to Ω_H. The problem of finding the coefficients of expansion is thus formally solved:

$$\Omega_H = \int_0^1\int_0^1\int_0^1 \Omega(x_1, x_2, x_3)\, e^{i2\pi\bar{B}_H\cdot\bar{r}}\, dx_1dx_2dx_3 \qquad [1\cdot29a]$$

The integral of Equation 1·29*a* may conveniently be written as a volume integral over the unit cell. Remembering that $\bar{r} = \sum x_j\bar{a}_j$ it is readily seen that a volume element of the unit cell may be expressed as follows.

$$dv = (\bar{a}_1\bar{a}_2\bar{a}_3)\, dx_1dx_2dx_3 = V\, dx_1dx_2dx_3 \qquad [1\cdot30]$$

Hence Equation 1·29*a* may be rewritten as

$$\Omega_H = V^{-1}\int_V \Omega(\bar{r})\, e^{i2\pi\bar{B}_H\cdot\bar{r}}\, dv \qquad [1\cdot29b]$$

The constant term in the series, Ω_{000}, corresponding to $H_1 = H_2 = H_3 = 0$, is given by

$$\Omega_{000} = V^{-1} \int_V \Omega(\bar{r})\, dv = \overline{\Omega} \qquad [1\cdot 31]$$

It is accordingly the average value of the function Ω throughout the unit cell — and hence throughout the entire crystal medium — and it is interesting to note that Ω_{000} becomes the only term of the series which can be obtained from macroscopic measurements.

The function Ω and the coefficients Ω_H are treated as complex quantities in the series 1·27. If it is known that a given property is to be represented by means of a real function Ω the corresponding Fourier series must be real. The expansion coefficients may be complex, but it is readily seen that they are subject to the condition $\Omega_{\overline{H}} = \Omega^*_H$, where the symbol Ω^*_H is used to represent the complex conjugate of Ω_H, and $\overline{H}$ stands for the triplet $-H_1$, $-H_2$, $-H_3$.

Each term in the Fourier series 1·27*b* is characterized by a different vector $\bar{B}_H$. By associating the coefficients Ω_H with the corresponding points of the reciprocal lattice one obtains a discrete tensor field, which may be considered as a representation of the function Ω. This visualization of the individual terms in the Fourier series is useful for many purposes and may often give considerable insight into problems connected with the Fourier expansion of lattice functions.

11. FOURIER SYNTHESIS OF LATTICE FUNCTIONS

The preceding section dealt with the problem of expanding a given lattice function Ω in a Fourier series. The results of these considerations may, however, be applied equally well to the converse problem, that of synthesizing the function by means of experimentally determined coefficients Ω_H. It is of importance to discuss this problem in considerable detail, for although the available experimental methods lead to complete or partial determination of the individual Fourier expansion coefficients for only a few of the crystal properties, one of these is the fundamentally important distribution function of physical matter.

It may be quite generally supposed that the Fourier series converges, which implies that the coefficients $\Omega_{H_1H_2H_3}$ become negligible if we go to sufficiently large values of $|H_1|$, $|H_2|$, or $|H_3|$. Accordingly it is justifiable to break the series at some particular point beyond which the coefficients are so small that they may be set equal to zero without serious error. Let us assume to begin with that all coefficients which are to be included in this finite series are completely known. The procedure leading to a synthesis of the function Ω is then simply the insertion of the known coefficients in the Fourier series and the evaluation of the series for so many different sets x_1, x_2, x_3 that the value of the function at any intermediate point may be obtained with sufficient accuracy by interpolation. It is often found that the amount of labor involved in this calculation is too great because the series contains hundreds of terms, and that it is necessary to carry out the summation for thousands of sets x_1, x_2, x_3 in order to attain the accuracy required for interpolation. However, in many such instances our main interest in the function Ω lies in its variation along a particularly important straight line or plane, and the synthesis of the function in such restricted regions is naturally less laborious. It is therefore useful to discuss cases of this type.

A. **Synthesis of the Function Ω along a Given Straight Line.** Suppose that the straight line is parallel to the lattice row $\bar{A}_l$ and that it passes through a point $\bar{s} = s_1\bar{a}_1 + s_2\bar{a}_2 + s_3\bar{a}_3$. The fixed reference point $\bar{s}$ is conveniently chosen as the intersection point between the straight line and one of the coordinate planes so that at least one (and possibly two or all three) of the components s_j becomes zero. Any arbitrary point on the given line is represented by

$$\bar{r} = \bar{s} + z\bar{A}_l \qquad [1{\cdot}32]$$

where z, because of the periodicity may be restricted to the range $0 \leq z < 1$. If Equation 1·32 is inserted in the series 1·27 there results the single sum,

$$\Omega(\bar{s} + z\bar{A}_l) = \sum_K C_K\, e^{-i2\pi Kz} \qquad [1{\cdot}33]$$

where $\bar{B}_H \cdot \bar{A}_l = \sum H_j l_j = K$, and where

$$C_K = \sum_{H_1}\sum_{H_2}\sum_{H_3} \Omega_{H_1H_2H_3}\, e^{-i2\pi(H_1s_1 + H_2s_2 + H_3s_3)} \qquad [1{\cdot}34]$$

which is a double rather than a triple sum since the set H_1, H_2, H_3 has to satisfy the condition $\sum H_j l_j = K$.

As an illustration we shall take the particular case corresponding to $\bar{s} = \frac{1}{2}\bar{a}_1 + \frac{1}{2}\bar{a}_2$, and $\bar{A}_l = \bar{a}_3$, i.e., $l_1 = l_2 = 0$, $l_3 = 1$. The quantities z and K become synonymous with x_3 and H_3, and the latter symbols may therefore be used in place of the former. Thus Equations 1·33 and 1·34 take the forms

$$\Omega(\tfrac{1}{2}\bar{a}_1 + \tfrac{1}{2}\bar{a}_2 + x_3\bar{a}_3) = \sum_{H_3} C_{H_3}\, e^{-i2\pi H_3x_3}$$

and

$$C_{H_3} = \sum_{H_1}\sum_{H_2} (-1)^{H_1+H_2}\, \Omega_{H_1H_2H_3}$$

B. **Synthesis of the Function Ω in a Given Plane.** Let the plane be parallel to a sequence of lattice planes $(h_1h_2h_3)$ and thus normal to the vector $\bar{B}_h$. The vector $\bar{s} = \sum s_j \bar{a}_j$ represents a convenient reference point in the plane; for instance, let us choose the intersection between the plane and one of the coordinate axes so that at least two (and possibly all three) components s_j are zero. Any point in the plane may be given in the form

$$\bar{r} = \bar{s} + z_1 \bar{A}_l + z_2 \bar{A}_{l'} \tag{1·35}$$

where $\bar{A}_l$ and $\bar{A}_{l'}$ are two lattice vectors parallel to the plane and where they consequently satisfy the conditions $\bar{A}_l \cdot \bar{B}_h = \bar{A}_{l'} \cdot \bar{B}_h = 0$. The Fourier series expansion of the function Ω in the given plane is therefore

$$\Omega(\bar{s} + z_1 \bar{A}_l + z_2 \bar{A}_{l'}) = \sum_{K_1} \sum_{K_2} C_{K_1 K_2} \, e^{-i2\pi(K_1 z_1 + K_2 z_2)} \tag{1·36}$$

where

$$K_1 = \bar{B}_H \cdot \bar{A}_l, \quad K_2 = \bar{B}_H \cdot \bar{A}_{l'} \tag{1·37}$$

and

$$C_{K_1 K_2} = \sum_H \Omega_H \, e^{-i2\pi \bar{B}_H \cdot \bar{s}} \tag{1·38}$$

The quantities $C_{K_1 K_2}$ as expressed by Equation 1·38 clearly represent single sums since only one of the indices H_j is independent because of Equations 1·37.

As an illustration let us choose $\bar{s} = \frac{1}{2}\bar{a}_3$, $\bar{A}_l = \bar{a}_1$, and $\bar{A}_{l'} = \bar{a}_2$. Thus the quantities z_1 and z_2 become synonymous with x_1 and x_2, the quantities K_1 and K_2 with H_1 and H_2, and the series becomes

$$\Omega(x_1 \bar{a}_1 + x_2 \bar{a}_2 + \tfrac{1}{2}\bar{a}_3) = \sum_{H_1} \sum_{H_2} C_{H_1 H_2} \, e^{-i2\pi(H_1 x_1 + H_2 x_2)}$$

with

$$C_{H_1 H_2} = \sum_{H_3} (-1)^{H_3} \Omega_{H_1 H_2 H_3}$$

We have so far assumed that complete information is available regarding all coefficients $\Omega_{H_1 H_2 H_3}$ (which are not small enough to be neglected). This assumption does not hold in many instances met with in actual practice, and a synthesis of the function Ω cannot be carried out. However, even a partial knowledge of the Fourier coefficients will sometimes give valuable information about the function Ω, and we shall therefore discuss two such cases of practical importance. In the instance to be dealt with first it will be assumed that only a plane section of the complete three-dimensional array of coefficients $\Omega_{H_1 H_2 H_3}$ is known. This two-dimensional set of coefficients is represented by a lattice plane $\bar{B}_H \cdot \bar{A}_l = 0$ in the reciprocal lattice, so that the experimental data somehow or other are restricted to one particular zone $\bar{A}_l$. In the second important case we shall imagine that only the moduli $|\Omega_{H_1 H_2 H_3}|$ of the Fourier coefficients can be found experimentally, and it will further be supposed that Ω is a real function, i.e., that $\Omega_H^* = \Omega_{\bar{H}}$.

C. Only the Coefficients Ω_H for Which $\bar{B}_H \cdot \bar{A}_l = 0$ Are Known. Any point in the crystal medium may be expressed in the form of Equation 1·32, with $\bar{s} = \sum s_j \bar{a}_j$ representing a vector, parallel to a certain plane, which may be chosen in any convenient way. Accordingly $\bar{s}$ is a variable vector; but only two of three components s_j are independent, and it is easily seen that one of the three components becomes zero if $\bar{s}$ is chosen parallel to a coordinate plane. The average value of the function along the straight lines parallel to the lattice row $\bar{A}_l$ becomes a function ϕ of the two independent components of $\bar{s}$, and it is given by the integral

$$\phi(\bar{s}) = \int_0^1 \Omega\, dz \qquad [1·39]$$

The product of the function ϕ and the period $|\bar{A}_l|$ accordingly represents the "projection" of the function Ω on a plane normal to the lattice row $\bar{A}_l$. Using the expansion for the function Ω given in Equation 1·27*b* the integral 1·39 becomes

$$\phi(\bar{s}) = \sum_H \Omega_H\, e^{-i2\pi \bar{B}_H \cdot \bar{s}} \int_0^1 e^{-i2\pi z \bar{B}_H \cdot \bar{A}_l}\, dz \qquad [1·40]$$

The integrals on the right side of Equation 1·40 vanish unless $\bar{B}_H \cdot \bar{A}_l = 0$. The triple series accordingly reduces to a double series of the form

$$\left.\begin{aligned} \phi(\bar{s}) &= \sum_H \Omega_H\, e^{-i2\pi \bar{B}_H \cdot \bar{s}} \\ \bar{B}_H \cdot \bar{A}_l &= 0 \end{aligned}\right\} \qquad [1·41]$$

The synthesis of the function ϕ can thus be carried out if we know the set of coefficients $\Omega_{H_1 H_2 H_3}$ for which the indices satisfy the auxiliary condition $\sum H_j l_j = 0$. The results will probably be clearer if we give an illustration. Suppose that we have determined experimentally only the coefficients $\Omega_{H_1 H_2 0}$, corresponding to $\bar{A}_l = \bar{a}_3$ in the equations given above. These experimental data do not suffice for a synthesis of the function Ω, but we are able to construct the function ϕ. The vector $\bar{s}$ can be chosen in any plane which is not parallel to $\bar{A}_l$; in the present case we may therefore set $\bar{s} = x_1 \bar{a}_1 + x_2 \bar{a}_2$. Inserting these particular values in Equations 1·41 we find

$$\phi(x_1, x_2) = \sum_{H_1} \sum_{H_2} \Omega_{H_1 H_2 0}\, e^{-i2\pi(H_1 x_1 + H_2 x_2)}$$

By means of an analogous procedure it is easily shown that we are able to synthesize a new function χ, representing the projection of the function onto a straight line, if the only known coefficients are of the type $\Omega_{nh_1, nh_2, nh_3}$, where h_1, h_2, h_3 are given integers while n assumes all possible integral values.

D. **Only the Moduli $\Omega_{H_1H_2H_3}$ Are Known.** A synthesis of the function Ω is not possible when only the moduli $|\Omega_H|$ are known; but as in the preceding case of partially known coefficients we can construct another function which is related to Ω. This new function, ψ, is obtained as follows.[7] Consider two points $\bar{r}$ and $\bar{r} + \bar{s}$ within the crystal medium. We shall vary $\bar{r}$, keeping $\bar{s}$ constant, throughout the entire unit cell, and at each location $\bar{r}$ we shall form the product $\Omega(\bar{r})\Omega(\bar{r} + \bar{s})$ of the values of the function Ω at the two ends of vector $\bar{s}$. The average value of this product is the function $\psi(\bar{s})$, i.e.,

$$\psi(\bar{s}) \equiv V^{-1} \int_V \Omega(\bar{r})\Omega(\bar{r} + \bar{s})\, dv \qquad [1{\cdot}42]$$

When we expand $\Omega(\bar{r})$ and $\Omega(\bar{r} + \bar{s})$ in Fourier series in accordance with Equation 1·27*b* the following result is obtained

$$\psi(\bar{s}) = V^{-1} \sum_H \sum_K \Omega_H \Omega_K\, e^{-i2\pi \bar{B}_K \cdot \bar{s}} \int_V e^{-i2\pi \bar{B}_{H+K} \cdot \bar{r}}\, dv \qquad [1{\cdot}43]$$

Every integral on the right side of Equation 1·43 vanishes unless $H + K = 0$ (actually $H_1 + K_1 = H_2 + K_2 = H_3 + K_3 = 0$), in which case the value is V. On the assumption that the function Ω is real we have furthermore $\Omega_{\bar{H}} = \Omega_H^*$. Accordingly Equation 1·43 reduces to a triple Fourier series

$$\psi(\bar{s}) = \sum_H |\Omega_H|^2\, e^{i2\pi \bar{B}_H \cdot \bar{s}} \qquad [1{\cdot}44]$$

which shows that the function ψ can be synthesized if all moduli $|\Omega_H|$ are known.

The restrictions regarding the function Ω and the coefficients Ω_H which were discussed under the headings *A*, *B*, and *C* of this section may equally well be imposed upon the function $\psi(\bar{s})$ and the coefficients $|\Omega_H|^2$ and obviously with quite analogous conclusions.

In subsequent chapters we shall have to draw heavily upon the results which have been obtained in this and in the preceding section.

12. PRIMITIVE AND NON-PRIMITIVE LATTICE REPRESENTATIONS

In formulating the lattice postulate it was stated that the vectors $\bar{a}_1$, $\bar{a}_2$, $\bar{a}_3$ are characteristic of the crystal medium. This statement does not imply that the vector set is unique, and we shall therefore inquire into the possible existence of equivalent sets. In order to investi-

[7] A. L. Patterson, *Phys. Rev.*, **46**, 372 (1934); *Zeitschr. f. Krist.*, **90**, 517 (1935).

gate this problem consider a lattice based upon the vectors $\bar{a}_1$, $\bar{a}_2$, $\bar{a}_3$. The lattice vectors are accordingly of the form $L_1\bar{a}_1 + L_2\bar{a}_2 + L_3\bar{a}_3$ where L_1, L_2, L_3 are any three integers. Any three vectors $\bar{a}_1'$, $\bar{a}_2'$, $\bar{a}_3'$ are defined as equivalent to the initial set if the following two conditions are fulfilled. (*a*) Every lattice vector of the given lattice can be described by means of a vector $L_1'\bar{a}_1' + L_2'\bar{a}_2' + L_3'\bar{a}_3'$ where L_1', L_2', L_3' are three integers, and (*b*) a vector $L_1'\bar{a}_1' + L_2'\bar{a}_2' + L_3'\bar{a}_3'$ where L_1', L_2', L_3' are any three integers represents one of the given lattice vectors.

It is clear that the vectors $\bar{a}_1'$, $\bar{a}_2'$, $\bar{a}_3'$ must be given as linear combinations of the initial vectors $\bar{a}_1$, $\bar{a}_2$, $\bar{a}_3$. The relationships between the two vector sets are accordingly of the type given by Equations 1·13 and 1·15 in section 6 of this chapter. If the two vector sets are equivalent, then any one lattice vector is characterized by two sets of three integers, namely, L_1, L_2, L_3 referring to the original vectors $\bar{a}_1$, $\bar{a}_2$, $\bar{a}_3$, and L_1', L_2', L_3' referring to the new vectors $\bar{a}_1'$, $\bar{a}_2'$, $\bar{a}_3'$. The quantities L_j transform as do the reciprocal vectors; hence we find with the aid of Equations 1·16

$$L_j' = \frac{1}{\Delta}\sum_k c_{j\,k}^* L_k, \quad L_j = \sum_k c_{kj} L_k' \qquad [1\cdot45]$$

where the symbol Δ stands for the determinant formed by the nine coefficients c_{jk}, and where $c_{j\,k}^*$ is the cofactor of the element c_{jk} in the determinant Δ. As shown by Equation 1·14, Δ measures the ratio between the volumes of the new and old unit cells, i.e., $(\bar{a}_1'\bar{a}_2'\bar{a}_3')/(\bar{a}_1\bar{a}_2\bar{a}_3) = \Delta$. The two conditions for the equivalence of the vector sets $\bar{a}_1$, $\bar{a}_2$, $\bar{a}_3$ and $\bar{a}_1'$, $\bar{a}_2'$, $\bar{a}_3'$ require that all coefficients c_{jk} be integers and in addition that the determinant Δ have the value $+1$ or -1. According to the latter requirement equivalent vector sets correspond to unit cells of equal volume. It is obviously possible to find an infinite number of different sets of nine integers c_{jk} which satisfy the condition $\Delta = \pm 1$, and it is hence to be concluded that there is an infinite number of equivalent vector sets in any crystal medium.

A vector set $\bar{a}_1$, $\bar{a}_2$, $\bar{a}_3$ is said to be primitive if it is impossible to find three vectors $\bar{s}_1$, $\bar{s}_2$, $\bar{s}_3$, for which $0 < |(\bar{s}_1\bar{s}_2\bar{s}_3)| < |(\bar{a}_1\bar{a}_2\bar{a}_3)|$ such that $\Omega(\bar{r}) = \Omega(\bar{r} + L_1\bar{s}_1 + L_2\bar{s}_2 + L_3\bar{s}_3)$ for any physical function Ω, for any $\bar{r}$ and for any three integers L_1, L_2, L_3. It is clear that if $\bar{a}_1$, $\bar{a}_2$, $\bar{a}_3$ is a primitive set, then any equivalent vector set is also primitive.

Consider a given lattice based upon a primitive vector set $\bar{a}_1$, $\bar{a}_2$, $\bar{a}_3$. Let us choose three new vectors $\bar{a}_1'$, $\bar{a}_2'$, $\bar{a}_3'$ equal to any three lattice vectors not all lying in a plane. The new vectors are thus of the form

$\bar{a}'_j = \sum_k c_{jk}\bar{a}_k$ with integral coefficients, and the determinant Δ is equal to some integer different from zero. If $\Delta = \pm 1$ the set $\bar{a}'_1, \bar{a}'_2, \bar{a}'_3$ is equivalent to $\bar{a}_1, \bar{a}_2, \bar{a}_3$ and a primitive set, while $\bar{a}'_1, \bar{a}'_2, \bar{a}'_3$ is a non-primitive set if $|\Delta| > 1$. We will assume that the set $\bar{a}'_1, \bar{a}'_2, \bar{a}'_3$ is non-primitive and investigate some of the properties of such a triplet. A lattice vector $\sum L_j\bar{a}_j$ will, according to Equation 1·15, be given by the expression

$$\sum_k \left(\sum_j \frac{1}{\Delta} c^*_{k\,j} L_j \right) \bar{a}'_k \qquad [1·46]$$

when referred to the new vectors $\bar{a}'_1, \bar{a}'_2, \bar{a}'_3$. The coefficients $\sum_j \frac{1}{\Delta} c^*_{k\,j} L_j$ are not integers for every set of three integral values L_j. A vector of the form $\sum L'_j\bar{a}'_j$, where L'_1, L'_2, L'_3 are integers, accordingly cannot represent all the lattice vectors of the given lattice. In order to obtain all the given lattice vectors by means of a non-primitive set $\bar{a}'_1, \bar{a}'_2, \bar{a}'_3$, fractional values of the coefficients L'_j must also be permitted. Such a representation of the lattice is called a non-primitive lattice representation.

If there were not in existence well-established conventions restricting our freedom in the choice of vector sets, it would be unnecessary ever to make use of non-primitive vector triplets. We have found it advisable to follow tradition rather than logic in this matter, and hence non-primitive lattice representations will on occasion be found in this book. It is, however, to be understood that any given lattice representation is to be considered primitive unless it is explicitly stated that it is non-primitive. Whenever we are free to choose the vectors $\bar{a}_1, \bar{a}_2, \bar{a}_3$ without interference from rules of convention it is convenient to use the following procedure. The vectors $\bar{a}_1, \bar{a}_2, \bar{a}_3$ are set equal to the three shortest lattice vectors which do not all lie in a plane. The positive directions of the vectors can always be so chosen that the angles $\alpha_1, \alpha_2, \alpha_3$ all lie in the range $\frac{\pi}{3} \leq \alpha_j \leq \frac{\pi}{2}$, or all in the range $\frac{\pi}{2} \leq \alpha_j \leq \frac{2\pi}{3}$. It is easily shown that the vectors $\bar{a}_1, \bar{a}_2, \bar{a}_3$ obtained in this manner form a primitive set.

We shall next illustrate our results by means of a series of examples. It will be assumed that the vector set $\bar{a}_1, \bar{a}_2, \bar{a}_3$ is known to be primitive, and a new set $\bar{a}'_1, \bar{a}'_2, \bar{a}'_3$ is introduced by means of equations of the form $\bar{a}'_j = \sum c_{jk}\bar{a}_k$ with integral coefficients. The transformations given in these examples lead to the only non-primitive lattice representations which will be used in subsequent chapters.

Example 1. The base- (or side-) centered lattice representation. Let the new set of vectors $\bar{a}_1', \bar{a}_2', \bar{a}_3'$ be defined by the equations

$$\begin{aligned} \bar{a}_1' &= \bar{a}_1 \\ \bar{a}_2' &= \quad \bar{a}_2 \\ \bar{a}_3' &= \bar{a}_1 \quad + 2\bar{a}_3 \end{aligned} \qquad [1\cdot47]$$

Thus $\Delta = +2$ and the new vector set is non-primitive. The converse transformation will accordingly contain fractional coefficients. Using Equation 1·15, we find

$$\begin{aligned} \bar{a}_1 &= \bar{a}_1' \\ \bar{a}_2 &= \quad \bar{a}_2' \\ \bar{a}_3 &= -\tfrac{1}{2}\bar{a}_1' \quad + \tfrac{1}{2}\bar{a}_3' \end{aligned} \qquad [1\cdot48]$$

When the equivalent points of the lattice are referred to the new vector set the representation takes the form

$$\bar{r} + K_1\bar{a}_1' + K_2\bar{a}_2' + K_3\bar{a}_3' + K(\tfrac{1}{2}\bar{a}_1' + \tfrac{1}{2}\bar{a}_3') \qquad [1\cdot49]$$

where K_1, K_2, K_3 are any three integers and where K may be set equal to 0 or 1. Since $\Delta = 2$ there are evidently two equivalent points in any one unit cell, namely, $\bar{r}$ and $\bar{r} + \frac{1}{2}\bar{a}_1' + \frac{1}{2}\bar{a}_3'$. If one of the two points is placed at a corner of the unit cell the other point will lie at the center of the base (or at the center of one side) of the unit cell, whence the name base-centered unit cell and base-centered lattice representation.

Example 2. The body-centered lattice representation. Consider next the transformation characterized by the equations

$$\begin{aligned} \bar{a}_1' &= \bar{a}_1 & \bar{a}_1 &= \bar{a}_1' \\ \bar{a}_2' &= \quad \bar{a}_2, & \bar{a}_2 &= \quad \bar{a}_2' \\ \bar{a}_3' &= \bar{a}_1 + \bar{a}_2 + 2\bar{a}_3 & \bar{a}_3 &= -\tfrac{1}{2}\bar{a}_1' - \tfrac{1}{2}\bar{a}_2' + \tfrac{1}{2}\bar{a}_3' \end{aligned} \qquad [1\cdot50]$$

The transformation determinant has again the value $+2$. In this case the equivalent points are represented not by Equation 1·49, but by

$$\bar{r} + K_1\bar{a}_1' + K_2\bar{a}_2' + K_3\bar{a}_3' + K(\tfrac{1}{2}\bar{a}_1' + \tfrac{1}{2}\bar{a}_2' + \tfrac{1}{2}\bar{a}_3') \qquad [1\cdot51]$$

The representation 1·51 is called body-centered because a corner and the center of a unit cell are equivalent points.

Example 3. The following transformation gives a non-primitive set $\bar{a}_1', \bar{a}_2', \bar{a}_3'$ for which $\Delta = 3$,

$$\begin{aligned} \bar{a}_1' &= -\bar{a}_1 + \bar{a}_2 & \bar{a}_1 &= -\tfrac{2}{3}\bar{a}_1' - \tfrac{1}{3}\bar{a}_2' + \tfrac{1}{3}\bar{a}_3' \\ \bar{a}_2' &= \quad - \bar{a}_2 + \bar{a}_3, & \bar{a}_2 &= \tfrac{1}{3}\bar{a}_1' - \tfrac{1}{3}\bar{a}_2' + \tfrac{1}{3}\bar{a}_3' \\ \bar{a}_3' &= \bar{a}_1 + \bar{a}_2 + \bar{a}_3 & \bar{a}_3 &= \tfrac{1}{3}\bar{a}_1' + \tfrac{2}{3}\bar{a}_2' + \tfrac{1}{3}\bar{a}_3' \end{aligned} \qquad [1\cdot52]$$

The equivalent points are expressed in the form

$$\bar{r} + K_1\bar{a}_1' + K_2\bar{a}_2' + K_3\bar{a}_3' + K(\tfrac{1}{3}\bar{a}_1' + \tfrac{2}{3}\bar{a}_2' + \tfrac{1}{3}\bar{a}_3') \qquad [1\cdot53]$$

where K_1, K_2, K_3 represent any three integers, while K is an integer which may be restricted to the values 0, 1, and 2. There are three equivalent points per unit cell. If one of these is the origin the three are

$$0, \quad \tfrac{1}{3}\bar{a}_1' + \tfrac{2}{3}\bar{a}_2' + \tfrac{1}{3}\bar{a}_3', \quad \tfrac{2}{3}\bar{a}_1' + \tfrac{1}{3}\bar{a}_2' + \tfrac{2}{3}\bar{a}_3'$$

Example 4. The face-centered lattice representation. In this final example we will set

$$\begin{aligned} \bar{a}_1' &= -\bar{a}_1 + \bar{a}_2 + \bar{a}_3 & \qquad \bar{a}_1 &= \tfrac{1}{2}\bar{a}_2' + \tfrac{1}{2}\bar{a}_3' \\ \bar{a}_2' &= \bar{a}_1 - \bar{a}_2 + \bar{a}_3, & \bar{a}_2 &= \tfrac{1}{2}\bar{a}_1' + \tfrac{1}{2}\bar{a}_3' \\ \bar{a}_3' &= \bar{a}_1 + \bar{a}_2 - \bar{a}_3 & \bar{a}_3 &= \tfrac{1}{2}\bar{a}_1' + \tfrac{1}{2}\bar{a}_2' \end{aligned} \qquad [1\cdot54]$$

The determinant $\Delta = +4$ and the representation of the equivalent points become

$$\bar{r} + K_1\bar{a}_1' + K_2\bar{a}_2' + K_3\bar{a}_3' + K_1'(\tfrac{1}{2}\bar{a}_2' + \tfrac{1}{2}\bar{a}_3') + K_2'(\tfrac{1}{2}\bar{a}_1' + \tfrac{1}{2}\bar{a}_3') + K_3'(\tfrac{1}{2}\bar{a}_1' + \tfrac{1}{2}\bar{a}_2') \qquad [1\cdot55]$$

where K_1, K_2, K_3 are any three integers and where K_1', K_2', K_3' assume the values 0 or 1 independently of one another. There are four equivalent points per unit cell, and if one of these is chosen at the corner of the unit cell the three others will be at the centers of the parallelopiped faces. The representation is therefore called face-centered.

CHAPTER II

THE SYMMETRY OF CRYSTALS

This chapter is devoted to a theoretical study of the symmetry properties of crystals. The subject can be presented in very elegant form if results taken from matrix algebra and group theory are used to full advantage. However, it is not fair to the reader to base the discussion on a presumed extensive knowledge of these fields of mathematics, and we shall therefore have to be satisfied with a less elegant treatment. On the other hand, a logical presentation of the theory of crystal symmetry cannot be achieved unless some use is made of matrix-algebraic and group-theoretical concepts. These might have been introduced according to need in the course of our investigation, but this procedure is not altogether satisfactory. We have found it preferable to give the elements of dyadic algebra and of group theory in separate appendices at the end of this volume. The reader who is not already familiar with these topics will probably find it necessary to study the appendices (or similar presentations) in order to follow the discussions in this chapter.

1. THE SYMMETRY CONCEPT

The subject of crystal symmetry cannot conveniently be approached until the symmetry concept has been properly introduced, and we shall therefore begin with a general definition of symmetry in relation to an object with a given set of properties.

Imagine that the space occupied by the object undergoes a transformation which preserves all linear dimensions. If the given properties of the object are invariant under this transformation it is by definition a symmetry operation. Thus, if a point $\bar{r}$ is transformed into a point $\bar{r}'$ by means of a symmetry operation the properties of the object have identical values at $\bar{r}$ and $\bar{r}'$, i.e., $\bar{r}$ and $\bar{r}'$ are equivalent points. It is possible that the object under consideration is initially defined in terms of the invariance of its properties under particular transformations of the type just described. Such symmetry operations which are used to define the object are said to be trivial. Any object has at least one trivial symmetry operation, and this is the identity operation which has the property of transforming every point into itself. Particular objects may have additional trivial symmetry operations. Thus any translation is a trivial symmetry operation of a homogeneous body, and any lattice translation is a trivial symmetry operation of a crystal lattice.

An object which has symmetry operations is said to have symmetry, and the complete collection of all symmetry operations of an object defines its symmetry. The symmetry of an object is trivial if all operations of the collection are trivial. The collection of all symmetry operations of any given object satisfies the group postulates (see Appendix B), and is thus a group. In order to show the truth of this statement we have to investigate some general properties of symmetry operations.

Let the symbol E designate the identity operation, and the symbol S any other symmetry operation. Any point $\bar{r}$ of the space under consideration is transformed by a symmetry operation S into an equivalent point $\bar{r}'$, and it is convenient to represent this transformation by means of the symbolic equation

$$\bar{r}' = \bar{r} \cdot S \tag{2·1}$$

The identity operation is accordingly defined by

$$\bar{r} = \bar{r} \cdot E \quad \text{for any } \bar{r} \tag{2·2}$$

Symmetry operations preserve all linear dimensions and they belong therefore to a particular type of linear transformations. Since the relationship between equivalent points $\bar{r}$ and $\bar{r}'$ is linear it has the general form

$$\bar{r}' = \bar{r} \cdot \boldsymbol{\phi} + \bar{t} \equiv \bar{r} \cdot [\boldsymbol{\phi}, \bar{t}] \tag{2·3}$$

where $\boldsymbol{\phi}$ is a dyadic (second-order tensor) and $\bar{t}$ a vector. Comparing with Equation 2·1 we may accordingly set $S \equiv [\boldsymbol{\phi}, \bar{t}]$ which operates on a vector in the manner defined by Equation 2·3. In particular the analytic form of the identity operation becomes

$$E \equiv [\mathbf{I}, 0] \equiv \mathbf{I} \tag{2·4}$$

where the symbol $\mathbf{I}$ as in Appendix A represents the idemfactor. The conservation of linear dimensions is expressed in the statement

$$|\bar{r}_1 - \bar{r}_2| = |(\bar{r}_1 - \bar{r}_2) \cdot S| \tag{2·5}$$

for any two vectors $\bar{r}_1$ and $\bar{r}_2$. This condition may be rewritten in the form

$$(\bar{r}_1 - \bar{r}_2) \cdot \mathbf{I} \cdot (\bar{r}_1 - \bar{r}_2) = (\bar{r}_1 - \bar{r}_2) \cdot \boldsymbol{\phi} \cdot \boldsymbol{\phi}_C \cdot (\bar{r}_1 - \bar{r}_2) \tag{2·5a}$$

which according to Equation A·52 requires

$$\boldsymbol{\phi} \cdot \boldsymbol{\phi}_C = \mathbf{I}, \quad \text{i.e.,} \quad \boldsymbol{\phi} = \boldsymbol{\phi}_C^{-1} \tag{2·5b}$$

where $\boldsymbol{\phi}_C$ and $\boldsymbol{\phi}^{-1}$ are the dyadics conjugate and reciprocal to $\boldsymbol{\phi}$.

Suppose that $S_1 = [\boldsymbol{\phi}_1, \bar{t}_1]$ and $S_2 = [\boldsymbol{\phi}_2, \bar{t}_2]$ are two symmetry operations and that space is transformed first by S_1 and then by S_2. Any initial point $\bar{r}$ will thus be transformed into an equivalent point $\bar{r}' = \bar{r} \cdot S_1$ and this will further be transformed into the equivalent point $\bar{r}'' = \bar{r}' \cdot S_2$. The single transformation which turns points $\bar{r}$ directly into points $\bar{r}''$ is equivalent to the transformation S_1 immediately followed by the transformation S_2; it is called the product of S_1 by S_2 and denoted by the symbol $S_1 \cdot S_2$, i.e., $\bar{r}'' = \bar{r} \cdot S_1 \cdot S_2$. With the aid of Equation 2·3 we find readily

$$S_1 \cdot S_2 = [\boldsymbol{\phi}_1, \bar{t}_1] \cdot [\boldsymbol{\phi}_2, \bar{t}_2] = [\boldsymbol{\phi}_1 \cdot \boldsymbol{\phi}_2, \bar{t}_1 \cdot \boldsymbol{\phi}_2 + \bar{t}_2] \qquad [2\cdot6]$$

which shows that in general $S_1 \cdot S_2 \neq S_2 \cdot S_1$. It follows immediately from Equations A·46 and 47 that the transformation $S_1 \cdot S_2$ satisfies the condition expressed in Equation 2·5*b* and that it thus conserves linear dimensions. Furthermore, it transforms points $\bar{r}$ into equivalent points $\bar{r}''$. Consequently $S_1 \cdot S_2$ is a symmetry operation, and we have obtained the important result that the product of any two symmetry operations is also a symmetry operation. Since we have shown that the theorem holds for the product of two symmetry operations, it becomes obvious that the theorem will hold for products involving any number of symmetry operations. In particular, the product $S \cdot S \cdots S$ containing the same symmetry operation j times is also a symmetry operation. This product is called the jth power of S and is denoted by S^j. Using Equation 2·6 one finds readily

$$S^j = [\boldsymbol{\phi}^j, \bar{t} \cdot \{\mathbf{I} + \boldsymbol{\phi} + \boldsymbol{\phi}^2 + \cdots + \boldsymbol{\phi}^{j-1}\}] \qquad [2\cdot7]$$

It is easily seen that the definition of the identity operation given in Equation 2·2 conveniently can be replaced by

$$E = E \cdot S = S \cdot E \quad \text{for any } S \qquad [2\cdot8]$$

The reciprocal (or inverse) transformation to the symmetry operation S is designated by S^{-1} and defined by

$$S \cdot S^{-1} = S^{-1} \cdot S = E \qquad [2\cdot9]$$

Since S transforms any point $\bar{r}$ into an equivalent point $\bar{r}' = \bar{r} \cdot S$, the reciprocal transformation S^{-1} will transform $\bar{r}'$ into $\bar{r}$, i.e., $\bar{r} = \bar{r}' \cdot S^{-1}$. The reciprocal transformation exists and has according to Equation 2·6 the form

$$S^{-1} = [\boldsymbol{\phi}^{-1}, -\bar{t} \cdot \boldsymbol{\phi}^{-1}] \qquad [2\cdot10]$$

on the assumption that $S \equiv [\boldsymbol{\phi}, \bar{t}]$. The condition expressed by Equation 2·5*b* is obviously fulfilled by the transformation S^{-1}, and since a set of points $\bar{r}'$ is transformed by S^{-1} into the equivalent set $\bar{r}$ it follows that the reciprocal transformation of any symmetry operation must again be a symmetry operation.

We have accordingly demonstrated that the complete collection of symmetry operations for any object has the following properties: it has the closure property; it contains the identity operation E as defined by Equation 2·8; it contains for every operation S an operation S^{-1} defined by Equation 2·9. These are just the group postulates given in Appendix B. The symmetry of an object is thus defined by a group in which the elements represent the various symmetry operations of the object. Groups of this kind may properly be called symmetry groups. Two different objects are said to have the same symmetry if the elements of their symmetry groups represent the same set of space transformations.

2. THE POSSIBLE SYMMETRY OPERATIONS OF CRYSTAL LATTICES

It has been known as an empirical fact since crystals were first studied that nearly all have non-trivial symmetry, and, indeed, symmetry has always been considered to be one of the most important properties of crystals. Nevertheless, it cannot truly be said that symmetry in a non-trivial sense is a universal property of crystals, and for this reason we omitted any reference to symmetry in the first chapter, which dealt with general properties. When the lattice hypothesis was proposed a hundred years ago there arose naturally the question of whether the empirically known symmetry properties of crystals could be explained on the basis of an assumed lattice structure. The confirmative answer to this question is contained in the theory of space groups which was developed during the latter half of the nineteenth century. The space group theory is concerned with the derivation of the symmetries which are possible for periodic media, and it has permanent value as an abstract mathematical development even if it should be found that periodic media cannot be used as models for crystal media. On the other hand, if the lattice hypothesis is correct then the space group theory is also a theory of crystal symmetry. The complete space group theory was published more than twenty years before the Laue experiment. At that time, therefore, only the macroscopic consequences of the theory could be compared with experimental observations. Direct confirmation of the theoretical predictions did not become possible until x-ray diffraction methods were developed.

The presentation of the theory of crystal symmetry to be given in this chapter is based upon the assumption that the lattice hypothesis is strictly correct. The experimental facts which justify this assumption cannot conveniently be given at this stage and they will therefore be divulged later. The particular objects the symmetry of which we wish to investigate are accordingly defined by the statement that they are media in which the physical properties, Ω, are periodic functions of position as defined by the condition given in Equation 1·17. The vectors $\bar{a}_1, \bar{a}_2, \bar{a}_3$ are characteristic of the medium and one has to assume that they form a primitive set unless there is evidence to the contrary. As a consequence conditions of the type

$$\Omega(\bar{r}) = \Omega(\bar{r} + \bar{s}) \qquad [2\cdot11]$$

for any $\bar{r}$ and for any Ω permit the conclusion to be drawn that the vector $\bar{s}$ represents one of the given lattice vectors $\bar{A}_L \equiv \sum L_j\bar{a}_j$. In order to make our considerations as general as possible it will be assumed that we have no a priori knowledge of the functions or of the vectors $\bar{a}_1, \bar{a}_2, \bar{a}_3$ beyond the facts already stated.

A group of operations which defines the symmetry of a crystal lattice is called a space group, and it is our problem to deduce all conceivable space groups. The construction of the various space groups must, however, be preceded by an investigation which determines the individual symmetry operations possible for crystal lattices.

Let $S \equiv [\boldsymbol{\phi}, \bar{t}]$ with $\boldsymbol{\phi} = \boldsymbol{\phi}_C^{-1}$ represent a symmetry operation of a crystal lattice. We already know an infinite number of such symmetry operations, namely, all lattice translations $\Gamma_{L_1L_2L_3}$, but they are trivial. The lattice translations may be given in the general form $[\boldsymbol{\phi}, \bar{t}]$, and we have

$$\begin{aligned} \Gamma_{L_1L_2L_3} &\equiv [\mathbf{I}, \bar{A}_L] \equiv [\mathbf{I}, L_1\bar{a}_1 + L_2\bar{a}_2 + L_3\bar{a}_3], \\ \Gamma_{000} &\equiv E \equiv [\mathbf{I}, 0] \equiv \mathbf{I} \end{aligned} \qquad [2\cdot12]$$

It is readily seen that the trivial symmetry operations of a crystal lattice form a group, the translation group (Γ), which thus is a subgroup of any space group. If the crystal lattice has only trivial symmetry operations the space group becomes identical with the translation group. The statement that S is a non-trivial symmetry operation of a crystal lattice imposes restrictions upon the analytic form of S, upon the vectors $\bar{a}_1$, $\bar{a}_2, \bar{a}_3$ and upon the functions Ω. The functions Ω are invariant under the symmetry operation and must therefore satisfy the condition

$$\Omega(\bar{r}) = \Omega(\bar{r} \cdot S) \qquad [2\cdot13]$$

for any $\bar{r}$. The invariance of the physical properties implies the invariance of their periodicity. Any transformation $S = [\boldsymbol{\phi}, \bar{t}]$ with $\boldsymbol{\phi} = \boldsymbol{\Phi}_C^{-1}$ which leaves the periodicity invariant will be called a *possible* symmetry operation. If in addition the condition expressed in Equation 2·13 is fulfilled then the possible symmetry operation is truly a symmetry operation.

The lattice vectors $\bar{A}_L$ are defined in terms of the natural coordinate system $\bar{a}_1, \bar{a}_2, \bar{a}_3$ and it becomes convenient to refer the other quantities to the same system or to the reciprocal system $\bar{b}_1, \bar{b}_2, \bar{b}_3$. Accordingly we set

$$\begin{aligned} \boldsymbol{\phi} &= \sum_k \bar{\phi}_k \bar{a}_k = \sum_j \bar{b}_j \bar{\phi}_j' = \sum_j \sum_k \phi_{jk} \bar{b}_j \bar{a}_k \\ \mathbf{I} &= \sum_j \bar{b}_j \bar{a}_j, \quad \bar{\phi}_k = \sum_j \phi_{jk} \bar{b}_j \\ \bar{t} &= \sum_j t_j \bar{a}_j, \quad \bar{\phi}_j' = \sum_k \phi_{jk} \bar{a}_k \end{aligned} \qquad [2\cdot14]$$

The condition $\boldsymbol{\phi} = \boldsymbol{\phi}_C^{-1}$, which insures the conservation of linear dimensions under the transformation $S \equiv [\boldsymbol{\phi}, \bar{t}]$, is readily expressed in terms of the components ϕ_{jk} and the reference vectors $\bar{a}_j$, and one finds

$$\bar{a}_j \cdot \bar{a}_k = \sum_l \sum_m \phi_{jl} \phi_{km} \bar{a}_l \cdot \bar{a}_m \qquad [2\cdot15]$$

According to results obtained in the preceding section we know that S^{-1} is a symmetry operation, if S is known to be one. Furthermore, we know that any product of symmetry operations is again a symmetry operation. Hence, if $S \equiv [\boldsymbol{\phi}, \bar{t}]$ is a symmetry operation of a crystal lattice, $S^{-1} \cdot \Gamma_L \cdot S$ is also a symmetry operation. This product is easily evaluated using Equation 2·6 and the result becomes

$$S^{-1} \cdot \Gamma_L \cdot S = [\mathbf{I}, \bar{A}_L \cdot \boldsymbol{\phi}] \qquad [2\cdot16]$$

which represents a translation. However, according to the statement of Equation 2·11, the only pure translations which are possible for the crystal lattice are by hypothesis the lattice translations. The invariance of the lattice structure under the transformation S is therefore contained in the condition

$$S^{-1} \cdot \Gamma_L \cdot S = \Gamma_{L'} \qquad [2\cdot17]$$

This requirement must be fulfilled for any translation Γ_L and we may hence set

$$S^{-1} \cdot (\Gamma) \cdot S = (\Gamma) \qquad [2\cdot18]$$

which shows that the translation group is an invariant subgroup of the space group (compare Equation B·15). In terms of the components ϕ_{jk} Equation 2·17 becomes

$$L_k' = \sum_j \phi_{jk} L_j \qquad [2\cdot19]$$

which must hold for any set of integers L_1, L_2, L_3 and L_1', L_2', L_3'. Accordingly we have the important result that all components ϕ_{jk} are integers. It is obvious — but we will nevertheless emphasize the point — that the components of $\boldsymbol{\Phi}$ are not necessarily whole numbers when the dyadic is referred to an arbitrary coordinate system. The conclusions that the components ϕ_{jk} are integral has a bearing on Equation 2·15 which is identically satisfied only if $\phi_{jk} = 0$ for $j \neq k$ and all $\phi_{jj} = +1$ or all $\phi_{jj} = -1$, i.e., only if $\boldsymbol{\Phi} = \mathbf{I}$ or if $\boldsymbol{\Phi} = -\mathbf{I}$. Accordingly, unless $\boldsymbol{\Phi} = \mathbf{I}$ or $\boldsymbol{\Phi} = -\mathbf{I}$ Equation 2·15 imposes conditions upon the vectors $\bar{a}_1$, $\bar{a}_2$, $\bar{a}_3$. For instance, if $\phi_{11} = \phi_{22} = +1$, $\phi_{33} = -1$ and all other components are zero, one finds $\bar{a}_1 \cdot \bar{a}_3 = \bar{a}_2 \cdot \bar{a}_3 = 0$.

The dyadics $\boldsymbol{\Phi} = \boldsymbol{\Phi}_C^{-1}$ are discussed in some detail in section A·5, and we shall make use of results which are obtained there. These dyadics represent rotations about an axis passing through the origin or such rotations combined with the inversion with respect to the origin. It is customary to refer to these transformations as proper or improper rotations respectively. The determinant $|\boldsymbol{\Phi}|$ is $+1$ if $\boldsymbol{\Phi}$ is proper and -1 if $\boldsymbol{\Phi}$ is improper. The complete set of all dyadics $\boldsymbol{\Phi} = \boldsymbol{\Phi}_C^{-1}$ is represented by

$$\boldsymbol{\Phi} = \pm\bar{u}\bar{u} \pm (\mathbf{I} - \bar{u}\bar{u}) \cos\varphi \pm \mathbf{I} \times \bar{u} \sin\varphi \qquad [2\cdot20]$$

where the upper sign corresponds to proper, the lower sign to improper rotations. The unit vector $\bar{u}$ satisfies the condition $\bar{u} \cdot \boldsymbol{\Phi} = \bar{u}$ when $\boldsymbol{\Phi}$ is proper, the condition $\bar{u} \cdot \boldsymbol{\Phi} = -\bar{u}$ when $\boldsymbol{\Phi}$ is improper and defines the proper or improper rotation axis, while φ is the rotation angle. When $\varphi = 0$ we have $\boldsymbol{\Phi} = \pm\mathbf{I}$, in which case any direction is a rotation axis. The jth power of $\boldsymbol{\Phi}$ is easily seen to be

$$\boldsymbol{\Phi}^j = |\boldsymbol{\Phi}|^j[\bar{u}\bar{u} + (\mathbf{I} - \bar{u}\bar{u}) \cos j\varphi + \mathbf{I} \times \bar{u} \sin j\varphi] \qquad [2\cdot21]$$

The dyadics $\boldsymbol{\Phi}$ which are contained in the symmetry operations of crystal lattices belong to the general type given in Equation 2·20, but they must in addition have integral components ϕ_{jk} in the coordinate system $\bar{a}_1$, $\bar{a}_2$, $\bar{a}_3$. This requirement imposes conditions upon the value of the rotation angle φ and upon the direction of the axis $\bar{u}$ relative to the crystal lattice. The particular values which φ may have are readily found when we recall that the scalar of a dyadic is an invariant quantity. In the reference frame $\bar{a}_1$, $\bar{a}_2$, $\bar{a}_3$ corresponding to the form of $\boldsymbol{\Phi}$ given in Equations 2·14, we have $\boldsymbol{\Phi}_S = \sum\phi_{jj}$, which is an integer since all components ϕ_{jk} are integers. On the other hand $\boldsymbol{\Phi}_S = \pm(1 + 2\cos\varphi)$ according to Equation 2·20. Setting the two expressions equal we obtain the result

$$1 + 2\cos\varphi = \pm\sum\phi_{jj} = \text{integer} \qquad [2\cdot22]$$

The only distinct values of φ which satisfy this equation are

$$\varphi = \frac{2\pi j}{n} \quad \text{with} \quad \begin{array}{l} n = 1, 2, 3, 4, \text{ or } 6 \\ j = 1, 2 \cdots n \end{array} \qquad [2\cdot23]$$

Since, according to Equation 2·21, $\mathbf{\Phi}^j(\varphi) = \pm\mathbf{\Phi}(j\varphi)$ we may state that the possible dyadics are powers of the dyadics given in Equation 2·20 with φ restricted to the values $\varphi = 2\pi/n$, $n = 1, 2, 3, 4$, and 6. It is convenient to introduce separate symbols for these dyadics and the following scheme will be adopted. A proper dyadic for which $\varphi = 2\pi/n$ will be denoted by $\mathbf{n}$ and the corresponding improper dyadic will be given the symbol $\bar{\mathbf{n}}$, and we recall that $\bar{\mathbf{n}} \equiv -\mathbf{n} \equiv -\mathbf{I}\cdot\mathbf{n} \equiv \mathbf{n}\cdot(-\mathbf{I})$. The complete list of possible dyadics $\mathbf{n}$ is

$$\begin{aligned} \mathbf{1} &\equiv \mathbf{I} \\ \mathbf{2} &\equiv 2\bar{u}\bar{u} - \mathbf{I} \\ \mathbf{3} &\equiv \tfrac{3}{2}\bar{u}\bar{u} - \tfrac{1}{2}\mathbf{I} + \tfrac{1}{2}\sqrt{3}\,\mathbf{I}\times\bar{u} \\ \mathbf{4} &\equiv \bar{u}\bar{u} + \mathbf{I}\times\bar{u} \\ \mathbf{6} &\equiv \tfrac{1}{2}\bar{u}\bar{u} + \tfrac{1}{2}\mathbf{I} + \tfrac{1}{2}\sqrt{3}\,\mathbf{I}\times\bar{u} \end{aligned} \qquad [2\cdot24]$$

Let us next find the restriction which must be imposed upon the orientation of the axes $\bar{u}$. Since $\bar{\mathbf{n}} = -\mathbf{n}$ it is evidently true that the restriction is the same for proper as for improper axes. It is shown in section A·5 that if $\mathbf{\Phi}$ is a proper dyadic (but $\mathbf{\Phi} \neq \mathbf{I}$), then $\mathbf{\Phi} - \mathbf{I}$ is a uniplanar dyadic with its plane normal to the rotation axis $\bar{u}$. When $\mathbf{\Phi}$ is expressed in the form given in Equations 2·14 we have

$$\mathbf{\Phi} - \mathbf{I} = \sum[\bar{\phi}_k - \bar{b}_k]\bar{a}_k = \sum\bar{b}_j[\bar{\phi}_j' - \bar{a}_j] \qquad [2\cdot25]$$

The components ϕ_{jk} are, however, integers and the three vectors $\bar{\phi}_j' - \bar{a}_j$ are therefore lattice vectors $\bar{A}_l$, while the three vectors $\bar{\phi}_k - \bar{b}_k$ are reciprocal lattice vectors $\bar{B}_h$. The plane of the dyadic $\mathbf{\Phi} - \mathbf{I}$ contains these six vectors and is thus a lattice plane in the initial as well as in the reciprocal lattice. The rotation axis $\bar{u}$, which is normal to this plane, is consequently parallel to a lattice vector $\bar{A}_l$ and to a reciprocal lattice vector $\bar{B}_h$.

We shall next deduce the condition which must be imposed upon the translational part $\bar{t}$ of symmetry operations $S \equiv [\mathbf{\Phi}, \bar{t}]$ of crystal lattices. All symmetry operations in the set $S\cdot(\Gamma)$ are equivalent in the sense that the existence of any one of them implies the existence of all others. A product $S\cdot\Gamma_L$ has the form

$$S\cdot\Gamma_L = [\mathbf{\Phi}, \bar{t} + \bar{A}_L] \qquad [2\cdot26]$$

It will suffice to consider just one of the transformations in the set

$S \cdot (\Gamma)$. If we let $S \equiv [\boldsymbol{\phi}, \bar{t}]$ be the operation representative of the set we may, as shown by Equation 2·26, restrict the translation vector $\bar{t} \equiv \sum t_j \bar{a}_j$ to the range $0 \leq t_j < 1$.

The dyadics $\boldsymbol{\phi}$ are of the type $\mathbf{n}^j$ or $\bar{\mathbf{n}}^j$. All the various powers of a given dyadic $\mathbf{n}$ or $\bar{\mathbf{n}}$ are not distinct, however, since there exists an integer m for every $\boldsymbol{\phi} = \mathbf{n}$ and for every $\boldsymbol{\phi} = \bar{\mathbf{n}}$ such that

$$\boldsymbol{\phi}^m = \mathbf{I} \qquad [2{\cdot}27]$$

Thus $\boldsymbol{\phi}^{m+j} = \boldsymbol{\phi}^j$, $\boldsymbol{\phi}^{-1} = \boldsymbol{\phi}^{m-1}$, and there are only m distinct powers of $\boldsymbol{\phi}$. The smallest positive integer m for which $\boldsymbol{\phi}^m = \mathbf{I}$ is the order of the dyadic. Clearly, $m = n$ for all dyadics $\mathbf{n}$ and for all dyadics $\bar{\mathbf{n}}$ with even n, while $m = 2n$ for dyadics $\bar{\mathbf{n}}$ with odd n. The transformation S^m is a symmetry operation if S is known to be one. Using Equations 2·7 and 2·27, we have

$$S^m = [\mathbf{I}, \bar{t} \cdot \{\boldsymbol{\phi}\}], \qquad [2{\cdot}28a]$$

where

$$\{\boldsymbol{\phi}\} \equiv \mathbf{I} + \boldsymbol{\phi} + \cdots \boldsymbol{\phi}^{m-1} \qquad [2{\cdot}28b]$$

Thus S^m is a pure translation and as stated in connection with Equation 2·11 we can therefore draw the conclusion that it represents one of the lattice translations Γ_L, i.e.,

$$S^m = \Gamma_L \quad \text{or} \quad \bar{t} \cdot \{\boldsymbol{\phi}\} = \bar{A}_L \qquad [2{\cdot}29]$$

This equation is identically satisfied only if $\{\boldsymbol{\phi}\} = 0$, and consequently $\bar{t}$ cannot be arbitrary when $\{\boldsymbol{\phi}\} \neq 0$. The dyadics $\{\mathbf{n}\}$ and $\{\bar{\mathbf{n}}\}$ are easily evaluated by direct summation in accordance with the definition of Equation 2·28 and they are

$$\begin{aligned} \{\mathbf{1}\} &= \mathbf{I} \\ \{\mathbf{n}\} &= n\,\bar{u}\bar{u} \quad \text{for } n = 2, 3, 4, \text{ or } 6 \\ \{\bar{\mathbf{n}}\} &= 0 \quad \text{for } n = 1, 3, 4, \text{ or } 6 \\ \{\bar{\mathbf{2}}\} &= 2(\mathbf{I} - \bar{u}\bar{u}) \end{aligned} \qquad [2{\cdot}30]$$

Thus the translation vector $\bar{t}$ of a symmetry operation $[\boldsymbol{\phi}, \bar{t}]$ of a crystal lattice may have any value when $\boldsymbol{\phi} = \bar{\mathbf{1}}, \bar{\mathbf{3}}, \bar{\mathbf{4}}$, or $\bar{\mathbf{6}}$, while it must be zero when $\boldsymbol{\phi} = \mathbf{1}$. When $\boldsymbol{\phi} = \mathbf{n}$ with $n = 2, 3, 4$, or 6, the vector $\bar{t}$ must satisfy the equation

$$(\bar{t} \cdot \bar{u})\bar{u} = \frac{1}{n}\bar{A}_L = \frac{j}{n}\bar{A}_l \qquad [2{\cdot}31]$$

This equation shows in the first place that the rotation axis $\bar{u}$ is parallel to a lattice vector, in corroboration of an earlier result, secondly that the component of the vector $\bar{t}$ along the rotation axis is equal to a fraction j/n, $j = 0, 1 \cdots n-1$, of the lattice period in that direction. However, there is no restriction upon the component of $\bar{t}$ normal to the axis $\bar{u}$. When $\boldsymbol{\phi} = \bar{\mathbf{2}}$ Equation 2·29 becomes

$$\bar{t} - (\bar{t} \cdot \bar{u})\bar{u} = j\bar{A}_l/2, \quad j = 0 \text{ or } 1 \qquad [2\cdot32]$$

In this case the component of the vector $\bar{t}$ along the axis $\bar{u}$ may have any value, while the component normal to $\bar{u}$ is either zero or equal to one-half of a lattice vector.

We have now deduced all the individual symmetry operations which crystal lattices may have. It is useful, however, to study in greater detail the results which so far have been obtained, before we pass on to a derivation of the space groups.

3. CLASSIFICATION OF THE POSSIBLE SYMMETRY OPERATIONS AND OF THEIR SYMMETRY ELEMENTS

Summarizing the results obtained in the preceding section we may state that the possible symmetry operations $S \equiv [\boldsymbol{\phi}, \bar{t}]$ of crystal lattices are solutions of Equation 2·29, i.e., of $S^m = \Gamma_L$, where $m = 1, 2, 3, 4$, or 6. Accordingly the dyadic part $\boldsymbol{\phi}$ is restricted to powers of the dyadics $\pm\mathbf{n}$, $n = 1, 2, 3, 4$, or 6, while the translation vector $\bar{t}$ satisfies the condition $\bar{t} \cdot \{\boldsymbol{\phi}\} = \bar{A}_L$. The scalar components ϕ_{jk} of $\boldsymbol{\phi}$ in the coordinate system $\bar{a}_1$, $\bar{a}_2$, $\bar{a}_3$ are all integers, and this requirement will in general lead to interrelationships between the vectors $\bar{a}_1$, $\bar{a}_2$, $\bar{a}_3$ as expressed in Equation 2·15.

In this section we shall investigate the nature of the space transformations which the possible symmetry operations represent and in the course of this investigation we shall find it convenient to make extensive use of the concept of symmetry elements. A symmetry element is a point, a straight line, or a plane which is transformed into itself under a symmetry operation and we speak thus of symmetry center, axis, or plane. There are different ways in which a straight line or a plane may be transformed into itself, and it is therefore useful to distinguish between different kinds of symmetry axes and symmetry planes. Accordingly we shall introduce the following definitions.

A point $\bar{r} = \bar{r}_0$ is said to be a *symmetry center* of the symmetry operation S, if it is transformed into itself, i.e., if

$$\bar{r}_0 \cdot S = \bar{r}_0 \quad \text{or} \quad \bar{r}_0 \cdot (\boldsymbol{\phi} - \mathbf{I}) + \bar{t} = 0 \qquad [2\cdot33]$$

A straight line $\bar{r} = \bar{s}_0 + k\bar{u}$ ($\bar{s}_0$ and $\bar{u}$ constants, k variable) is a *symmetry axis* of the symmetry operation S if, for any k,

$$(\bar{s}_0 + k\bar{u}) \cdot S = \bar{s}_0 + k'\bar{u} \qquad [2\cdot34]$$

The symmetry axis is a *proper rotation axis* if, for any k,

$$(\bar{s}_0 + k\bar{u}) \cdot S = \bar{s}_0 + k\bar{u} \qquad [2{\cdot}35]$$

it is an *improper rotation axis* if, for any k,

$$(\bar{s}_0 + k\bar{u}) \cdot S = \bar{s}_0 - k\bar{u} \qquad [2{\cdot}36]$$

and it is a *screw axis* if, for any k,

$$(\bar{s}_0 + k\bar{u}) \cdot S = \bar{s}_0 + (k + t_0)\bar{u} \qquad [2{\cdot}37]$$

where t_0 is a constant.

A plane $\bar{r} = \bar{s}_0 + \bar{s}$, $\bar{s} \cdot \bar{u} = 0$ ($\bar{s}_0$ and $\bar{u}$ constants) is a *symmetry plane* of the operation S if for any point in the plane

$$(\bar{s}_0 + \bar{s}) \cdot S = \bar{s}_0 + \bar{s}', \quad \text{where} \quad \bar{s}' \cdot \bar{u} = 0 \qquad [2{\cdot}38]$$

The symmetry plane is a *reflection plane* if, for any $\bar{s}$ for which $\bar{s} \cdot \bar{u} = 0$,

$$(\bar{s}_0 + \bar{s}) \cdot S = \bar{s}_0 + \bar{s} \qquad [2{\cdot}39]$$

and it is a *glide plane* if, for any $\bar{s}$ for which $\bar{s} \cdot \bar{u} = 0$,

$$(\bar{s}_0 + \bar{s}) \cdot S = \bar{s}_0 + \bar{s} + \bar{t}_0 \qquad [2{\cdot}40]$$

where $\bar{t}_0$ is constant and $\bar{t}_0 \cdot \bar{u} = 0$.

We note that every point of a proper rotation axis and of a reflection plane is a symmetry center, while only one point of an improper rotation axis, namely, the point $\bar{r} = \bar{s}_0$, is a symmetry center.

The dyadic part $\boldsymbol{\phi}$ of a possible symmetry operation represents, as we shall learn in section A·5, a proper or improper rotation about an axis (about any axis if $\boldsymbol{\phi} = \pm\mathbf{I}$) through the origin, and since

$$[\boldsymbol{\phi}, \bar{t}] \equiv \boldsymbol{\phi} \cdot [\mathbf{I}, \bar{t}] \qquad [2{\cdot}41]$$

we may consider the possible symmetry operations to be combinations of such rotations with translations. These combinations may represent proper or improper rotations, although about axes which do not pass through the origin, or they may represent types of transformations which we have not hitherto discussed.

In order to classify the possible symmetry operations it is useful to divide them into two main types. The first type includes only the operations which satisfy the equation

$$S^m = \Gamma_{000} = E, \quad \text{i.e.,} \quad \bar{t} \cdot \{\boldsymbol{\phi}\} = 0 \qquad [2{\cdot}42]$$

and we will call them *closed* operations since the equivalent points $\bar{r}$, $\bar{r} \cdot S$, $\bar{r} \cdot S^2 \cdots \bar{r} \cdot S^m \cdots$ when interconnected by straight lines evidently form a closed geometrical structure. All the transformations for which

$$S^m = \Gamma_L \neq \Gamma_{000}, \quad \text{i.e.,} \quad \bar{t} \cdot \{\boldsymbol{\phi}\} = \bar{A}_L \neq 0 \qquad [2\cdot43]$$

belong to the second or *open* type of symmetry operations. With the aid of the definition given in Equation 2·42, the complete list of closed symmetry operations is readily prepared and is

$$[\mathbf{n}, \bar{t}] \quad \text{where} \quad \begin{cases} \bar{t} = 0 & \text{for } n = 1 \\ \bar{t} \cdot \bar{u} = 0 & \text{for } n = 2, 3, 4, 6 \end{cases} \qquad [2\cdot44a]$$

$$[\bar{\mathbf{n}}, \bar{t}] \quad \text{where} \quad \begin{cases} \bar{t} \text{ is arbitrary for } n = 1, 3, 4, 6 \\ \bar{t} \times \bar{u} = 0 \quad \text{for } n = 2 \end{cases} \qquad [2\cdot44b]$$

The dyadics $\boldsymbol{\phi}$ with which we are dealing are solutions of the equation $\boldsymbol{\phi}^m - \mathbf{I} = 0$. One root of this equation is $\boldsymbol{\phi} = \mathbf{I}$, hence $\boldsymbol{\phi} - \mathbf{I}$ is a factor and we have

$$\boldsymbol{\phi}^m - \mathbf{I} = \{\boldsymbol{\phi}\} \cdot (\boldsymbol{\phi} - \mathbf{I}) = (\boldsymbol{\phi} - \mathbf{I}) \cdot \{\boldsymbol{\phi}\} = 0 \qquad [2\cdot45]$$

In our considerations we have often encountered the dyadics $\boldsymbol{\phi} - \mathbf{I}$ and $\{\boldsymbol{\phi}\}$, and Equation 2·45 shows that they are intimately connected. Thus, if one of them is non-singular, the other must be zero; similarly if one is uniplanar, the other must be unilinear, the plane of one being normal to the axis of the other.

Suppose that a symmetry operation $[\boldsymbol{\phi}, \bar{t}]$ has a symmetry center. If we choose the origin in the symmetry center the vector $\bar{t}$ obviously vanishes as seen from Equation 2·33, and the analytic form reduces to $[\boldsymbol{\phi}, 0] \equiv \boldsymbol{\phi}$. Accordingly a symmetry operation which has a symmetry center represents a proper or improper rotation. One verifies readily that Equation 2·33 has a solution if Equation 2·42 is satisfied. Any closed symmetry operation has therefore at least one symmetry center. Closed symmetry operations consequently represent proper or improper rotations and any one of them may be reduced to the form $\mathbf{n}$ or $\bar{\mathbf{n}}$ by a proper choice of origin.

Let us examine Equation 2·33 in greater detail. The solution of this equation gives a symmetry center, a proper rotation axis or a reflection plane, depending upon the nature of the dyadic $\boldsymbol{\phi} - \mathbf{I}$, whether it is non-singular, uniplanar, or unilinear. We know from earlier results that $\boldsymbol{\phi} - \mathbf{I}$ is non-singular when $\boldsymbol{\phi} = \bar{\mathbf{1}}, \bar{\mathbf{3}}, \bar{\mathbf{4}}$, or $\bar{\mathbf{6}}$, and each of the symmetry operations $[\bar{\mathbf{n}}, \bar{t}]$ with $n = 1, 3, 4$, or 6 has thus one symmetry center. The location of this symmetry center is given by the equation

$$\bar{r}_0 = -\bar{t} \cdot (\boldsymbol{\phi} - \mathbf{I})^{-1} \qquad [2\cdot46]$$

and is, of course, dependent upon the value of the translation vector $\bar{t}$. We see for instance that the operation $[\bar{\mathbf{1}}, \bar{t}]$ is an inversion with $\bar{r}_0 = \bar{t}/2$

as inversion center. The operations $[\bar{3}, \bar{t}]$, $[\bar{4}, \bar{t}]$ and $[\bar{6}, \bar{t}]$ are improper rotations about a unique axis. This improper rotation axis is $\bar{r} = \bar{r}_0 + k\bar{u}$ where $\bar{r}_0$ is the symmetry center given by Equation 2·46.

The dyadic $\boldsymbol{\phi} - \mathbf{I}$ is uniplanar if $[\boldsymbol{\phi}, \bar{t}]$ is equal to $[\mathbf{2}, \bar{t}]$, $[\mathbf{3}, \bar{t}]$, $[\mathbf{4}, \bar{t}]$, or $[\mathbf{6}, \bar{t}]$ with $\bar{t} \cdot \{\mathbf{n}\} = 0$ and the solution of Equation 2·33 gives a straight line, the proper rotation axis. Finally $\boldsymbol{\phi} - \mathbf{I}$ is unilinear if $[\boldsymbol{\phi}, \bar{t}] = [\bar{\mathbf{2}}, \bar{t}]$ with $\bar{t} \times \bar{u} = 0$, in which case the solution of Equation 2·33 gives a plane, the reflection plane.

The existence of the following additional symmetry elements of closed operations is readily verified. Any normal to the reflection plane is an improper rotation axis. Any plane containing a proper or improper rotation axis of even order is a symmetry plane. Any plane normal to a proper rotation axis is a symmetry plane. The plane through a symmetry center normal to an improper rotation axis is a symmetry plane.

The open symmetry operations are:

$$[\mathbf{n}, \bar{t}] \text{ with } n = 2, 3, 4, \text{ or } 6$$

where

$$(\bar{t} \cdot \bar{u})\bar{u} = \frac{j}{n} \bar{A}_l, \quad j = 1, 2 \cdots n - 1 \qquad [2\cdot47a]$$

$$[\bar{\mathbf{2}}, \bar{t}] \quad \text{where} \quad \bar{t} - (\bar{t} \cdot \bar{u})\bar{u} = \frac{j}{2}\bar{A}_1 + \frac{k}{2}\bar{A}_2 \neq 0 \qquad [2\cdot47b]$$

with $j = 0$ or 1, $k = 0$ or 1.

In writing down the open symmetry operations in the form given in Equations 2·47*a* and *b*, we have taken into account the fact that we limit our considerations to only one of the operations in the set $S \cdot (\Gamma)$ in agreement with the discussion of Equation 2·26. The vector $\bar{A}_l$ of Equation 2·47*a* is the lattice period in the direction $\bar{u}$, while in Equation 2·47*b* the vectors $\bar{A}_1$ and $\bar{A}_2$ designate the two shortest lattice vectors normal to direction $\bar{u}$.

Any open operation may be written as the product of a closed operation and a translation as shown by the identities

$$\begin{aligned} [\mathbf{n}, \bar{t}] &= [\mathbf{n}, \bar{t} - (\bar{t} \cdot \bar{u})\bar{u}] \cdot [\mathbf{I}, (\bar{t} \cdot \bar{u})\bar{u}] \\ [\bar{\mathbf{2}}, \bar{t}] &= [\bar{\mathbf{2}}, (\bar{t} \cdot \bar{u})\bar{u}] \cdot [\mathbf{I}, \bar{t} - (\bar{t} \cdot \bar{u})\bar{u}] \end{aligned} \qquad [2\cdot48]$$

If the origin is chosen on the proper rotation axis or in the reflection plane of the closed factor in Equations 2·48, the open operations will assume simpler forms, namely,

$$[\mathbf{n}, \frac{j}{n}\bar{A}_l], \quad j = 1, 2 \cdots n - 1 \quad \text{and} \quad \bar{A}_l \times \bar{u} = 0 \qquad [2\cdot49a]$$

$$[\bar{\mathbf{2}}, \tfrac{1}{2}\bar{A}_1], \quad [\bar{\mathbf{2}}, \tfrac{1}{2}\bar{A}_2] \quad \text{or} \quad [\bar{\mathbf{2}}, \tfrac{1}{2}\bar{A}_1 + \tfrac{1}{2}\bar{A}_2] \qquad [2\cdot49b]$$

with $\bar{A}_1 \cdot \bar{u} = \bar{A}_2 \cdot \bar{u} = 0$.

An operation of the type given in Equation 2·47*a* is called an *n*-fold screw (or glide rotation) of pitch j/n. The screw is left-handed if $0 < j/n < 1/2$, right-handed if $1/2 < j/n < 1$ and neutral if $j/n = 1/2$. It is seen that a proper rotation may be considered as a screw of zero pitch. The equation

$$\bar{r} \cdot (\mathbf{n} - \mathbf{I}) + \bar{t} - (\bar{t} \cdot \bar{u})\bar{u} = 0 \qquad [2\cdot50]$$

has as solution a straight line which is the screw axis. The operation given in Equation 2·47*b* is called a glide reflection. The solution of the equation

$$\bar{r} \cdot (\bar{\mathbf{2}} - \mathbf{I}) + (\bar{t} \cdot \bar{u})\bar{u} = 0 \qquad [2\cdot51]$$

is a plane and this is the glide plane. Evidently the screw axis coincides with the proper rotation axis, the glide plane with the reflection plane of the corresponding closed operations given in Equations 2·48.

Some of the results obtained in this section are for convenience compiled in Table 2·1.

TABLE 2·1

THE POSSIBLE SYMMETRY OPERATIONS

A. The Closed Operations, $S^m = E$

$[\boldsymbol{\Phi}, \bar{t}]$	Condition on $\bar{t}$	Name of Operation	Order m
$[\mathbf{1}, \bar{t}]$	$\bar{t} = 0$	identity	1
$[\mathbf{n}, \bar{t}] = [\mathbf{2}, \bar{t}], [\mathbf{3}, \bar{t}], [\mathbf{4}, \bar{t}], [\mathbf{6}, \bar{t}]$	$\bar{t} \cdot \bar{u} = 0$	*n*-fold proper rotation	n
$[\bar{\mathbf{1}}, \bar{t}]$	none	inversion	2
$[\bar{\mathbf{n}}, \bar{t}] = [\bar{\mathbf{3}}, \bar{t}]$	none	*n*-fold improper rotation	6
$[\bar{\mathbf{4}}, \bar{t}]$			4
$[\bar{\mathbf{6}}, \bar{t}]$			6
$[\bar{\mathbf{2}}, \bar{t}]$	$\bar{t} - (\bar{t} \cdot \bar{u})\bar{u} = 0$	reflection	2

B. The Open Operations, $S^m = \Gamma_L \neq E$

$[\boldsymbol{\Phi}, \bar{t}]$	Condition on $\bar{t}$	Name of Operation	Order m
$[\mathbf{1}, \bar{t}]$	$\bar{t} = \bar{A}_L \neq 0$	lattice translation	1
$[\mathbf{n}, \bar{t}] = [\mathbf{2}, \bar{t}], [\mathbf{3}, \bar{t}], [\mathbf{4}, \bar{t}], [\mathbf{6}, \bar{t}]$	$(\bar{t} \cdot \bar{u})\bar{u} = \frac{j}{n}\bar{A}_l \neq 0$, $j = 1, 2 \cdots n - 1$	*n*-fold screw of pitch j/n	n
$[\bar{\mathbf{2}}, \bar{t}]$	$\bar{t} - (\bar{t} \cdot \bar{u})\bar{u} = \frac{j}{2}\bar{A}_1 + \frac{k}{2}\bar{A}_2 \neq 0$, $j = 0$ or 1, $k = 0$ or 1	glide reflection	2

4. THE POINT GROUPS

The fundamental problem of the theory of crystal lattice symmetry is the derivation of all conceivable space groups. In the two preceding sections the possible symmetry operations of crystal lattices, i.e., the possible elements of space groups, were deduced and discussed; hence the first step toward the solution of our problem has been completed. In order to formulate an intelligent plan for further investigations it is useful to consider some of the general properties of space groups.

We know from Equation 2·18 that the translation group (Γ) is an invariant subgroup of every space group. Hence, using the result of Equation B·18, any space group (G) may be written as the direct product of the translation group and its factor group, i.e.,

$$(G) = (\Gamma) \cdot (G/\Gamma) = (G/\Gamma) \cdot (\Gamma) \qquad [2{\cdot}52]$$

The factor group (G/Γ) has the form

$$(G/\Gamma) = (E, S_1, S_2, \cdots) \qquad [2{\cdot}53]$$

where the identity element E represents a lattice translation while all other elements $S_1 \equiv [\boldsymbol{\phi}_1, \bar{t}_1]$, $S_2 \equiv [\boldsymbol{\phi}_2, \bar{t}_2] \cdots$ are non-trivial symmetry operations. Since (G/Γ) is a group it follows that the set

$$(\mathbf{I}, \boldsymbol{\phi}_1, \boldsymbol{\phi}_2, \cdots) \qquad [2{\cdot}54]$$

formed by the dyadic parts of the elements in the factor group is also a group, and the groups of Equations 2·53 and 2·54 are evidently simply isomorphic. Such a group as that of Equation 2·54 in which all elements are dyadics $\mathbf{n}$ or $\bar{\mathbf{n}}$, with $n = 1, 2, 3, 4$, or 6, is called a point group.

These considerations show that the factor groups may be obtained with comparative ease from the point groups and the space groups from the factor groups. Thus the derivation of all possible point groups logically becomes the next step in our investigations, and we shall devote this section to a detailed study of the point groups.

A point group containing an element $\mathbf{n}$ or $\bar{\mathbf{n}}$ necessarily contains all powers $\mathbf{n}^j$ or $\bar{\mathbf{n}}^j$ of that element. The set of all powers $\mathbf{n}^j$ or $\bar{\mathbf{n}}^j$ forms a cyclic group which we shall denote by $(\mathbf{n})$ or $(\bar{\mathbf{n}})$. A point group consequently has a cyclic subgroup $(\mathbf{n})$ or $(\bar{\mathbf{n}})$ for every element $\mathbf{n}$ or $\bar{\mathbf{n}}$ which it contains. The groups $(\mathbf{n})$ and $(\bar{\mathbf{n}})$ are, of course, legitimate point groups and we have thus the following ten cyclic point groups

$$\begin{matrix} (\mathbf{1}), & (\mathbf{2}), & (\mathbf{3}), & (\mathbf{4}), & (\mathbf{6}) \\ (\bar{\mathbf{1}}), & (\bar{\mathbf{2}}), & (\bar{\mathbf{3}}), & (\bar{\mathbf{4}}), & (\bar{\mathbf{6}}) \end{matrix} \qquad [2{\cdot}55]$$

The complete list of the elements of these groups is given in Table 2·2. The following statements are readily verified by means of Equations 2·21 or 2·24.

TABLE 2·2

THE ELEMENTS OF THE CYCLIC POINT GROUPS

Point Group	Elements				
(1)	**1**				
(2)	**2**,	**1**			
(3)	**3**,	$\mathbf{3}^2$,	**1**		
(4)	**4**,	$\mathbf{4}^2 = \mathbf{2}$,	$\mathbf{4}^3$,	**1**	
(6)	**6**,	$\mathbf{6}^2 = \mathbf{3}$	$\mathbf{6}^3 = \mathbf{2}$,	$\mathbf{6}^4 = \mathbf{3}^2$,	$\mathbf{6}^5$,	**1**
($\bar{\mathbf{1}}$)	$\bar{\mathbf{1}}$,	**1**			
($\bar{\mathbf{2}}$)	$\bar{\mathbf{2}}$,	**1**			
($\bar{\mathbf{3}}$)	$\bar{\mathbf{3}}$,	$\bar{\mathbf{3}}^2 = \mathbf{3}^2$,	$\bar{\mathbf{3}}^3 = \bar{\mathbf{1}}$,	$\bar{\mathbf{3}}^4 = \mathbf{3}$,	$\bar{\mathbf{3}}^5$,	**1**
($\bar{\mathbf{4}}$)	$\bar{\mathbf{4}}$,	$\bar{\mathbf{4}}^2 = \mathbf{2}$,	$\bar{\mathbf{4}}^3$,	**1**	
($\bar{\mathbf{6}}$)	$\bar{\mathbf{6}}$,	$\bar{\mathbf{6}}^2 = \mathbf{3}$,	$\bar{\mathbf{6}}^3 = \bar{\mathbf{2}}$,	$\bar{\mathbf{6}}^4 = \mathbf{3}^2$,	$\bar{\mathbf{6}}^5$,	**1**

$$\begin{aligned}&(\mathbf{2}) \text{ is a subgroup of } (\mathbf{4}), \text{ of } (\mathbf{6}), \text{ and of } (\bar{\mathbf{4}})\\&(\mathbf{3}) \text{ is a subgroup of } (\mathbf{6}), \text{ of } (\bar{\mathbf{3}}), \text{ and of } (\bar{\mathbf{6}})\\&(\bar{\mathbf{1}}) \text{ is a subgroup of } (\bar{\mathbf{3}})\\&(\bar{\mathbf{2}}) \text{ is a subgroup of } (\bar{\mathbf{6}})\end{aligned} \qquad [2{\cdot}56]$$

The three groups of order six may according to Equation B·19 be written as direct products of subgroups, i.e.,

$$\begin{aligned}(\mathbf{6}) &= [(\mathbf{3}) \cdot (\mathbf{2})] = [(\mathbf{2}) \cdot (\mathbf{3})]\\(\bar{\mathbf{3}}) &= [(\mathbf{3}) \cdot (\bar{\mathbf{1}})] = [(\bar{\mathbf{1}}) \cdot (\mathbf{3})]\\(\bar{\mathbf{6}}) &= [(\mathbf{3}) \cdot (\bar{\mathbf{2}})] = [(\bar{\mathbf{2}}) \cdot (\mathbf{3})]\end{aligned} \qquad [2{\cdot}57]$$

In order to indicate that the two subgroups have the same proper or improper rotation axis their direct products have been enclosed in brackets.

It is convenient to speak of a point group as proper if all its elements are proper, whereas an improper point group contains both proper and improper elements. The product of two proper or of two improper elements is proper, but the product of a proper and an improper element is improper. An improper point group must therefore contain proper and improper elements in equal number, and the proper elements must form a proper subgroup.

An improper point group of which $\bar{\mathbf{1}}$ is an element contains an element $-\boldsymbol{\phi}$ for every element $\boldsymbol{\phi}$, and since $\bar{\mathbf{1}} \cdot \boldsymbol{\phi} = \boldsymbol{\phi} \cdot \bar{\mathbf{1}}$, it follows that the inversion group $(\bar{\mathbf{1}})$ is an invariant subgroup. Hence all improper point groups of this type have the form

$$(\bar{\mathbf{1}}) \cdot (\mathbf{P}) = (\mathbf{P}) \cdot (\bar{\mathbf{1}}) \qquad [2{\cdot}58]$$

where $(\mathbf{P})$ denotes the subgroup formed by the proper elements. Conversely, if $(\mathbf{P})$ is any one of the proper point groups, we may augment it with the inversion group and construct an improper point group $(\bar{\mathbf{1}}) \cdot (\mathbf{P})$.

An improper point group which does not contain the element $\bar{\mathbf{1}}$ will be given the symbol $(\bar{\mathbf{P}})$. Since $\bar{\mathbf{3}}^3 = \bar{\mathbf{1}}$ a group $(\bar{\mathbf{P}})$ may not contain the element $\bar{\mathbf{3}}$ and hence the improper elements must be odd powers of $\bar{\mathbf{2}}$, $\bar{\mathbf{4}}$, or $\bar{\mathbf{6}}$. Let $-\boldsymbol{\phi}$ represent any one of the improper elements of $(\bar{\mathbf{P}})$. The product $-\boldsymbol{\phi}^{-1} \cdot \boldsymbol{\phi} = \bar{\mathbf{1}}$ and consequently the corresponding proper operation $\boldsymbol{\phi}$ cannot be an element of $(\bar{\mathbf{P}})$. If we expand the group $(\bar{\mathbf{P}})$ in cosets of the proper subgroup $(\mathbf{P}')$ of index two we find

$$(\bar{\mathbf{P}}) = (\mathbf{P}'), -\boldsymbol{\phi} \cdot (\mathbf{P}') = (\mathbf{P}'), (\mathbf{P}') \cdot -\boldsymbol{\phi} \qquad [2{\cdot}59]$$

where $-\boldsymbol{\phi}$ is any one of the improper elements. Since $-\boldsymbol{\phi} \cdot (\mathbf{P}') = (\mathbf{P}') \cdot -\boldsymbol{\phi}$ it follows that $\boldsymbol{\phi} \cdot (\mathbf{P}') = (\mathbf{P}') \cdot \boldsymbol{\phi}$ where $\boldsymbol{\phi}$ — we recall — is not an element of $(\bar{\mathbf{P}})$. This being the case it must be true that the two sets $(\mathbf{P}')$ and $\boldsymbol{\phi} \cdot (\mathbf{P}')$ form a group, obviously one of the proper point groups $(\mathbf{P})$, i.e.,

$$(\mathbf{P}) = (\mathbf{P}'), \quad \boldsymbol{\phi} \cdot (\mathbf{P}') \qquad [2{\cdot}60]$$

Thus the two groups of Equations 2·59 and 2·60 are simply isomorphic. Accordingly we have the useful result that every group $(\bar{\mathbf{P}})$ is simply isomorphic with a proper point group $(\mathbf{P})$ which has a subgroup of index two. Conversely, to every proper point group $(\mathbf{P})$ with a subgroup $(\mathbf{P}')$ of index two, there is a corresponding improper point group $(\bar{\mathbf{P}})$.

These results show that only the proper point groups need to be deduced in detail, for once they have been found we are able to write down all the improper groups.

Let

$$(\mathbf{P}) = (\mathbf{1}, \mathbf{n}_1, \mathbf{n}_2 \cdots) \qquad [2{\cdot}61]$$

represent any one of the non-cyclic proper point groups. The characteristic dyadic of the group will be denoted by the symbol $\{\mathbf{P}\}$ and it is defined by

$$\{\mathbf{P}\} = \mathbf{1} + \mathbf{n}_1 + \mathbf{n}_2 + \cdots \qquad [2{\cdot}62]$$

i.e., by the sum of all elements. The scalar of the characteristic dyadic obviously is the sum of the scalars of the elements contained in the group and we will call it the characteristic scalar.

A non-cyclic proper point group must contain elements representing rotations about different axes, for otherwise the group would be cyclic. All elements which represent rotations about the same axis form a cyclic subgroup. Consequently the elements of the group $(\mathbf{P})$ may be arranged into cyclic subgroups, each subgroup associated with a different rotation axis and any two of these subgroups having only the identity element in common. Let there be s_6 such cyclic subgroups of order six, s_4 subgroups of order four, s_3 of order three, and s_2 of order two. The total number of elements in $(\mathbf{P})$, i.e., the order k of $(\mathbf{P})$, is seen to be

$$k = 1 + \sum_{2}^{6} (n - 1)s_n = 1 + s_2 + 2s_3 + 3s_4 + 5s_6 \qquad [2\cdot63]$$

while $s_2 + s_3 + s_4 + s_6$ is the number of different rotation axes. The characteristic scalar of a cyclic group $(\mathbf{n})$, $n = 2, 3, 4$, or 6 is just n according to Equation 2·30, while the scalar of the identity has the value 3. Thus the characteristic scalar of the point group $(\mathbf{P})$ becomes

$$\{\mathbf{P}\}_S = 3 + \sum_{2}^{6} (n - 3)s_n = 3 - s_2 + s_4 + 3s_6 \qquad [2\cdot64]$$

Let $\mathbf{n}_1$ and $\mathbf{n}_2$ be two elements of $(\mathbf{P})$, representing rotations about two different axes. Since $\mathbf{n}_1$ and $\mathbf{n}_2$ are elements of $(\mathbf{P})$ we have $(\mathbf{P}) \cdot \mathbf{n}_1 = (\mathbf{P}) \cdot \mathbf{n}_2 = (\mathbf{P})$. In any relation such as this it is, of course, permissible to replace the group by its characteristic dyadic, and hence it may be stated that $\{\mathbf{P}\} = \{\mathbf{P}\} \cdot \mathbf{n}_1 = \{\mathbf{P}\} \cdot \mathbf{n}_2$. Let $\bar{r}$ be an arbitrary vector and let the three dyadics $\{\mathbf{P}\}$, $\{\mathbf{P}\} \cdot \mathbf{n}_1$ and $\{\mathbf{P}\} \cdot \mathbf{n}_2$ operate on it. We have just found that these three dyadics are equal and hence their scalar products with the arbitrary vector $\bar{r}$ must be equal, i.e.,

$$\bar{r} \cdot \{\mathbf{P}\} = \bar{r} \cdot \{\mathbf{P}\} \cdot \mathbf{n}_1 = \bar{r} \cdot \{\mathbf{P}\} \cdot \mathbf{n}_2 \qquad [2\cdot65]$$

This equation shows that $\bar{r} \cdot \{\mathbf{P}\}$ is a point on the rotation axis of $\mathbf{n}_1$ as well as of $\mathbf{n}_2$, but this is possible only if $\{\mathbf{P}\}$ is identically zero. Consequently, setting $\{\mathbf{P}\}_S = 0$ in Equation 2·64, we obtain the following interesting relation between the number of cyclic subgroups

$$s_2 = 3 + s_4 + 3s_6 \qquad [2\cdot66]$$

If $\mathbf{n}_1$ and $\mathbf{n}_2$ are two elements (representing rotations about two different axes $\bar{u}_1$ and $\bar{u}_2$) of a point group $(\mathbf{P})$ any product $\mathbf{n}_1^j \cdot \mathbf{n}_2^k$ is also contained in the group, and consequently the product must represent a proper rotation of order 2, 3, 4, or 6 about a third axis. The scalar $[\mathbf{n}_1^j \cdot \mathbf{n}_2^k]_S$ accordingly must have the value -1, 0, 1, or 2 corresponding to a rotation angle $2\pi/n$ with $n = 2, 3, 4$, or 6. The vector $[\mathbf{n}_1^j \cdot \mathbf{n}_2^k]_V$ is, according to Equation 2·20, equal to $-2\bar{u} \sin \varphi$ where $\bar{u}$ is the rotation axis and φ the rotation angle of the product $\mathbf{n}_1^j \cdot \mathbf{n}_2^k$. With the aid of Equations 2·20 and 2·21 the scalar and vector of $\mathbf{n}_1^j \cdot \mathbf{n}_2^k$ are readily evaluated and we find

$$[\mathbf{n}_1^j \cdot \mathbf{n}_2^k]_S = (1 - \cos j\varphi_1)(1 - \cos k\varphi_2)\cos^2\chi - 2\sin j\varphi_1 \sin k\varphi_2 \cos\chi + (1 + \cos j\varphi_1)(1 + \cos k\varphi_2) - 1 = 1 + 2\cos\varphi \qquad [2\cdot67]$$

$$\begin{aligned}[\mathbf{n}_1^j \cdot \mathbf{n}_2^k]_V = {} & [\cos\chi\,(1 - \cos j\varphi_1)\sin k\varphi_2 - \sin j\varphi_1\,(1 + \cos k\varphi_2)]\bar{u}_1 \\ & + [\cos\chi\,(1 - \cos k\varphi_2)\sin j\varphi_1 - \sin k\varphi_2\,(1 + \cos j\varphi_1)]\bar{u}_2 \\ & + [\cos\chi\,(1 - \cos j\varphi_1)(1 - \cos k\varphi_2) - \sin j\varphi_1 \sin k\varphi_2]\bar{u}_1 \times \bar{u}_2 \\ = {} & -2\bar{u}\sin\varphi \qquad [2\cdot68]\end{aligned}$$

In these equations φ_1 and φ_2 are the rotation angles, $\bar{u}_1$ and $\bar{u}_2$ the rotation axes of $\mathbf{n}_1$ and $\mathbf{n}_2$, while $\cos\chi = \bar{u}_1 \cdot \bar{u}_2$.

Suppose that $\mathbf{n}_1$ and $\mathbf{n}_2$ are rotations of even order so that the point group contains the element $\mathbf{n}_1^{n_1/2} \cdot \mathbf{n}_2^{n_2/2}$. The scalar and vector of this product are

$$[\mathbf{n}_1^{n_1/2} \cdot \mathbf{n}_2^{n_2/2}]_S = 1 + 2\cos 2\chi = 1 + 2\cos\varphi \qquad [2\cdot69a]$$

$$[\mathbf{n}_1^{n_1/2} \cdot \mathbf{n}_2^{n_2/2}]_V = 4\bar{u}_1 \times \bar{u}_2 \cos\chi = -2\bar{u}\sin\varphi \qquad [2\cdot69b]$$

Thus the product represents a rotation about an axis normal to the plane containing $\bar{u}_1$ and $\bar{u}_2$, and since the rotation must be of order 2, 3, 4, or 6 the angle χ may assume only certain discrete values, namely multiples of π/n with $n = 2, 3, 4$, or 6. On the basis of Equations 2·69 the following table may be constructed.

TABLE 2·3

POSSIBLE INTERSECTION ANGLES FOR ROTATION AXES OF EVEN ORDER

χ	φ	Nature of Rotation Axis Parallel to $\bar{u}_1 \times \bar{u}_2$
$\pi/6$	$2\pi/6$	Sixfold
$\pi/4$	$2\pi/4$	Fourfold
$\pi/3$	$2\pi/3$	Threefold or sixfold
$\pi/2$	$2\pi/2$	Twofold, fourfold, or sixfold

Let us next investigate the possible intersection angles χ for threefold rotation axes. Setting $\mathbf{n}_1 = \mathbf{3}_1$ and $\mathbf{n}_2 = \mathbf{3}_2$, Equation 2·67 gives the following results

$$[\mathbf{3}_1 \cdot \mathbf{3}_2]_S = [\mathbf{3}_1^2 \cdot \mathbf{3}_2^2]_S = \tfrac{9}{4}\cos^2\chi - \tfrac{3}{2}\cos\chi - \tfrac{3}{4} \qquad [2\cdot70a]$$

$$[\mathbf{3}_1^2 \cdot \mathbf{3}_2]_S = [\mathbf{3}_1 \cdot \mathbf{3}_2^2]_S = \tfrac{9}{4}\cos^2\chi + \tfrac{3}{2}\cos\chi - \tfrac{3}{4} \qquad [7\cdot20b]$$

Accordingly $\cos\chi = \pm\,1/3$ and two of the four operations of Equations 2·70 become rotations of order three. Thus, if $s_3 > 1$, then its only possible value is $s_3 = 4$ and the four threefold rotation axes intersect at an angle of 109° 28′ (or 70° 32′), i.e., they are directed towards the corners of a regular tetrahedron.

Sixfold rotation axes are also threefold rotation axes since (**3**) is a subgroup of (**6**), and they must therefore intersect at the same angles as do threefold axes. This requirement cannot, however, be reconciled with Equation 2·69*a*, and consequently no proper point group (**P**) may contain more than one subgroup (**6**), i.e., $s_6 = 0$ or 1.

Consider next the case for which $s_4 > 1$. If one sets $\mathbf{n}_1 = \mathbf{4}_1$ and $\mathbf{n}_2 = \mathbf{4}_2$ Equations 2·67 and 2·68 give

$$[\mathbf{4}_1 \cdot \mathbf{4}_2]_S = \cos^2 \chi - 2 \cos \chi = 1 + 2 \cos \varphi \qquad [2{\cdot}71a]$$

$$[\mathbf{4}_1 \cdot \mathbf{4}_2]_V = (\cos \chi - 1)(\bar{u}_1 + \bar{u}_2 + \bar{u}_1 \times \bar{u}_2) = -2\bar{u} \sin \varphi \qquad [2{\cdot}71b]$$

The only possible value of χ is thus $\pi/2$, i.e., $\bar{u}_1 \cdot \bar{u}_2 = 0$, and the product $\mathbf{4}_1 \cdot \mathbf{4}_2$ is a rotation of order three about the axis $\frac{1}{\sqrt{3}} (\bar{u}_1 + \bar{u}_2 + \bar{u}_1 \times \bar{u}_2)$. It is readily seen that $\bar{u}_1 \cdot \mathbf{4}_1 \cdot \mathbf{4}_2 = \bar{u}_1 \times \bar{u}_2$. As a consequence $\bar{u}_1 \times \bar{u}_2$ is a fourfold rotation axis and we have $s_4 = 3$. Similarly the fourfold rotations will transform the axis of the threefold rotation $\mathbf{4}_1 \cdot \mathbf{4}_2$ into three others making $s_3 = 4$. In other words, if we assume $s_4 > 1$, then $s_4 = 3$ and simultaneously $s_3 = 4$.

On the basis of the considerations given above we shall proceed to deduce the possible non-cyclic proper point groups one by one.

Let us begin with the case for which $s_6 = s_4 = s_3 = 0$. According to Equation 2·66, $s_2 = 3$, while the order of the group is $k = 4$ according to Equation 2·63. Table 2·3 shows further that the three rotation axes are mutually orthogonal. The rotation axes are thus $\bar{u}_1$, $\bar{u}_2$, and $\bar{u}_1 \times \bar{u}_2$ with $\bar{u}_1 \cdot \bar{u}_2 = 0$. A proper point group in which there is one rotation axis of order n and normal to it n twofold rotation axes separated by angles π/n is called a dihedral group of order $2n$ and is given the symbol D_n. The group under consideration belongs to this type and is obviously D_2, the dihedral group of order four. According to the result obtained in Appendix B and expressed in Equation B·19 the group may be written as the direct product of any two of the three subgroups of order two, i.e.,

$$\begin{gathered} D_2 = (\mathbf{2}) \cdot (\mathbf{2}') = (\mathbf{2}') \cdot (\mathbf{2}) \\ \mathbf{2} = 2\bar{u}_1\bar{u}_1 - \mathbf{I}, \quad \mathbf{2}' = 2\bar{u}_2\bar{u}_2 - \mathbf{I}, \quad \bar{u}_1 \cdot \bar{u}_2 = 0 \end{gathered} \qquad [2{\cdot}72]$$

Axes which are transformed into one another by the operations of a point group are said to be equivalent. Clearly, equivalent axes are of the same order, but axes of the same order need not be equivalent. If an an axis $\bar{u}$ is transformed into $-\bar{u}$ it is called a non-polar axis, if not, it is said to be a polar axis. Thus all three twofold axes of D_2 ($\bar{u}_1$, $\bar{u}_2$, and $\bar{u}_1 \times \bar{u}_2$) are non-equivalent and non-polar.

If one of the three quantities s_3, s_4, s_6 is equal to 1, then the rotation axis $\bar{u}_1$ associated with this subgroup must be transformed into itself by all rotations $\mathbf{n}'$ of other subgroups of the point group, i.e.,

$$\bar{u}_1 \cdot \mathbf{n}' = \pm \bar{u}_1 \qquad [2{\cdot}73]$$

Since $\bar{u}_1$ is not to be the axis of $\mathbf{n}'$ this equation is satisfied only if $\mathbf{n}' = 2\bar{u}_2\bar{u}_2 - \mathbf{I}$ where $\bar{u}_1 \cdot \bar{u}_2 = 0$. Hence we obtain the following combinations of values s_n

s_6	s_4	s_3	s_2	k
0	0	1	3	6
0	1	0	4	8
1	0	0	6	12

These sets s_n evidently correspond to the dihedral point groups D_3, D_4, and D_6, and according to the oft-used Equation B·19 we have

$$D_n = (\mathbf{n}) \cdot (\mathbf{2}') = (\mathbf{2}') \cdot (\mathbf{n})$$

$$\mathbf{n} = \bar{u}_1\bar{u}_1 + (\mathbf{I} - \bar{u}_1\bar{u}_1) \cos\frac{2\pi}{n} + \mathbf{I} \times \bar{u}_1 \sin\frac{2\pi}{n} \qquad [2{\cdot}74]$$

$$\mathbf{2}' = 2\bar{u}_2\bar{u}_2 - \mathbf{I}, \quad \bar{u}_1 \cdot \bar{u}_2 = 0$$

The three twofold rotation axes of D_3 are

$$\bar{u}_2 \cdot (\mathbf{3}) = \bar{u}_2, \quad -\tfrac{1}{2}\bar{u}_2 - \tfrac{1}{2}\sqrt{3}\bar{u}_1 \times \bar{u}_2, \quad -\tfrac{1}{2}\bar{u}_2 + \tfrac{1}{2}\sqrt{3}\bar{u}_1 \times \bar{u}_2 \qquad [2{\cdot}75]$$

They are thus equivalent and polar. In the point group D_4 the twofold axes are all non-polar, but they fall into two sets of two equivalent axes. The two sets are

$$\bar{u}_2 \cdot (\mathbf{4}) = \pm \bar{u}_2, \quad \pm \bar{u}_1 \times \bar{u}_2$$

and [2·76]

$$\frac{1}{\sqrt{2}}(\bar{u}_2 + \bar{u}_1 \times \bar{u}_2) \cdot (\mathbf{4}) = \pm \frac{1}{\sqrt{2}}(\bar{u}_2 \pm \bar{u}_1 \times \bar{u}_2)$$

There are six twofold axes in D_6. They are all non-polar, but they are not all equivalent; they form two sets, each set containing three equivalent axes. The six twofold axes are

$$\bar{u}_2 \cdot (\mathbf{6}) = \pm \bar{u}_2, \quad \pm(\tfrac{1}{2}\bar{u}_2 \pm \tfrac{1}{2}\sqrt{3}\bar{u}_1 \times \bar{u}_2)$$

and [2·77]

$$\bar{u}_1 \times \bar{u}_2 \cdot (\mathbf{6}) = \pm \bar{u}_1 \times \bar{u}_2, \quad \pm(\tfrac{1}{2}\sqrt{3}\bar{u}_2 \pm \tfrac{1}{2}\bar{u}_1 \times \bar{u}_2)$$

We have now deduced all point groups (**P**) for which s_6, s_4, or $s_3 = 1$, while D_2 is the only point group for which $s_3 = s_4 = s_6 = 0$. The point groups yet to be derived must have $s_6 = 0$ (since $s_6 = 1$ gives D_6 and since $s_6 = 0$ or 1 are the only two possibilities). With the aid of Equations 2·70 and 2·71, it was shown that if $s_3 > 1$, then $s_3 = 4$, and if $s_4 > 1$ then $s_4 = 3$ and simultaneously $s_3 = 4$. Consequently there are only two additional point groups and these correspond to the following combinations of s_n values

s_6	s_4	s_3	s_2	k	Symbol
0	0	4	3	12	T
0	3	4	6	24	O

The three axes of order two in the point group T may intersect only at angles $\pi/3$ or $\pi/2$ as shown by Table 2·3. The former value leads to $s_3 = 1$ and gives the already known point group D_3. The twofold axes must therefore be orthogonal as in the point group D_2 which thus becomes a subgroup of T. The four axes of order three are directed towards the corners of a regular tetrahedron according to Equations 2·70. The threefold rotations must furthermore transform the three twofold axes into one another, i.e., they must satisfy the equation

$$\bar{u}_1 \cdot \mathbf{3}' = \pm\bar{u}_1, \quad \pm\bar{u}_2, \quad \text{or} \quad \pm\bar{u}_1 \times \bar{u}_2 \qquad [2\cdot78]$$

These requirements give the following directions for the threefold axes

$$\begin{array}{ll} (\bar{u}_1 + \bar{u}_2 + \bar{u}_1 \times \bar{u}_2)/\sqrt{3}, & (\bar{u}_1 - \bar{u}_2 - \bar{u}_1 \times \bar{u}_2)/\sqrt{3} \\ (-\bar{u}_1 - \bar{u}_2 + \bar{u}_1 \times \bar{u}_2)/\sqrt{3}, & (-\bar{u}_1 + \bar{u}_2 - \bar{u}_1 \times \bar{u}_2)/\sqrt{3} \end{array} \qquad [2\cdot79]$$

The four axes of order three are equivalent and polar, while the three axes of order two are equivalent and non-polar. According to Equation B·19 we have

$$\begin{aligned} T &= (\mathbf{3}') \cdot D_2 = D_2 \cdot (\mathbf{3}') = (\mathbf{3}') \cdot ((\mathbf{2}) \cdot (\mathbf{2}')) = ((\mathbf{2}) \cdot (\mathbf{2}')) \cdot (\mathbf{3}') \\ \mathbf{2} &= 2\bar{u}_1\bar{u}_1 - \mathbf{I}, \quad \mathbf{2}' = 2\bar{u}_2\bar{u}_2 - \mathbf{I}, \quad \bar{u}_1 \cdot \bar{u}_2 = 0 \qquad [2\cdot80] \\ \mathbf{3}' &= \tfrac{3}{2}\bar{u}\bar{u} - \tfrac{1}{2}\mathbf{I} + \tfrac{1}{2}\sqrt{3}\mathbf{I} \times \bar{u}, \quad \bar{u} = (\bar{u}_1 + \bar{u}_2 + \bar{u}_1 \times \bar{u}_2)/\sqrt{3} \end{aligned}$$

The group is usually referred to as the tetrahedral group since it contains the proper rotations characteristic of a regular tetrahedron.

The three fourfold rotation axes of the point group O must intersect orthogonally as shown by Equations 2·71. If these axes are $\bar{u}_1$, $\bar{u}_2$ and $\bar{u}_1 \times \bar{u}_2$ with $\bar{u}_1 \cdot \bar{u}_2 = 0$ any one of the four threefold rotations must satisfy Equation 2·78, so that the directions of the threefold axes are again given by Equations 2·79. The six axes of order two become

$$\pm(\bar{u}_1 \pm \bar{u}_2)/\sqrt{2}, \quad \pm(\bar{u}_1 \pm \bar{u}_1 \times \bar{u}_2)/\sqrt{2}, \quad \pm(\bar{u}_2 \pm \bar{u}_1 \times \bar{u}_2)/\sqrt{2} \qquad [2\cdot81]$$

Since fourfold rotation axes are also twofold rotation axes (because $\mathbf{4}^2 = \mathbf{2}$) it is seen that T and D_4 are subgroups. There are three twofold axes normal to every axis of order three and consequently D_3 is also a subgroup. Accordingly the point group O may be represented in the following manner.

$$\begin{aligned} O &= (\mathbf{4}) \cdot D_3 = D_3 \cdot (\mathbf{4}) = (\mathbf{3}') \cdot D_4 = D_4 \cdot (\mathbf{3}') \\ &= (\mathbf{4}) \cdot ((\mathbf{3}') \cdot (\mathbf{2}'')) = (\mathbf{3}') \cdot ((\mathbf{4}) \cdot (\mathbf{2}'')) \end{aligned} \qquad [2\cdot82]$$

$$\mathbf{4} = \bar{u}_1\bar{u}_1 + \mathbf{I} \times \bar{u}_1, \quad \mathbf{2}'' = (\bar{u}_1 + \bar{u}_2)(\bar{u}_1 + \bar{u}_2) - \mathbf{I}$$

$$\mathbf{3}' = \tfrac{3}{2}\bar{u}\bar{u} - \tfrac{1}{2}\mathbf{I} + \tfrac{1}{2}\sqrt{3}\mathbf{I} \times \bar{u}, \quad \bar{u}_1 \cdot \bar{u}_2 = 0, \quad \bar{u} = (\bar{u}_1 + \bar{u}_2 + \bar{u}_1 \times \bar{u}_2)/\sqrt{3}$$

All axes of O are non-polar and axes of the same order are equivalent. The group contains all the rotations to which a regular octahedron may be subjected, and it is therefore called the octahedral group.

We have thus deduced all possible proper point groups. They are the five cyclic groups $(\mathbf{n}) \equiv C_n$, the four dihedral groups $(\mathbf{n}) \cdot (\mathbf{2}) \equiv D_n$, the tetrahedral group T and the octahedral group O. The complete list of these eleven groups and their subgroups is given in Table 2·4. Subgroups of index two are printed in roman type. It is seen from Table 2·4 that all proper point groups are subgroups of D_6 or O.

TABLE 2·4

THE PROPER POINT GROUPS AND THEIR SUBGROUPS

Point Group	Subgroups									
C_1	C_1									
C_2	C_1	C_2								
C_3	C_1		C_3							
C_4	C_1	C_2		C_4						
C_6	C_1	C_2	C_3		C_6					
D_2	C_1	C_2				D_2				
D_3	C_1	C_2	C_3				D_3			
D_4	C_1	C_2		C_4		D_2		D_4		
D_6	C_1	C_2	C_3		C_6	D_2	D_3		D_6	
T	C_1	C_2	C_3			D_2				T	
O	C_1	C_2	C_3	C_4		D_2	D_3	D_4		T	O

The improper point groups are either of the form given by Equation 2·58 or of the form expressed in Equation 2·59. The latter groups are simply isomorphic with proper point groups which have a subgroup of index two. The groups C_1, C_3, and T have no subgroup of index two, and consequently no point groups of the type of Equation 2·59 may be constructed from them. The other groups of Table 2·4 have all subgroups of index two and are thus isomorphic with improper groups $(\bar{\mathbf{P}})$. Altogether ten groups $(\bar{\mathbf{P}})$ may be formed, one for every group C_2, C_4, C_6, D_2, D_3, and T, and two each for the groups D_4 and D_6. Evidently there are eleven groups $(\bar{\mathbf{1}}) \cdot (\mathbf{P})$, one for every proper group $(\mathbf{P})$. Five of the twenty-one improper point groups are cyclic; they have been derived earlier and are included in the list of cyclic groups 2·55. The improper point groups and the proper point groups to which they correspond are given in Table 2·5. Clearly the improper point groups have the same axial directions as the corresponding proper groups, but in passing from the latter to the former some or all of the proper axes become improper.

TABLE 2·5

THE PROPER AND IMPROPER GROUPS

Proper Point Group, (P)	Subgroup of (P) of Index Two	Improper Point Groups	
		Type $(\bar{\mathbf{P}})$	Type $(\bar{\mathbf{1}}) \cdot (\mathbf{P})$
$C_1(\mathbf{1})$			$C_i(\bar{\mathbf{1}})$
$C_2(\mathbf{2})$	$(\mathbf{1})$	$C_s(\bar{\mathbf{2}})$	$C_{2h}(\bar{\mathbf{1}}) \cdot (\mathbf{2})$
$D_2(\mathbf{2}) \cdot (\mathbf{2}')$	$(\mathbf{2})$	$C_{2v}(\mathbf{2}) \cdot (\bar{\mathbf{2}}')$	$D_{2h}(\bar{\mathbf{1}}) \cdot (\mathbf{2}) \cdot (\mathbf{2}')$
$C_3(\mathbf{3})$			$C_{3i}(\bar{\mathbf{3}})$
$D_3(\mathbf{3}) \cdot (\mathbf{2}')$	$(\mathbf{3})$	$C_{3v}(\mathbf{3}) \cdot (\bar{\mathbf{2}}')$	$D_{3d}(\bar{\mathbf{3}}) \cdot (\mathbf{2}')$
$C_4(\mathbf{4})$	$(\mathbf{2})$	$S_4(\bar{\mathbf{4}})$	$C_{4h}(\bar{\mathbf{1}}) \cdot (\mathbf{4})$
$D_4(\mathbf{4}) \cdot (\mathbf{2}')$	$(\mathbf{4})$	$C_{4v}(\mathbf{4}) \cdot (\bar{\mathbf{2}}')$	$D_{4h}(\bar{\mathbf{1}}) \cdot (\mathbf{4}) \cdot (\mathbf{2}')$
	$(\mathbf{2}) \cdot (\mathbf{2}')$	$V_d(\bar{\mathbf{4}}) \cdot (\mathbf{2}')$	
$C_6(\mathbf{6})$	$(\mathbf{3})$	$C_{3h}(\bar{\mathbf{6}})$	$C_{6h}(\bar{\mathbf{1}}) \cdot (\mathbf{6})$
$D_6(\mathbf{6}) \cdot (\mathbf{2}')$	$(\mathbf{6})$	$C_{6v}(\mathbf{6}) \cdot (\bar{\mathbf{2}}')$	$D_{6h}(\bar{\mathbf{1}}) \cdot (\mathbf{6}) \cdot (\mathbf{2}')$
	$(\mathbf{3}) \cdot (\mathbf{2}')$	$D_{3h}(\bar{\mathbf{6}}) \cdot (\mathbf{2}')$	
$T(\mathbf{3}') \cdot ((\mathbf{2}) \cdot (\mathbf{2}'))$			$T_h(\bar{\mathbf{3}}') \cdot ((\mathbf{2}) \cdot (\mathbf{2}'))$
$O(\mathbf{3}') \cdot ((\mathbf{4}) \cdot (\mathbf{2}''))$	$(\mathbf{3}') \cdot ((\mathbf{2}) \cdot (\mathbf{2}'))$	$T_d(\mathbf{3}') \cdot ((\bar{\mathbf{4}}) \cdot (\bar{\mathbf{2}}''))$	$O_h(\bar{\mathbf{3}}') \cdot ((\mathbf{4}) \cdot (\mathbf{2}''))$

Generating elements:

$$\mathbf{n} = \bar{u}_1\bar{u}_1 + (\mathbf{I} - \bar{u}_1\bar{u}_1) \cos \frac{2\pi}{n} + \mathbf{I} \times \bar{u}_1 \sin \frac{2\pi}{n}$$

$$\mathbf{2}' = 2\bar{u}_2\bar{u}_2 - \mathbf{I} \quad \text{with} \quad \bar{u}_1 \cdot \bar{u}_2 = 0$$

$$\mathbf{2}'' = (\bar{u}_2 + \bar{u}_1 \times \bar{u}_2)(\bar{u}_2 + \bar{u}_1 \times \bar{u}_2) - \mathbf{I}$$

$$\mathbf{3}' = (\bar{u}_1 + \bar{u}_2 + \bar{u}_1 \times \bar{u}_2)(\bar{u}_1 + \bar{u}_2 + \bar{u}_1 \times \bar{u}_2)/2 - \mathbf{I}/2 + \mathbf{I} \times (\bar{u}_1 + \bar{u}_2 + \bar{u}_1 \times \bar{u}_2)/2$$

It is of interest to note that the various elements of any point group may be represented as the products of powers of not more than three of the elements. These we shall call the generating elements of the point group. For instance, $\bar{\mathbf{3}}$ is the generating element of C_{3i}, $\mathbf{4}$ and $\mathbf{2}'$ are the generating elements of D_4, while $\bar{\mathbf{3}}'$, $\mathbf{4}$, and $\mathbf{2}''$ are the generating elements of O_h. The symbols of the point groups given in Table 2·5 are those introduced by Schoenflies. The correlations between the symbols and the group compositions as shown by the direct product form are neither obvious nor consistent, and the Schoenflies nomenclature will therefore in the next section be replaced by the more logical Mauguin-Hermann nomenclature.

5. THE TRANSLATION GROUPS

In order to synthesize the space groups we must, as shown by Equation 2·52, know all translation groups and factor groups of which they are composed. In the preceding section the point groups were derived. Having determined all point groups it becomes possible to deduce translation groups as well as factor groups with comparative ease. Since translation groups and factor groups are not independent, the order in which they are derived is of some importance. An acceptable translation group must be invariant under the symmetry operations of the crystal lattice as expressed in Equation 2·18 where $S \equiv [\boldsymbol{\phi}, \bar{t}]$ denotes any one element of the space group. It is readily seen that Equation 2·18 can be expressed in the form

$$\boldsymbol{\phi}^{-1} \cdot (\Gamma) \cdot \boldsymbol{\phi} = (\Gamma) \qquad [2\cdot83]$$

which involves only the dyadic parts of the symmetry operations. The translation group is in other words an invariant subgroup of the space group if it is invariant under the operations of the corresponding point group. Since all the point groups are known we are consequently in a position to derive all translation groups without first having to find all factor groups. We will therefore devote this section to an investigation of the possible translation groups, while the derivation of the factor groups, which thus represents the final stage in the space group synthesis, will be discussed in section 6 of this chapter.

All the elements of the translation group are the lattice translations. If the lattice is described by means of a primitive vector set $\bar{a}_1$, $\bar{a}_2$, $\bar{a}_3$, the lattice vectors have the form $\bar{A}_L = L_1\bar{a}_1 + L_2\bar{a}_2 + L_3\bar{a}_3$ where L_1, L_2, L_3 are any three integers, positive, negative or zero. The corresponding lattice translations are $\Gamma_{L_1L_2L_3} \equiv \Gamma_L \equiv [\mathrm{I}, \bar{A}_L]$ and the translation group is the set of all conceivable operations Γ_L, i.e., $(\Gamma) = (\Gamma_L)$. When the lattice is represented by means of a non-primitive triplet $\bar{a}_1$, $\bar{a}_2$, $\bar{a}_3$ the lattice vectors have fractional as well as integral components, as was shown by the discussion in section 12 of Chapter I, and the group (Γ_L) is then merely a subgroup of the translation group. Consider the body-centered representation as an example. Since the lattice vectors referred to a body-centered set $\bar{a}_1$, $\bar{a}_2$, $\bar{a}_3$ have the general form given by Equation 1·51, the corresponding lattice translations are either $\Gamma_{L_1L_2L_3}$ or $\Gamma_{L_1L_2L_3} \cdot \Gamma_{\frac{1}{2}\frac{1}{2}\frac{1}{2}}$. The group (Γ_L) is thus a subgroup of index two and the translation group may be expressed in the form

$$\text{Body-centered} \quad (\Gamma) = (\Gamma_L) \cdot (E, \Gamma_{\frac{1}{2}\frac{1}{2}\frac{1}{2}}) \qquad [2{\cdot}84]$$

In a similar manner we find the following results for the translation group in base-centered and face-centered lattice representations (using the results expressed in Equations 1·49 and 1·55).

$$\begin{aligned} \text{Base-centered} \quad (\Gamma) &= (\Gamma_L) \cdot (E, \Gamma_{0\frac{1}{2}\frac{1}{2}}) \\ &= (\Gamma_L) \cdot (E, \Gamma_{\frac{1}{2}0\frac{1}{2}}) \\ &= (\Gamma_L) \cdot (E, \Gamma_{\frac{1}{2}\frac{1}{2}0}) \end{aligned} \qquad [2{\cdot}85]$$

$$\text{Face-centered} \quad (\Gamma) = (\Gamma_L) \cdot (E, \Gamma_{0\frac{1}{2}\frac{1}{2}}, \Gamma_{\frac{1}{2}0\frac{1}{2}}, \Gamma_{0\frac{1}{2}\frac{1}{2}}) \qquad [2{\cdot}86]$$

Since the only non-primitive representations which will be used in the following investigations are the ones just mentioned, it is convenient to introduce separate symbols for the corresponding translation groups. Following the Mauguin-Hermann notation we will adopt the following scheme.

$$\begin{array}{ll} \text{Primitive translation group} & (\Gamma_L) \equiv \mathcal{P} \\ \text{Body-centered translation group} & (\Gamma_L) \cdot (E, \Gamma_{\frac{1}{2}\frac{1}{2}\frac{1}{2}}) \equiv \mathfrak{J} \\ \text{Base-centered translation group} & (\Gamma_L) \cdot (E, \Gamma_{0\frac{1}{2}\frac{1}{2}}) \equiv \mathcal{A} \\ & (\Gamma_L) \cdot (E, \Gamma_{\frac{1}{2}0\frac{1}{2}}) \equiv \mathcal{B} \\ & (\Gamma_L) \cdot (E, \Gamma_{\frac{1}{2}\frac{1}{2}0}) \equiv \mathcal{C} \\ \text{Face-centered translation group} & (\Gamma_L) \cdot (E, \Gamma_{0\frac{1}{2}\frac{1}{2}}, \Gamma_{\frac{1}{2}0\frac{1}{2}}, \Gamma_{\frac{1}{2}\frac{1}{2}0}) \equiv \mathfrak{F} \end{array} \qquad [2{\cdot}87]$$

Equation 2·83, as shown by Equation 2·19, is equivalent to the statement that all components ϕ_{jk} are integers. In other words, if the vector set $\bar{a}_1, \bar{a}_2, \bar{a}_3$ of the translation group (Γ) is such that all elements $\boldsymbol{\phi}$ of a given point group have integral components ϕ_{jk} when referred to the coordinate system $\bar{a}_1, \bar{a}_2, \bar{a}_3$, then (Γ) is an invariant subgroup of all space groups which correspond to the given point group. Since identically

$$\boldsymbol{\phi} \equiv \sum_j \sum_k (\bar{a}_j \cdot \boldsymbol{\phi} \cdot \bar{b}_k)\bar{b}_j\bar{a}_k \qquad [2{\cdot}88]$$

it follows that Equation 2·83 may be expressed in the form

$$\phi_{jk} = \bar{a}_j \cdot \boldsymbol{\phi} \cdot \bar{b}_k = \text{integer} \qquad [2{\cdot}89]$$

In any point group there is a set of constant dyadics $\boldsymbol{\phi}$ which we know and the variables of Equation 2·89 are therefore the vectors $\bar{a}_1, \bar{a}_2, \bar{a}_3$. This equation is identically satisfied only if $\boldsymbol{\phi} = \mathbf{I}$ or if $\boldsymbol{\phi} = -\mathbf{I}$, i.e., when the point group is $C_1(\mathbf{1})$ or $C_i(\bar{\mathbf{1}})$. For all other point groups Equation 2·89 represents scalar relationships between the three vectors $\bar{a}_1$, $\bar{a}_2$, $\bar{a}_3$ and thus the six quantities a_1, a_2, a_3, α_1, α_2, α_3, which define the lengths and relative orientation of these vectors, are no longer independent.

The complete set of all possible translation groups will be deduced with the aid of Equation 2·89. The derivation is greatly simplified by the fact that it is not necessary to consider each point group separately. Clearly if Equation 2·89 is satisfied for a dyadic $\boldsymbol{\phi}$ it will also be satisfied for the corresponding dyadic $-\boldsymbol{\phi}$. Consequently Equation 2·89 will have the same solutions for a proper point group (**P**) as for the corresponding improper groups ($\bar{\mathbf{P}}$) and $(\bar{\mathbf{1}}) \cdot (\mathbf{P})$, so that it is sufficient to solve Equation 2·89 for the proper point groups. It may further be shown that Equation 2·89 gives the same solutions for a dihedral point group D_n with $n > 2$ as for the corresponding cyclic group C_n and the same solutions for the tetrahedral group T as for the octahedral group O.

TABLE 2·6. THE

System	Point Groups
Triclinic	$C_1(\mathbf{1})$, $C_i(\bar{\mathbf{1}})$
Monoclinic	$C_2(\mathbf{2})$, $C_s(\bar{\mathbf{2}})$, $C_{2h}(\bar{\mathbf{1}}) \cdot (\mathbf{2})$
Orthorhombic	$D_2(\mathbf{2}) \cdot (\mathbf{2}')$, $C_{2v}(\mathbf{2}) \cdot (\bar{\mathbf{2}}')$, $D_{2h}(\bar{\mathbf{1}}) \cdot (\mathbf{2}) \cdot (\mathbf{2}')$
Trigonal	$C_3(\mathbf{3})$, $C_{3i}(\bar{\mathbf{3}})$ $D_3(\mathbf{3}) \cdot (\mathbf{2}')$, $C_{3v}(\mathbf{3}) \cdot (\bar{\mathbf{2}}')$, $D_{3d}(\bar{\mathbf{3}}) \cdot (\mathbf{2}')$
Tetragonal	$C_4(\mathbf{4})$, $S_4(\bar{\mathbf{4}})$, $C_{4h}(\bar{\mathbf{1}}) \cdot (\mathbf{4})$ $D_4(\mathbf{4}) \cdot (\mathbf{2}')$, $C_{4v}(\mathbf{4}) \cdot (\bar{\mathbf{2}}')$, $V_d(\bar{\mathbf{4}}) \cdot (\mathbf{2}')$, $D_{4h}(\bar{\mathbf{1}}) \cdot (\mathbf{4}) \cdot (\mathbf{2}')$
Hexagonal	$C_6(\mathbf{6})$, $C_{3h}(\bar{\mathbf{6}})$, $C_{6h}(\bar{\mathbf{1}}) \cdot (\mathbf{6})$ $D_6(\mathbf{6}) \cdot (\mathbf{2}')$, $C_{6v}(\mathbf{6}) \cdot (\bar{\mathbf{2}}')$, $D_{3h}(\bar{\mathbf{6}}) \cdot (\mathbf{2}')$, $D_{6h}(\bar{\mathbf{1}}) \cdot (\mathbf{6}) \cdot (\mathbf{2}')$
Cubic	$T(\mathbf{3}') \cdot ((\mathbf{2}) \cdot (\mathbf{2}'))$, $T_h(\bar{\mathbf{3}}') \cdot ((\mathbf{2}) \cdot (\mathbf{2}'))$ $O(\mathbf{3}') \cdot ((\mathbf{4}) \cdot (\mathbf{2}''))$, $T_d(\mathbf{3}') \cdot ((\bar{\mathbf{4}}) \cdot (\bar{\mathbf{2}}''))$, $O_h(\bar{\mathbf{3}}') \cdot ((\mathbf{4}) \cdot (\mathbf{2}''))$

On the basis of these considerations it becomes convenient to arrange the thirty-two point groups into seven so-called systems in such a way that a translation group which is invariant with respect to any one point group of a given system necessarily is invariant with respect to all other point groups of the same system. The distribution of the point groups among these seven systems is shown in Table 2·6.

In section 12 of Chapter I, it was shown that there are an infinite number of equivalent vector sets $\bar{a}_1, \bar{a}_2, \bar{a}_3$ by means of which any given translation lattice may be described. We arrive at the same conclusion when Equation 2·89 is considered. Suppose in particular that $\bar{a}_1, \bar{a}_2, \bar{a}_3$ is a set of vectors which satisfies Equation 2·89. If we introduce new vectors $\bar{a}_1', \bar{a}_2', \bar{a}_3'$ defined by $\bar{a}_j' = \sum c_{jk}\bar{a}_k$ where all coefficients c_{jk} are integers, it is obviously true that the new vector set also satisfies Equation 2·89. It is, of course, sufficient to deal with just one of these equivalent sets, and this one set is selected according to universally adopted rules which are described in Table 2·6. The vector set so obtained is not

Seven Systems

Rules for the Selection of the Vector Set $\bar{a}_1, \bar{a}_2, \bar{a}_3$
$\bar{a}_1$, $\bar{a}_2$, and $\bar{a}_3$ are chosen as the three shortest lattice vectors which do not all lie in a plane. $a_1, a_2, a_3, \alpha_1, \alpha_2, \alpha_3$ are independent.
$\bar{a}_2$ is chosen as the shortest lattice vector along the twofold axis, while $\bar{a}_1$ and $\bar{a}_3$ are taken to be the two shortest lattice vectors normal to the twofold axis. a_1, a_2, a_3, α_2 are independent while $\alpha_1 = \alpha_3 = \pi/2$.
$\bar{a}_1$, $\bar{a}_2$, and $\bar{a}_3$ are chosen as the three shortest lattice vectors along the three orthogonal twofold axes. a_1, a_2, a_3 are independent while $\alpha_1 = \alpha_2 = \alpha_3 = \pi/2$.
Case I. $\bar{a}_3$ is chosen as the shortest lattice vector along the threefold axis, while $\bar{a}_1$ is taken to be the shortest lattice vector normal to the threefold axis and $\bar{a}_2$ is chosen so that $\bar{a}_2 = \bar{a}_1 \cdot \mathbf{3}$. a_1 and a_3 are independent while $a_2 = a_1$, $\alpha_1 = \alpha_2 = \pi/2$, and $\alpha_3 = 2\pi/3$. Case II. $\bar{a}_1$ is chosen as the shortest lattice vector which is neither parallel nor normal to the threefold axis, while $\bar{a}_2 = \bar{a}_1 \cdot \mathbf{3}$ and $\bar{a}_3 = \bar{a}_2 \cdot \mathbf{3} = \bar{a}_1 \cdot \mathbf{3}^2$. a_1 and α_1 are independent while $a_2 = a_3 = a_1$ and $\alpha_1 = \alpha_2 = \alpha_3$.
$\bar{a}_3$ is chosen as the shortest lattice vector along the fourfold axis, while $\bar{a}_1$ is taken to be the shortest lattice vector normal to the fourfold axis and $\bar{a}_2 = \bar{a}_1 \cdot \mathbf{4}$. a_1, a_3 are independent while $a_2 = a_1$ and $\alpha_1 = \alpha_2 = \alpha_3 = \pi/2$.
$\bar{a}_3$ is chosen as the shortest lattice vector along the sixfold axis, while $\bar{a}_1$ is taken to be the shortest lattice vector normal to the sixfold axis and $\bar{a}_2 = \bar{a}_1 \cdot \mathbf{3}$. a_1, a_3 are independent while $a_2 = a_1$, $\alpha_1 = \alpha_2 = \pi/2$, and $\alpha_3 = 2\pi/3$.
$\bar{a}_1$, $\bar{a}_2$, and $\bar{a}_3$ are chosen along the three equivalent and orthogonal axes of order two in T and T_h, of order four in O, T_d and O_h. a_1 is independent while $a_2 = a_3 = a_1$ and $\alpha_1 = \alpha_2 = \alpha_3 = \pi/2$.

necessarily primitive and we must therefore in the following make detailed investigations of the translation groups which come into consideration for the various systems.

Triclinic System. Since Equation 2·89 is identically satisfied for $\boldsymbol{\phi} = \mathbf{1}$ or $\bar{\mathbf{1}}$ no restriction is imposed upon the vector set $\bar{a}_1, \bar{a}_2, \bar{a}_3$. It may therefore be assumed, as indicated in Table 2·6, that the three shortest lattice vectors (not all lying in a plane) serve as the vector triplet $\bar{a}_1, \bar{a}_2, \bar{a}_3$. This vector set is obviously primitive and we have thus

Triclinic translation group $\mathcal{P}$

According to the rules given in Table 2·6, we have obtained a specific coordinate system $\bar{a}_1, \bar{a}_2, \bar{a}_3$ for each of the seven systems and it becomes convenient to express all our dyadics $\boldsymbol{\phi}$ in terms of their components in this reference frame. We will use the general form given in Equations 2·14 or the corresponding matrix form, i.e.,

$$\boldsymbol{\phi} \equiv \sum_{k}\sum \phi_{jk}\bar{b}_j\bar{a}_k \equiv \begin{pmatrix} \phi_{11} & \phi_{21} & \phi_{31} \\ \phi_{12} & \phi_{22} & \phi_{32} \\ \phi_{13} & \phi_{23} & \phi_{33} \end{pmatrix} \qquad [2\cdot 90]$$

All the operations of any point group may be obtained with ease from the generating elements, and we will therefore list the specific forms of these elements. The generating elements of the triclinic point groups are $\mathbf{1}$ and $\bar{\mathbf{1}}$ which have the same simple forms in all systems, namely,

$$\mathbf{1} = \bar{b}_1\bar{a}_1 + \bar{b}_2\bar{a}_2 + \bar{b}_3\bar{a}_3 = \begin{pmatrix} 1 & 0 & 0 \\ 0 & 1 & 0 \\ 0 & 0 & 1 \end{pmatrix} \qquad [2\cdot 91a]$$

$$\bar{\mathbf{1}} = -\bar{b}_1\bar{a}_1 - \bar{b}_2\bar{a}_2 - \bar{b}_3\bar{a}_3 = \begin{pmatrix} \bar{1} & 0 & 0 \\ 0 & \bar{1} & 0 \\ 0 & 0 & \bar{1} \end{pmatrix} \qquad [2\cdot 91b]$$

Monoclinic System. Since the vectors $\bar{a}_1$, $\bar{a}_2$, and $\bar{a}_3$ are chosen either parallel or normal to the only twofold axis of the monoclinic point groups, any one of the three vectors is transformed into itself by the symmetry operations which come into consideration in this system, i.e., $\bar{a}_j \cdot \boldsymbol{\phi} = \pm\bar{a}_j$, and Equation 2·89 is satisfied. When referred to the coordinate system $\bar{a}_1, \bar{a}_2, \bar{a}_3$ the generating elements $\mathbf{2}$ and $\bar{\mathbf{2}}$ become

$$\mathbf{2} = -\bar{b}_1\bar{a}_1 + \bar{b}_2\bar{a}_2 - \bar{b}_3\bar{a}_3 = \begin{pmatrix} \bar{1} & 0 & 0 \\ 0 & 1 & 0 \\ 0 & 0 & \bar{1} \end{pmatrix} \qquad [2\cdot 92a]$$

$$\bar{\mathbf{2}} = \bar{b}_1\bar{a}_1 - \bar{b}_2\bar{a}_2 + \bar{b}_3\bar{a}_3 = \begin{pmatrix} 1 & 0 & 0 \\ 0 & \bar{1} & 0 \\ 0 & 0 & 1 \end{pmatrix} \qquad [2{\cdot}92b]$$

Reference to Table 2·6 shows that the vectors $\bar{a}_1$, $\bar{a}_2$, $\bar{a}_3$ have not been selected in such a manner that they necessarily form a primitive set. We must therefore investigate the possibility that the triplet is non-primitive. According to the results obtained in section 12 of Chapter I a lattice representation is primitive if all lattice vectors are of the type $\bar{A}_L \equiv L_1\bar{a}_1 + L_2\bar{a}_2 + L_3\bar{a}_3$ with only integral values L_1, L_2, L_3. The lattice vectors of non-primitive representations have on the other hand fractional as well as integral components and they are thus either of the form $\bar{A}_L$ or of the form $\bar{A}_L + \sum f_j\bar{a}_j$ where the components f_j of the vector $\bar{f} \equiv \sum f_j\bar{a}_j$ are fractions which because of the periodicity may be restricted to the range $0 \leq f_j < 1$. The corresponding lattice translations are $\Gamma_{L_1L_2L_3}$ and $\Gamma_{L_1L_2L_3} \cdot \Gamma_{f_1f_2f_3}$. (For example, $\bar{f} = \frac{1}{2}(\bar{a}_1 + \bar{a}_2 + \bar{a}_3)$ in the body-centered representation and the translation group is therefore $(\Gamma_L) \cdot (E, \Gamma_{\frac{1}{2}\frac{1}{2}\frac{1}{2}})$.) In order to find out if a given vector set $\bar{a}_1$, $\bar{a}_2$, $\bar{a}_3$ is primitive or both primitive and non-primitive we shall proceed as follows. We assume the existence of a lattice vector $\bar{f} \equiv \sum f_j\bar{a}_j$ with $0 \leq f_j < 1$. The existence of additional and equivalent lattice vectors $\bar{f} \cdot \boldsymbol{\phi}$ (where $\boldsymbol{\phi}$ is any one element of the point group under consideration) and of lattice vectors $\bar{f} \pm \bar{f} \cdot \boldsymbol{\phi}$ is then implied. It is easily shown, as demonstrated below, that these lattice vectors cannot exist unless the components f_j assume specific values. The solution $\bar{f} = 0$ is, of course, trivial and the set $\bar{a}_1$, $\bar{a}_2$, $\bar{a}_3$ is necessarily primitive if $\bar{f} = 0$ is the only solution. However, if we find an additional solution for $\bar{f}$, then the set $\bar{a}_1$, $\bar{a}_2$, $\bar{a}_3$ may be primitive or non-primitive. For example, if the two solutions are $\bar{f} = 0$ and $\bar{f} = \frac{1}{2}(\bar{a}_1 + \bar{a}_2 + \bar{a}_3)$ the representation is either primitive or body-centered, and the corresponding translation group is $\mathcal{P}$ or $\mathfrak{I}$.

According to the rules given in Table 2·6, the vectors $\bar{a}_1$, $\bar{a}_2$, $\bar{a}_3$ of the monoclinic system are so chosen that any lattice vector parallel to the twofold axis has the form $L_2\bar{a}_2$, any lattice vector normal to the twofold axis the form $L_1\bar{a}_1 + L_3\bar{a}_3$. Since the same translation groups correspond to a point group $(\mathbf{P})$ as to the analogous improper groups $(\bar{\mathbf{P}})$ and $(\bar{\mathbf{1}}) \cdot (\mathbf{P})$, it is sufficient to consider the point group $(\mathbf{2})$ in the monoclinic system. The vectors $\bar{f} + \bar{f} \cdot \mathbf{2}$ and $\bar{f} - \bar{f} \cdot \mathbf{2}$ are respectively parallel and normal to the twofold axis. Hence we must set $\bar{f} + \bar{f} \cdot \mathbf{2} = L_2\bar{a}_2$ and $\bar{f} - \bar{f} \cdot \mathbf{2} = L_1\bar{a}_1 + L_3\bar{a}_3$. The possible values are therefore $f_j = 0$ or $\frac{1}{2}$. The various solutions for $\bar{f}$ and the corresponding translation groups (using the notation introduced in Equations 2·87) are thus

$$\begin{aligned}
&(1)\quad \bar{f} = 0, && \text{translation group } \mathcal{P} \\
&(2)\quad \bar{f} = \tfrac{1}{2}(\bar{a}_2 + \bar{a}_3), && \text{translation group } \mathcal{A} \\
&(3)\quad \bar{f} = \tfrac{1}{2}(\bar{a}_1 + \bar{a}_2), && \text{translation group } \mathcal{C} \\
&(4)\quad \bar{f} = \tfrac{1}{2}(\bar{a}_1 + \bar{a}_2 + \bar{a}_3), && \text{translation group } \mathfrak{I}
\end{aligned} \qquad [2{\cdot}93]$$

It should be noted that it is not necessary to make use of all three translation groups $\mathcal{A}$, $\mathcal{C}$, and $\mathfrak{I}$. The group $\mathcal{C}$ is transformed into $\mathcal{A}$ if the vectors $\bar{a}_1$ and $\bar{a}_3$ are interchanged. Similarly the group $\mathfrak{I}$ is transformed into $\mathcal{A}$ when we introduce a new vector $\bar{a}_3'$ defined by $\bar{a}_3' = \bar{a}_1 + \bar{a}_3$.

Orthorhombic System. In the orthorhombic system the vectors $\bar{a}_1$, $\bar{a}_2$, $\bar{a}_3$ are the shortest lattice vectors along the three orthogonal axes of order two. Since $\bar{a}_j \cdot \boldsymbol{\phi} = \pm\bar{a}_j$ for any operation which comes into consideration it follows that Equation 2·89 is satisfied and the translation group is thus invariant. All the three twofold axes are proper in point groups $(\mathbf{2}) \cdot (\mathbf{2}')$ and $(\bar{\mathbf{1}}) \cdot (\mathbf{2}) \cdot (\mathbf{2}')$ (in the latter group they are also all improper), while the point group $(\mathbf{2}) \cdot (\bar{\mathbf{2}}')$ contains only one proper axis. We shall agree to choose the vector $\bar{a}_3$ along a proper twofold axis, and we may therefore take $\bar{a}_3$ along the axis $\bar{u}_1$ of the operation $\mathbf{2}$, $\bar{a}_1$ along the axis $\bar{u}_2$ of the element $\mathbf{2}'$ and $\bar{a}_2$ along the axis $\bar{u}_1 \times \bar{u}_2$ of the element $\mathbf{2} \cdot \mathbf{2}'$. Referring the generating elements to the coordinate system $\bar{a}_1$, $\bar{a}_2$, $\bar{a}_3$ we find

$$\mathbf{2} = -\bar{b}_1\bar{a}_1 - \bar{b}_2\bar{a}_2 + \bar{b}_3\bar{a}_3 = \begin{pmatrix} \bar{1} & 0 & 0 \\ 0 & \bar{1} & 0 \\ 0 & 0 & 1 \end{pmatrix} \qquad [2{\cdot}94a]$$

$$\pm\mathbf{2}' = \pm(\bar{b}_1\bar{a}_1 - \bar{b}_2\bar{a}_2 - \bar{b}_3\bar{a}_3) = \pm\begin{pmatrix} 1 & 0 & 0 \\ 0 & \bar{1} & 0 \\ 0 & 0 & \bar{1} \end{pmatrix} \qquad [2{\cdot}94b]$$

In order to find out if the translation group may be non-primitive we follow the procedure outlined in our discussion of the monoclinic system. The vectors $\bar{f} + \bar{f} \cdot \mathbf{2}, \bar{f} + \bar{f} \cdot \mathbf{2}'$, and $\bar{f} + \bar{f} \cdot \mathbf{2} \cdot \mathbf{2}'$ are parallel to the three twofold axes, and they must therefore be of the form $L_j\bar{a}_j$. Accordingly we find $f_j = 0$ or $\frac{1}{2}$, and the following solutions are obtained.

$$\begin{aligned}
&(1)\quad \bar{f} = 0, && \text{translation group } \mathcal{P} \\
&(2)\quad \bar{f} = \tfrac{1}{2}(\bar{a}_2 + \bar{a}_3), && \text{translation group } \mathcal{A} \\
&(3)\quad \bar{f} = \tfrac{1}{2}(\bar{a}_1 + \bar{a}_3), && \text{translation group } \mathcal{B} \\
&(4)\quad \bar{f} = \tfrac{1}{2}(\bar{a}_1 + \bar{a}_2), && \text{translation group } \mathcal{C} \\
&(5)\quad \bar{f} = \tfrac{1}{2}(\bar{a}_1 + \bar{a}_2 + \bar{a}_3), && \text{translation group } \mathfrak{I} \\
&(6)\quad \bar{f} = \tfrac{1}{2}(\bar{a}_2 + \bar{a}_3),\ \tfrac{1}{2}(\bar{a}_1 + \bar{a}_3), && \\
&\qquad\quad \text{and } \tfrac{1}{2}(\bar{a}_1 + \bar{a}_2), && \text{translation group } \mathfrak{F}
\end{aligned} \qquad [2{\cdot}95]$$

It is not necessary to use all three of the base-centered translation groups $\mathfrak{A}$, $\mathfrak{B}$, and $\mathfrak{C}$. Only one of the base-centered groups, say $\mathfrak{A}$, needs to be used with the point groups $(\mathbf{2}) \cdot (\mathbf{2}')$ and $(\bar{\mathbf{1}}) \cdot (\mathbf{2}) \cdot (\mathbf{2}')$ since $\bar{a}_1$, $\bar{a}_2$, $\bar{a}_3$ are all proper axes and thus may be interchanged. In the point group $(\mathbf{2}) \cdot (\bar{\mathbf{2}}')$, $\bar{a}_1$ and $\bar{a}_2$ are both improper axes and may be interchanged, but they cannot be interchanged with the proper axis $\bar{a}_3$ and hence two of the three base-centered translation groups, namely, $\mathfrak{A}$ and $\mathfrak{C}$ (or $\mathfrak{B}$ and $\mathfrak{C}$) must be considered.

Trigonal System. In order to avoid the use of non-primitive representations there are two alternatives for the choice of the vector set $\bar{a}_1$, $\bar{a}_2$, $\bar{a}_3$ in this system.

Case I. Let us begin by selecting the vectors $\bar{a}_1$, $\bar{a}_2$, $\bar{a}_3$ according to the rules given under Case I in Table 2·6. According to this procedure, we set $\bar{a}_3$ equal to the shortest lattice vector along the threefold axis, $\bar{a}_1$ equal to the shortest lattice vector normal to the threefold axis and $\bar{a}_2 = \bar{a}_1 \cdot \mathbf{3}$. However, we shall use this vector set only if it is primitive.

It is readily seen that Equation 2·89 is satisfied for the point groups $(\mathbf{3})$ and $(\bar{\mathbf{3}})$. However, the vector set $\bar{a}_1$, $\bar{a}_2$, $\bar{a}_3$ is transformed into $\bar{a}_1$, $-(\bar{a}_1 + \bar{a}_2)$, $-\bar{a}_3$ by a twofold rotation about the vector $\bar{a}_1$ and into $\bar{a}_1 + \bar{a}_2$, $-\bar{a}_2$, $-\bar{a}_3$ by a twofold rotation about the vector $2\bar{a}_1 + \bar{a}_2$. Hence, Equation 2·89 is satisfied also for the point groups $(\mathbf{3}) \cdot (\mathbf{2}')$, $(\mathbf{3}) \cdot (\bar{\mathbf{2}}')$, and $(\bar{\mathbf{3}}) \cdot (\mathbf{2}')$, provided the axis $\bar{u}_2$ of the generating elements $\mathbf{2}'$ or $\bar{\mathbf{2}}'$ is parallel to $\bar{a}_1$ or to $2\bar{a}_1 + \bar{a}_2$. In order to distinguish between the two possible orientations of $\bar{u}_2$ we shall designate the twofold operation by $\mathbf{2}'$ when $\bar{u}_2$ is along $\bar{a}_1$, by $\mathbf{2}''$ when $\bar{u}_2$ is along $2\bar{a}_1 + \bar{a}_2$. The point groups of the trigonal system may accordingly be written as $C_3(\mathbf{3})$, $C_{3i}(\bar{\mathbf{3}})$, $D_3(\mathbf{3}) \cdot (\mathbf{2}')$ or $(\mathbf{3}) \cdot (\mathbf{2}'')$, $C_{3v}(\mathbf{3}) \cdot (\bar{\mathbf{2}}')$ or $(\mathbf{3}) \cdot (\bar{\mathbf{2}}'')$, $D_{3d}(\bar{\mathbf{3}}) \cdot (\mathbf{2}')$ or $(\bar{\mathbf{3}}) \cdot (\mathbf{2}'')$ with the following generating elements.

$$\pm\mathbf{3} = \pm\bar{b}_1\bar{a}_2 \mp \bar{b}_2(\bar{a}_1 + \bar{a}_2) \pm \bar{b}_3\bar{a}_3 = \pm\begin{pmatrix} 0 & \bar{1} & 0 \\ 1 & \bar{1} & 0 \\ 0 & 0 & 1 \end{pmatrix} \qquad [2\cdot96a]$$

$$\pm\mathbf{2}' = \pm\bar{b}_1\bar{a}_1 \mp \bar{b}_2(\bar{a}_1 + \bar{a}_2) \mp \bar{b}_3\bar{a}_3 = \pm\begin{pmatrix} 1 & \bar{1} & 0 \\ 0 & \bar{1} & 0 \\ 0 & 0 & \bar{1} \end{pmatrix} \qquad [2\cdot96b]$$

$$\pm\mathbf{2}'' = \pm\bar{b}_1(\bar{a}_1 + \bar{a}_2) \mp \bar{b}_2\bar{a}_2 \mp \bar{b}_3\bar{a}_3 = \pm\begin{pmatrix} 1 & 0 & 0 \\ 1 & \bar{1} & 0 \\ 0 & 0 & \bar{1} \end{pmatrix} \qquad [2\cdot96c]$$

We shall next investigate whether non-primitive translation groups come into consideration. Let again $\bar{f} \equiv \sum f_j\bar{a}_j$ represent a hypothetical lattice vector for which $0 \leq f_j < 1$. $\bar{f}$ cannot be a lattice vector unless the following sum and difference are also lattice vectors, $\bar{f} + \bar{f} \cdot \mathbf{3} + \bar{f} \cdot \mathbf{3}^2 = 3f_3\bar{a}_3$, $\bar{f} - \bar{f} \cdot \mathbf{3} = (f_1 + f_2)\bar{a}_1 + (2f_2 - f_1)\bar{a}_2$. Hence it must be required that $f_j = 0$, $\frac{1}{3}$ or $\frac{2}{3}$, and the possible values of $\bar{f}$ become

(1) $\bar{f} = 0$, translation group $(\Gamma_L) \equiv \mathcal{P}$

(2) $\bar{f} = \frac{1}{3}\bar{a}_1 + \frac{2}{3}\bar{a}_2 + \frac{1}{3}\bar{a}_3$ and $\frac{2}{3}\bar{a}_1 + \frac{1}{3}\bar{a}_2 + \frac{2}{3}\bar{a}_3$, translation group $(\Gamma_L) \cdot (E, \Gamma_{\frac{1}{3}\frac{2}{3}\frac{1}{3}}, \Gamma_{\frac{2}{3}\frac{1}{3}\frac{2}{3}})$ [2·97]

(3) $\bar{f} = \frac{2}{3}\bar{a}_1 + \frac{1}{3}\bar{a}_2 + \frac{1}{3}\bar{a}_3$ and $\frac{1}{3}\bar{a}_1 + \frac{2}{3}\bar{a}_2 + \frac{2}{3}\bar{a}_3$, translation group $(\Gamma_L) \cdot (E, \Gamma_{\frac{2}{3}\frac{1}{3}\frac{1}{3}}, \Gamma_{\frac{1}{3}\frac{2}{3}\frac{2}{3}})$

Since $\bar{a}_1$ and $\bar{a}_2$ are equivalent vectors they may be interchanged and the non-primitive translation groups given under (2) and (3) are thus entirely equivalent. The non-primitive translation group $(\Gamma_L) \cdot (E, \Gamma_{\frac{1}{3}\frac{2}{3}\frac{1}{3}}, \Gamma_{\frac{2}{3}\frac{1}{3}\frac{2}{3}})$ respectively $(\Gamma_L) \cdot (E, \Gamma_{\frac{2}{3}\frac{1}{3}\frac{1}{3}}, \Gamma_{\frac{1}{3}\frac{2}{3}\frac{2}{3}})$ is readily transformed into a primitive translation group by means of a proper choice of new vectors $\bar{a}_1'$, $\bar{a}_2'$, $\bar{a}_3'$ defined by $\bar{a}_1' = \bar{f} = \frac{1}{3}\bar{a}_1 + \frac{2}{3}\bar{a}_2 + \frac{1}{3}\bar{a}_3$, $\bar{a}_2' = \bar{a}_1' \cdot \mathbf{3}$, and $\bar{a}_3' = \bar{a}_2' \cdot \mathbf{3}$, i.e.,

$$
\begin{aligned}
\bar{a}_1' &= +\tfrac{1}{3}\bar{a}_1 + \tfrac{2}{3}\bar{a}_2 + \tfrac{1}{3}\bar{a}_3 \\
\bar{a}_2' &= -\tfrac{2}{3}\bar{a}_1 - \tfrac{1}{3}\bar{a}_2 + \tfrac{1}{3}\bar{a}_3 \\
\bar{a}_3' &= +\tfrac{1}{3}\bar{a}_1 - \tfrac{1}{3}\bar{a}_2 + \tfrac{1}{3}\bar{a}_3
\end{aligned}
\qquad [2{\cdot}98]
$$

This transformation was discussed in section 12 of Chapter I (compare Equations 1·52) and the new set $\bar{a}_1'$, $\bar{a}_2'$, $\bar{a}_3'$ is evidently primitive. The vectors $\bar{a}_1'$, $\bar{a}_2'$, $\bar{a}_3'$ are chosen in accordance with the rules given under Case II of Table 2·6. In other words, the non-primitive translation group of Case I becomes a primitive translation group when referred to the vector set of Case II.

Case II. In accordance with the discussion given above we shall employ the reference frame of Case II whenever the translation group of Case I is non-primitive. The corresponding translation group of Case II is then, as we have seen, primitive. It is customary to say that the vector set $\bar{a}_1$, $\bar{a}_2$, $\bar{a}_3$ of Case I is of hexagonal type, while the vector set $\bar{a}_1$, $\bar{a}_2$, $\bar{a}_3$ of Case II is called rhombohedral. The two translation groups which come into consideration in the trigonal system are both primitive, but one is based upon a vector set of hexagonal type, the other upon a vector set of rhombohedral type. In order to distinguish between them, we shall continue to use the customary symbol $\mathcal{P}$ for the primitive translation group of hexagonal type and introduce the new symbol $\mathcal{R}$ for the primitive translation group of rhombohedral type.

The rhombohedral vector set $\bar{a}_1$, $\bar{a}_2$, $\bar{a}_3$ is obviously invariant under a rotation **3** about the axis $\bar{a}_1 + \bar{a}_2 + \bar{a}_3$, and it is also invariant under twofold rotations about an axis $\bar{a}_1 - \bar{a}_2$. The latter direction is normal to the threefold axis. The vector set $\bar{a}_1$, $\bar{a}_2$, $\bar{a}_3$ will therefore satisfy Equation 2·89 for all operations of trigonal point groups provided the axis $\bar{u}_2$ of the generating element $\mathbf{2}'$ or $\bar{\mathbf{2}}'$ coincides with the lattice vector $\bar{a}_1 - \bar{a}_2$ (or with either of the equivalent vectors $\bar{a}_2 - \bar{a}_3$ or $\bar{a}_3 - \bar{a}_1$). It will be recalled that there were two non-equivalent, possible directions for $\bar{u}_2$ in a reference frame of hexagonal type, but this is not true of the rhombohedral reference frame, and accordingly we do not now have to consider alternative forms of the point groups D_3, C_{3v}, and D_{3d}. Thus, using a rhombohedral vector set we have the following point groups $C_3(\mathbf{3})$, $C_{3i}(\bar{\mathbf{3}})$, $D_3(\mathbf{3}) \cdot (\mathbf{2}')$, $C_{3v}(\mathbf{3}) \cdot (\bar{\mathbf{2}}')$, $D_{3d}(\bar{\mathbf{3}}) \cdot (\mathbf{2}')$, and the generating elements $\pm\mathbf{3}$ and $\pm\mathbf{2}'$ become

$$\pm\mathbf{3} = \pm(\bar{b}_1\bar{a}_2 + \bar{b}_2\bar{a}_3 + \bar{b}_3\bar{a}_1) = \pm\begin{pmatrix} 0 & 0 & 1 \\ 1 & 0 & 0 \\ 0 & 1 & 0 \end{pmatrix} \qquad [2\cdot 99a]$$

$$\pm\mathbf{2}' = \mp(\bar{b}_1\bar{a}_2 + \bar{b}_2\bar{a}_1 + \bar{b}_3\bar{a}_3) = \pm\begin{pmatrix} 0 & \bar{1} & 0 \\ \bar{1} & 0 & 0 \\ 0 & 0 & \bar{1} \end{pmatrix} \qquad [2\cdot 99b]$$

Tetragonal System. The vectors $\bar{a}_1$, $\bar{a}_2$, $\bar{a}_3$ of the tetragonal system are chosen, according to Table 2·6, in such a manner that Equation 2·89 is satisfied for the point groups $(\mathbf{4})$, $(\bar{\mathbf{4}})$, and $(\bar{\mathbf{1}}) \cdot (\mathbf{4})$. The vector set $\bar{a}_1$, $\bar{a}_2$, $\bar{a}_3$ is, however, turned into $\bar{a}_1$, $-\bar{a}_2$, $-\bar{a}_3$ by a twofold rotation about the vector $\bar{a}_1$, into $\bar{a}_2$, $\bar{a}_1$, $-\bar{a}_3$ by a twofold rotation about the vector $\bar{a}_1 + \bar{a}_2$. Accordingly the triplet $\bar{a}_1$, $\bar{a}_2$, $\bar{a}_3$ satisfies Equation 2·89 also for the remaining tetragonal point groups provided the axis $\bar{u}_2$ of the generating element $\mathbf{2}'$ or $\bar{\mathbf{2}}'$ is chosen along $\bar{a}_1$ or along $\bar{a}_1 + \bar{a}_2$ (or along one of the other vectors equivalent to $\bar{a}_1$ or to $\bar{a}_1 + \bar{a}_2$). We shall agree to designate the twofold operation by $\mathbf{2}'$ or $\bar{\mathbf{2}}'$ when its axis is along vector $\bar{a}_1$, by $\mathbf{2}''$ or $\bar{\mathbf{2}}''$ when its axis is along the vector $\bar{a}_1 + \bar{a}_2$. The two possible orientations for the axis $\bar{u}_2$ lead to two distinct forms of the point group D_{2d}, namely, $(\bar{\mathbf{4}}) \cdot (\mathbf{2}')$ and $(\bar{\mathbf{4}}) \cdot (\mathbf{2}'')$, but distinct forms do not come into consideration for the point groups D_4, C_{4v} and D_{4h} since $(\mathbf{4}) \cdot (\mathbf{2}') = (\mathbf{4}) \cdot (\mathbf{2}'')$ and $(\mathbf{4}) \cdot (\bar{\mathbf{2}}') = (\mathbf{4}) \cdot (\bar{\mathbf{2}}'')$. The generating elements are

$$\pm\mathbf{4} = \pm(\bar{b}_1\bar{a}_2 - \bar{b}_2\bar{a}_1 + \bar{b}_3\bar{a}_3) = \pm\begin{pmatrix} 0 & \bar{1} & 0 \\ 1 & 0 & 0 \\ 0 & 0 & 1 \end{pmatrix} \qquad [2\cdot 100a]$$

$$\pm\mathbf{2}' = \pm(\bar{b}_1\bar{a}_1 - \bar{b}_2\bar{a}_2 - \bar{b}_3\bar{a}_3) = \pm\begin{pmatrix}1 & 0 & 0\\ 0 & \bar{1} & 0\\ 0 & 0 & \bar{1}\end{pmatrix} \qquad [2\cdot100b]$$

$$\mathbf{2}'' = \bar{b}_1\bar{a}_2 + \bar{b}_2\bar{a}_1 - \bar{b}_3\bar{a}_3 = \begin{pmatrix}0 & 1 & 0\\ 1 & 0 & 0\\ 0 & 0 & \bar{1}\end{pmatrix} \qquad [2\cdot100c]$$

The monoclinic point groups are subgroups of the tetragonal point groups. According to Table 2·6, the tetragonal vector set $\bar{a}_1$, $\bar{a}_2$, $\bar{a}_3$ may be considered a special case of a monoclinic triplet in which the vectors $\bar{a}_2$ and $\bar{a}_3$ have been interchanged. Accordingly the tetragonal translation groups must be sought among the monoclinic translation groups. These we found to be $\mathcal{P}$, $\mathcal{A}$, $\mathcal{B}$, $\mathcal{I}$ (the groups $\mathcal{P}$, $\mathcal{A}$, $\mathcal{C}$, $\mathcal{I}$ were actually deduced, but the vectors $\bar{a}_2$ and $\bar{a}_3$ are to be interchanged so that $\mathcal{C}$ is transformed into $\mathcal{B}$). In the tetragonal system the vectors $\bar{a}_1$ and $\bar{a}_2$ are equivalent and it must therefore be required of a tetragonal translation group that it remain invariant under an interchange of $\bar{a}_1$ and $\bar{a}_2$. The groups $\mathcal{A}$ and $\mathcal{B}$ do not fulfil this condition. Tetragonal translation groups are therefore either primitive or body-centered, i.e., $\mathcal{P}$ or $\mathcal{I}$.

Hexagonal System. It is seen from Table 2·6 that the vector set $\bar{a}_1$, $\bar{a}_2$, $\bar{a}_3$ of the hexagonal system is the same as that of Case I of the trigonal system. We know that this vector set satisfies Equation 2·89 for all trigonal point groups. Since the triplet is transformed into itself by a twofold rotation about $\bar{a}_3$ it follows that $\bar{a}_1$, $\bar{a}_2$, $\bar{a}_3$ satisfy Equation 2·89 also for all hexagonal point groups.

According to results obtained in the discussion of the trigonal system the axis $\bar{u}_2$ of the twofold generating element of D_6, C_{6v}, D_{3h}, and D_{6h} is either along the vector $\bar{a}_1$ or along the vector $2\bar{a}_1 + \bar{a}_2$. In the former case the symbol $\mathbf{2}'$ or $\bar{\mathbf{2}}'$ is used to designate the twofold operation, in the latter case the symbol $\mathbf{2}''$ or $\bar{\mathbf{2}}''$. It is readily verified that $(\mathbf{6})\cdot(\mathbf{2}') = (\mathbf{6})\cdot(\mathbf{2}'')$ and $(\mathbf{6})\cdot(\bar{\mathbf{2}}') = (\mathbf{6})\cdot(\bar{\mathbf{2}}'')$ while $(\bar{\mathbf{6}})\cdot(\mathbf{2}') \neq (\bar{\mathbf{6}})\cdot(\mathbf{2}'')$. The two alternatives for the direction of $\bar{u}_2$ thus lead to two distinct forms of D_{3h}, while only one form of the remaining hexagonal point groups needs to be considered. The generating elements $\pm\mathbf{2}'$ and $\pm\mathbf{2}''$ are given in Equations 2·96*b* and *c* and the elements $\pm\mathbf{6}$ are

$$\pm\mathbf{6} = \pm\bar{b}_1(\bar{a}_1 + \bar{a}_2) \mp \bar{b}_2\bar{a}_1 \pm \bar{b}_3\bar{a}_3 = \pm\begin{pmatrix}1 & \bar{1} & 0\\ 1 & 0 & 0\\ 0 & 0 & 1\end{pmatrix} \qquad [2\cdot101]$$

Monoclinic as well as trigonal point groups are subgroups of hexagonal point groups. Hexagonal translation groups must therefore be sought among the translation groups which are common to the monoclinic and trigonal systems. Monoclinic translation groups are either primitive, base-centered or body-centered, while trigonal translation groups (referred to the vector set of Case I) are either primitive or of the non-primitive type shown in Equations 2·97. The two systems have only the primitive translation group in common, and this is consequently the only possible hexagonal translation group.

TABLE 2·7

THE FOURTEEN TRANSLATION GROUPS

System	Nature of Vector Set $\bar{a}_1$, $\bar{a}_2$, $\bar{a}_3$	Translation Groups
Triclinic	$a_1,\ a_2,\ a_3,\ \alpha_1,\ \alpha_2,\ \alpha_3$	$\mathcal{P}$
Monoclinic	$a_1,\ a_2,\ a_3,\ \alpha_2$ $\alpha_1 = \alpha_3 = \dfrac{\pi}{2}$	$\mathcal{P}$ or $\mathcal{A}$ (or $\mathcal{C}$ or $\mathcal{I}$)
Orthorhombic	$a_1,\ a_2,\ a_3$ $\alpha_1 = \alpha_2 = \alpha_3 = \dfrac{\pi}{2}$	$\mathcal{P}$, $\mathcal{A}$ (or $\mathcal{B}$ or $\mathcal{C}$), $\mathcal{I}$, or $\mathcal{F}$
Tetragonal	$a_1,\ a_3$ $a_2 = a_1,\quad \alpha_1 = \alpha_2 = \alpha_3 = \dfrac{\pi}{2}$	$\mathcal{P}$ or $\mathcal{I}$
	$a_1,\ \alpha_1$ $a_2 = a_3 = a_1,\quad \alpha_1 = \alpha_2 = \alpha_3$	$\mathcal{R}$
Trigonal ↗↘		
Hexagonal	$a_1,\ a_3$ $a_2 = a_1,\quad \alpha_1 = \alpha_2 = \dfrac{\pi}{2},\quad \alpha_3 = \dfrac{2\pi}{3}$	$\mathcal{P}$
Cubic	a_1 $a_2 = a_3 = a_1,\quad \alpha_1 = \alpha_2 = \alpha_3 = \dfrac{\pi}{2}$	$\mathcal{P}$, $\mathcal{I}$, or $\mathcal{F}$

Cubic System. It is readily verified that the cubic vector set $\bar{a}_1$, $\bar{a}_2$, $\bar{a}_3$ chosen according to the convention given in Table 2·6 satisfies Equation 2·89 for all cubic point groups. The generating elements of cubic point groups are $\pm\mathbf{3}'$, $\pm\mathbf{4}$, $\pm\mathbf{2}$, $\pm\mathbf{2}'$, and $\pm\mathbf{2}''$. The elements $\pm\mathbf{2}$ and $\pm\mathbf{2}'$ are given by Equations 2·94*a* and *b*, the elements $\pm\mathbf{3}'$ by Equation 2·99*a*, the elements $\pm\mathbf{4}$ and $\pm\mathbf{2}''$ by Equations 2·100*a* and *c*.

The cubic vector set $\bar{a}_1$, $\bar{a}_2$, $\bar{a}_3$ can be considered a special case of the orthorhombic set, the difference being that the three vectors are equivalent in the cubic system. In the orthorhombic system the translation groups were found to be $\mathcal{P}$, $\mathcal{A}$, $\mathcal{B}$, $\mathcal{C}$, $\mathcal{I}$, or $\mathcal{F}$. Since the base-centered

TABLE 2·8. TRANSLATION GROUPS

Type of Translation Group	Point Groups	Rotation Axes		
Triclinic				
$\mathcal{P}$	$C_1(1)$			
	$C_i(\bar{1})$			
Monoclinic			$\bar{a}_2$	
$\mathcal{P}, \mathcal{A}$	$C_2(2)$		2	
	$C_s(\bar{2})$		$\bar{2}$	
	$C_{2h}(\bar{1})(2)$		± 2	
Orthorhombic		$\bar{a}_3$	$\bar{a}_1$	$\bar{a}_2$
$\mathcal{P}, \mathcal{A}, \mathcal{C}, \mathcal{I}, \mathcal{F}$	$C_{2v}(2)(\bar{2}')$	2	$\bar{2}$	$\bar{2}$
$\mathcal{P}, \mathcal{A}, \mathcal{I}, \mathcal{F}$	$D_2(2)(2')$	2	2	2
	$D_{2h}(\bar{1})(2)(2')$	± 2	± 2	± 2
Tetragonal		$\bar{a}_3$	$\bar{a}_1$	$\bar{a}_1 + \bar{a}_2$
	$C_4(4)$	4		
	$S_4(\bar{4})$	$\bar{4}$		
	$C_{4h}(\bar{1})(4)$	± 4		
	$D_4(4)(2')$	4	2	2
$\mathcal{P}, \mathcal{I}$	$C_{4v}(4)(\bar{2}')$	4	$\bar{2}$	$\bar{2}$
	$D_{2d}(\bar{4})(2')$	$\bar{4}$	2	$\bar{2}$
	$(\bar{4})(2'')$	$\bar{4}$	$\bar{2}$	2
	$D_{4h}(\bar{1})(4)(2')$	± 4	± 2	± 2
Cubic		$\bar{a}_1$	$\bar{a}_1 + \bar{a}_2 + \bar{a}_3$	$\bar{a}_1 + \bar{a}_2$
	$T(3')((2)(2'))$	2	3	
$\mathcal{P}, \mathcal{I}, \mathcal{F}$	$T_h(\bar{3}')((2)(2'))$	± 2	$\bar{3}$	
	$O(3')((4)(2''))$	4	3	2
	$T_d(3')((\bar{4})(\bar{2}''))$	$\bar{4}$	3	$\bar{2}$
	$O_h(\bar{3}')((4)(2''))$	± 4	$\bar{3}$	± 2
Rhombohedral		$\bar{a}_1 + \bar{a}_2 + \bar{a}_3$		$\bar{a}_1 - \bar{a}_2$
	$C_3(3)$	3		
	$C_{3i}(\bar{3})$	$\bar{3}$		
$\mathcal{R}$	$D_3(3)(2')$	3		2
	$C_{3v}(3)(\bar{2}')$	3		$\bar{2}$
	$D_{3d}(\bar{3})(2')$	$\bar{3}$		± 2
Hexagonal		$\bar{a}_3$	$\bar{a}_1$	$2\bar{a}_1 + \bar{a}_2$
	$C_3(3)$	3		
	$C_{3i}(\bar{3})$	$\bar{3}$		
	D_3 $(3)(2')$	3	2	
	$(3)(2'')$	3		2
	C_{3v} $(3)(\bar{2}')$	3	$\bar{2}$	
$\mathcal{P}$	$(3)(\bar{2}'')$	3		$\bar{2}$
	D_{3d} $(\bar{3})(2')$	$\bar{3}$	± 2	
	$(\bar{3})(2'')$	$\bar{3}$		± 2
	$C_6(6)$	6		
	$C_{3h}(\bar{6})$	$\bar{6}$		
	$C_{6h}(\bar{1})(6)$	± 6		
	$D_6(6)(2')$	6	2	2
	$C_{6v}(6)(\bar{2}')$	6	$\bar{2}$	$\bar{2}$
	D_{3h} $(\bar{6})(2')$	$\bar{6}$	2	$\bar{2}$
	$(\bar{6})(2'')$	$\bar{6}$	$\bar{2}$	2
	$D_{6h}(\bar{1})(6)(2')$	± 6	± 2	± 2

AND POINT GROUPS

Generating Elements	$\{\Phi\}$
$\pm\mathbf{1} = \pm\begin{pmatrix}1 & 0 & 0\\ 0 & 1 & 0\\ 0 & 0 & 1\end{pmatrix}$	
$\pm\mathbf{2} = \pm\begin{pmatrix}\bar{1} & 0 & 0\\ 0 & 1 & 0\\ 0 & 0 & \bar{1}\end{pmatrix}$	$\{\mathbf{2}\} = 2\bar{b}_2\bar{a}_2$
$\pm\mathbf{2} = \pm\begin{pmatrix}\bar{1} & 0 & 0\\ 0 & \bar{1} & 0\\ 0 & 0 & 1\end{pmatrix}$	$\{\mathbf{2}\} = 2\bar{b}_3\bar{a}_3$
$\pm\mathbf{2}' = \pm\begin{pmatrix}1 & 0 & 0\\ 0 & \bar{1} & 0\\ 0 & 0 & \bar{1}\end{pmatrix}$	$\{\mathbf{2}'\} = 2\bar{b}_1\bar{a}_1$
$\pm\mathbf{4} = \pm\begin{pmatrix}0 & \bar{1} & 0\\ 1 & 0 & 0\\ 0 & 0 & 1\end{pmatrix}$	$\{\mathbf{4}\} = 4\bar{b}_3\bar{a}_3$
$\pm\mathbf{2}'' = \pm\begin{pmatrix}0 & 1 & 0\\ 1 & 0 & 0\\ 0 & 0 & \bar{1}\end{pmatrix}$	$\{\mathbf{2}''\} = (\bar{b}_1 + \bar{b}_2)(\bar{a}_1 + \bar{a}_2)$
$\pm\mathbf{3}' = \pm\begin{pmatrix}0 & 0 & 1\\ 1 & 0 & 0\\ 0 & 1 & 0\end{pmatrix}$	$\{\mathbf{3}'\} = (\bar{b}_1 + \bar{b}_2 + \bar{b}_3)(\bar{a}_1 + \bar{a}_2 + \bar{a}_3)$
$\pm\mathbf{3} = \pm\begin{pmatrix}0 & 0 & 1\\ 1 & 0 & 0\\ 0 & 1 & 0\end{pmatrix}$	$\{\mathbf{3}\} = (\bar{b}_1 + \bar{b}_2 + \bar{b}_3)(\bar{a}_1 + \bar{a}_2 + \bar{a}_3)$
$\pm\mathbf{2}' = \pm\begin{pmatrix}0 & \bar{1} & 0\\ \bar{1} & 0 & 0\\ 0 & 0 & \bar{1}\end{pmatrix}$	$\{\mathbf{2}'\} = (\bar{b}_1 - \bar{b}_2)(\bar{a}_1 - \bar{a}_2)$
$\pm\mathbf{3} = \pm\begin{pmatrix}0 & \bar{1} & 0\\ 1 & \bar{1} & 0\\ 0 & 0 & 1\end{pmatrix}$	$\{\mathbf{3}\} = 3\bar{b}_3\bar{a}_3$
$\pm\mathbf{2}' = \pm\begin{pmatrix}1 & \bar{1} & 0\\ 0 & \bar{1} & 0\\ 0 & 0 & \bar{1}\end{pmatrix}$	$\{\mathbf{2}'\} = (2\bar{b}_1 - \bar{b}_2)\bar{a}_1$
$\pm\mathbf{2}'' = \pm\begin{pmatrix}1 & 0 & 0\\ 1 & \bar{1} & 0\\ 0 & 0 & \bar{1}\end{pmatrix}$	$\{\mathbf{2}''\} = \bar{b}_1(2\bar{a}_1 + \bar{a}_2)$
$\pm\mathbf{6} = \pm\begin{pmatrix}1 & \bar{1} & 0\\ 1 & 0 & 0\\ 0 & 0 & 1\end{pmatrix}$	$\{\mathbf{6}\} = 6\bar{b}_3\bar{a}_3$

groups are not invariant under an interchange of $\bar{a}_1$, $\bar{a}_2$, and $\bar{a}_3$ they cannot come into consideration in the cubic system. The cubic translation groups are therefore $\mathcal{P}$, $\mathfrak{J}$, or $\mathfrak{F}$, i.e., primitive, body-centered, or face-centered.

All translation groups have now been deduced and the results have for the sake of convenience been compiled in Table 2·7. The translation groups are either primitive, base-centered, body-centered, or face-centered, but they are based upon different vector sets $\bar{a}_1$, $\bar{a}_2$, $\bar{a}_3$ in the different systems. As a consequence there are, as shown by Table 2·7, fourteen distinct translation groups.

In Table 2·8 are listed all translation groups and the point groups to which they correspond. This table also contains useful information about the direction and nature of the rotation axes in the various point groups and gives the matrix form of the generating elements. In the last column are given the characteristic dyadics $\{\mathbf{n}\}$ of the proper generating elements. According to Equation 2·30 this characteristic dyadic has the value $\{\mathbf{n}\} = n\,\bar{u}\bar{u}$ where $\bar{u}$ is a unit vector along the rotation axis. The antecedent of the dyad in the last column of Table 2·8 therefore represents the direction of the rotation axis in the reciprocal lattice, the consequent the direction of the rotation axis in the initial lattice. The rotation axes of the various point groups are given in the third column. The information in this column is complete except for the fact that only one representative of each set of equivalent axes is listed. The symbol $\mathbf{n}$ as usual indicates an n-fold proper axis, the symbol $\bar{\mathbf{n}}$ an n-fold improper axis, while the symbol $\pm\mathbf{n}$ shows that the axis is proper as well as improper. In the Mauguin-Hermann notation the point groups (and space groups) are characterized by the nature of their rotation axes. Thus the symbols given in the third column are simply the Mauguin-Hermann symbols for the point groups. (Actually Mauguin-Hermann use the symbol m instead of $\bar{\mathbf{2}}$, the symbol $\frac{n}{m}$ instead of $\pm\mathbf{n}$.)

In the point groups where the generating elements are associated with different rotation axes it has been found advisable to differentiate between the generating elements by affixing accents to their symbols. The scheme which we are using is given in Table 2·9.

6. THE SPACE GROUPS

According to results obtained in preceding sections of this chapter we know that any space group can be written as the direct product of the translation group and its factor group. When the translation vectors $\bar{t}$ of the elements $[\boldsymbol{\phi}, \bar{t}]$ are omitted the factor groups reduce to the thirty-

TABLE 2·9

NOMENCLATURE FOR THE GENERATING ELEMENTS

Type of Translation Group	Rotation Axes of Generating Elements $\bar{a}_3$	$\bar{a}_1$	$\bar{a}_1 + \bar{a}_2 + \bar{a}_3$	$\bar{a}_1 + \bar{a}_2$	$2\bar{a}_1 + \bar{a}_2$	$\bar{a}_1 - \bar{a}_2$
Orthorhombic	$\pm\mathbf{2}$	$\pm\mathbf{2}'$				
Tetragonal	$\pm\mathbf{4}$	$\pm\mathbf{2}'$		$\pm\mathbf{2}''$		
Cubic	$\pm\mathbf{2}$	$\pm\mathbf{2}'$				
			$\pm\mathbf{3}'$	$\pm\mathbf{2}''$		
	$\pm\mathbf{4}$					
Rhombohedral			$\pm\mathbf{3}$			$\pm\mathbf{2}'$
Hexagonal	$\pm\mathbf{3}$					
		$\pm\mathbf{2}'$			$\pm\mathbf{2}''$	
	$\pm\mathbf{6}$					

two possible point groups which were deduced in section 2·4. The point groups are either cyclic or such that they may be written as the direct product of two or three cyclic subgroups. Thus the point groups may be given in the following general form

$$(\boldsymbol{\phi})(\boldsymbol{\phi}_1)(\boldsymbol{\phi}_2) \qquad [2\cdot 102]$$

where $\boldsymbol{\phi}$, $\boldsymbol{\phi}_1$, and $\boldsymbol{\phi}_2$ are the generating elements. (If the point group under consideration can be written as the direct product of only two cyclic subgroups we set $\boldsymbol{\phi}_2 = \mathbf{I}$, and if it is cyclic we set $\boldsymbol{\phi}_1 = \boldsymbol{\phi}_2 = \mathbf{I}$.) Because of the isomorphism the factor groups corresponding to the point group of Equation 2·102 will have the form

$$(\boldsymbol{\phi}, \bar{t})(\boldsymbol{\phi}_1, \bar{t}')(\boldsymbol{\phi}_2, \bar{t}'') \qquad [2\cdot 103]$$

while the space groups may be represented by the product

$$(\Gamma)(\boldsymbol{\phi}, \bar{t})(\boldsymbol{\phi}_1, \bar{t}')(\boldsymbol{\phi}_2, \bar{t}'') \qquad [2\cdot 104]$$

We have deduced all point groups, i.e., all possible sets $\boldsymbol{\phi}$, $\boldsymbol{\phi}_1$, $\boldsymbol{\phi}_2$, and we have also derived all translation groups (Γ) which may be combined with each set $\boldsymbol{\phi}$, $\boldsymbol{\phi}_1$, $\boldsymbol{\phi}_2$. Thus the translation vectors $\bar{t}$, $\bar{t}'$, and $\bar{t}''$ are the only unknown quantities. In order to determine the translation vectors we shall in the first place make use of the fact that the generating elements $[\boldsymbol{\phi}, \bar{t}]$, $[\boldsymbol{\phi}_1, \bar{t}']$, and $[\boldsymbol{\phi}_2, \bar{t}'']$ must be possible symmetry operations of the crystal lattice. Accordingly the translation vectors are subject to the condition expressed in Equation 2·29, i.e.,

$$\begin{aligned} \bar{t} \cdot \{\boldsymbol{\phi}\} &= \text{a lattice vector} \\ \bar{t}' \cdot \{\boldsymbol{\phi}_1\} &= \text{a lattice vector} \\ \bar{t}'' \cdot \{\boldsymbol{\phi}_2\} &= \text{a lattice vector} \end{aligned} \qquad [2\cdot 105]$$

The conditions given in Equations 2·105 are necessary conditions, but they are not sufficient. If the product represented by Equation 2·103 is to be a factor group it must be a group and this requirement imposes in general additional conditions upon the vectors $\bar{t}$, $\bar{t}'$, and $\bar{t}''$. Conversely it may be stated that the product given in Equation 2·103 is a possible factor group, if its three generating elements represent possible symmetry operations and if in addition the product is a group. These two requirements are obviously fulfilled when $\bar{t} = \bar{t}' = \bar{t}'' = 0$. Accordingly the point groups themselves are acceptable as factor groups, and we may construct some of the space groups without further investigation. These space groups are the direct products of the translation groups with the point groups. They are easily listed with the aid of Table 2·8 in which the possible translation groups are given in the first column and the possible point groups in the second column. The seventy-three space groups so obtained are compiled in Table 2·10. They may appropriately be called the seventy-three point space groups. (In Table 2·10 we have introduced some obvious simplifications in the nomenclature. The script symbols for the translation groups have been replaced by the corresponding italic symbols. The parentheses (the group symbol) around the generating elements have been omitted, while the $\pm$ sign has been substituted for the inversion group.)

The seventy-three point space groups represent less than one-third of all space groups, and we shall next have to consider in some detail the methods by means of which all conceivable space groups can be derived. Unless systematic procedures are followed it will frequently happen that apparently different space groups are derived which on closer examination prove to be merely different representations of the same space group. Difficulties of this nature can be attributed to the lack of definite rules for the choice of origin of our reference frame. The elements of space groups define transformations from one set of points in space to another set of points in the same space (compare section 1 of this chapter). The initial and transformed set were described by means of vectors drawn from a fixed point, the origin. Let $\bar{r}$ and $\bar{r}'$ as in Equation 2·3 be two such vectors representing an initial point and the transformed point. Suppose that the origin is shifted to the point $\bar{r}_0$ and that $\bar{r}_1$ and $\bar{r}_1'$ are the position vectors of the initial and of the transformed point relative to the new origin. Obviously we have $\bar{r} = \bar{r}_1 + \bar{r}_0$ and $\bar{r}' = \bar{r}_1' + \bar{r}_0$. With the aid of Equation 2·3 we find

$$\bar{r}_1' = \bar{r}_1 \cdot \boldsymbol{\varphi} + \bar{t} + \bar{r}_0 \cdot (\boldsymbol{\varphi} - \mathbf{I}) = \bar{r}_1 \cdot [\boldsymbol{\varphi}, \bar{t} + \bar{r}_0 \cdot (\boldsymbol{\varphi} - \mathbf{I})] \quad [2{\cdot}106]$$

Clearly the two symbols $[\boldsymbol{\varphi}, \bar{t}]$ and $[\boldsymbol{\varphi}, \bar{t} + \bar{r}_0 \cdot (\boldsymbol{\varphi} - \mathbf{I})]$, where $\bar{r}_0$ is arbitrary, represent the same transformation. Accordingly we set

$$[\boldsymbol{\varphi}, \bar{t}] = [\boldsymbol{\varphi}, \bar{t} + \bar{r}_0 \cdot (\boldsymbol{\varphi} - \mathbf{I})] \quad [2{\cdot}107]$$

TABLE 2·10

THE SEVENTY-THREE POINT SPACE GROUPS

Space Group	Mauguin-Hermann	Schoenflies
$P1$	$P1$	C_1^1
$P\bar{1}$	$P\bar{1}$	C_i^1
$P2$	$P2$	C_2^1
$A2$	$A2$	C_2^3
$P\bar{2}$	Pm	C_s^1
$A\bar{2}$	Am	C_s^3
$P \pm 2$	$P\frac{2}{m}$	C_{2h}^1
$A \pm 2$	$A\frac{2}{m}$	C_{2h}^3
$P22'$	$P222$	D_2^1
$A22'$	$A222$	D_2^6
$I22'$	$I222$	D_2^8
$F22'$	$F222$	D_2^7
$P2\bar{2}'$	$Pmm2$	C_{2v}^1
$A2\bar{2}'$	$Amm2$	C_{2v}^{14}
$C2\bar{2}'$	$Cmm2$	C_{2v}^{11}
$I2\bar{2}'$	$Imm2$	C_{2v}^{20}
$F2\bar{2}'$	$Fmm2$	C_{2v}^{18}
$P \pm 22'$	$P\frac{2}{m}\frac{2}{m}\frac{2}{m}$	D_{2h}^1
$A \pm 22'$	$A\frac{2}{m}\frac{2}{m}\frac{2}{m}$	D_{2h}^{19}
$I \pm 22'$	$I\frac{2}{m}\frac{2}{m}\frac{2}{m}$	D_{2h}^{25}
$F \pm 22'$	$F\frac{2}{m}\frac{2}{m}\frac{2}{m}$	D_{2h}^{23}
$P4$	$P4$	C_4^1
$I4$	$I4$	C_4^5
$P\bar{4}$	$P\bar{4}$	S_4^1
$I\bar{4}$	$I\bar{4}$	S_4^2
$P \pm 4$	$P\frac{4}{m}$	C_{4h}^1
$I \pm 4$	$I\frac{4}{m}$	C_{4h}^5
$P42'$	$P422$	D_4^1
$I42'$	$I422$	D_4^9
$P4\bar{2}'$	$P4mm$	C_{4v}^1
$I4\bar{2}'$	$I4mm$	C_{4v}^9
$P\bar{4}2'$	$P\bar{4}2m$	D_{2d}^1
$I\bar{4}2'$	$I\bar{4}2m$	D_{2d}^{11}
$P\bar{4}2''$	$P\bar{4}m2$	D_{2d}^5
$I\bar{4}2''$	$I\bar{4}m2$	D_{2d}^9
$P \pm 42'$	$P\frac{4}{m}\frac{2}{m}\frac{2}{m}$	D_{4h}^1
$I \pm 42'$	$I\frac{4}{m}\frac{2}{m}\frac{2}{m}$	D_{4h}^{17}

Space Group	Mauguin-Hermann	Schoenflies
$P3$	$C3$	C_3^1
$R3$	$R3$	C_3^4
$P\bar{3}$	$C\bar{3}$	C_{3i}^1
$R\bar{3}$	$R\bar{3}$	C_{3i}^2
$P32'$	$C321$	D_3^2
$P32''$	$C312$	D_3^1
$R32'$	$R32$	D_3^7
$P3\bar{2}'$	$C3m1$	C_{3v}^1
$P3\bar{2}''$	$C31m$	C_{3v}^2
$R3\bar{2}'$	$R3m$	C_{3v}^5
$P\bar{3}2'$	$C\bar{3}\frac{2}{m}1$	D_{3d}^3
$P\bar{3}2''$	$C\bar{3}1\frac{2}{m}$	D_{3d}^1
$R\bar{3}2'$	$R\bar{3}m$	D_{3d}^5
$P6$	$C6$	C_6^1
$P\bar{6}$	$C\bar{6}$	C_{3h}^1
$P \pm 6$	$C\frac{6}{m}$	C_{6h}^1
$P62'$	$C622$	D_6^1
$P6\bar{2}'$	$C6mm$	C_{6v}^1
$P\bar{6}2'$	$C\bar{6}2m$	D_{3h}^3
$P\bar{6}2''$	$C\bar{6}m2$	D_{3h}^1
$P \pm 62'$	$C\frac{6}{m}\frac{2}{m}\frac{2}{m}$	D_{6h}^1
$P3'22'$	$P23$	T^1
$I3'22'$	$I23$	T^3
$F3'22'$	$F23$	T^2
$P\bar{3}'22'$	$P\frac{2}{m}\bar{3}$	T_h^1
$I\bar{3}'22'$	$I\frac{2}{m}\bar{3}$	T_h^5
$F\bar{3}'22'$	$F\frac{2}{m}\bar{3}$	T_h^3
$P3'42''$	$P432$	O^1
$I3'42''$	$I432$	O^5
$F3'42''$	$F432$	O^3
$P3'\bar{4}\bar{2}''$	$P\bar{4}3m$	T_d^1
$I3'\bar{4}\bar{2}''$	$I\bar{4}3m$	T_d^3
$F3'\bar{4}\bar{2}''$	$F\bar{4}3m$	T_d^2
$P\bar{3}'42''$	$P\frac{4}{m}\bar{3}\frac{2}{m}$	O_h^1
$I\bar{3}'42''$	$I\frac{4}{m}\bar{3}\frac{2}{m}$	O_h^9
$F\bar{3}'42''$	$F\frac{4}{m}\bar{3}\frac{2}{m}$	O_h^5

It is consequently permissible to increase any translation vector by an amount $\bar{r}_0 \cdot (\mathbf{\phi} - \mathbf{I})$. Although the vector $\bar{r}_0$ is arbitrary, this is not necessarily true of the increment $\bar{r}_0 \cdot (\mathbf{\phi} - \mathbf{I})$. The dyadics $\mathbf{\phi}$ which come into consideration in our investigations are $\pm\mathbf{n}$. If $\mathbf{\phi} = \bar{\mathbf{1}}, \bar{\mathbf{3}}, \bar{\mathbf{4}}$, or $\bar{\mathbf{6}}$ the dyadic $\mathbf{\phi} - \mathbf{I}$ is non-singular (compare the discussion of section 3 of Chapter II) in which case the vector $\bar{r}_0 \cdot (\mathbf{\phi} - \mathbf{I})$ can assume any value. The dyadic $\mathbf{\phi} - \mathbf{I}$ is uniplanar if $\mathbf{\phi} = \mathbf{2}, \mathbf{3}, \mathbf{4}$, or $\mathbf{6}$ and $\bar{r}_0 \cdot (\mathbf{\phi} - \mathbf{I})$ is then an arbitrary vector normal to the rotation axis. The dyadic $\bar{\mathbf{2}} - \mathbf{I}$ is unilinear and hence $\bar{r}_0 \cdot (\bar{\mathbf{2}} - \mathbf{I})$ is an arbitrary vector parallel to the improper rotation axis. Finally the increment $\bar{r}_0 \cdot (\mathbf{\phi} - \mathbf{I}) = 0$, if $\mathbf{\phi} = \mathbf{1}$. In accordance with Equation 2·107 we may set

$$(\Gamma)(\mathbf{\phi}, \bar{t})(\mathbf{\phi}_1, \bar{t}')(\mathbf{\phi}_2, \bar{t}'') = (\Gamma)(\mathbf{\phi}, \bar{t} + \bar{r}_0 \cdot (\mathbf{\phi} - \mathbf{I}))$$
$$(\mathbf{\phi}_1, \bar{t}' + \bar{r}_0 \cdot (\mathbf{\phi}_1 - \mathbf{I}))(\mathbf{\phi}_2, \bar{t}'' + \bar{r}_0 \cdot (\mathbf{\phi}_2 - \mathbf{I})) \quad [2\cdot108]$$

Since the vector $\bar{r}_0$ is arbitrary we may choose it in such a way that the translation vector for one of the three generating elements assumes the simplest possible value. For the sake of convenience let us agree upon a definite order in which to write down the generating elements of any given space group. In Tables 2·6 and 2·8 the generating elements of the various point groups are given in a specific order, and we will adopt the same order for the corresponding space groups as indicated by Equations 2·102 and 2·104. According to this scheme the space groups may be classed into three types as follows.

Type A. The first generating element of the space group is $[\bar{\mathbf{n}}, \bar{t}]$ with $n = 1, 3, 4$, or 6. The dyadic $\mathbf{\phi} - \mathbf{I}$ is then non-singular. The space groups which correspond to the following point groups belong to this type: C_i, C_{2h}, D_{2h}, S_4, C_{4h}, D_{2d}, D_{4h}, C_{3i}, D_{3d}, C_{3h}, C_{6h}, D_{3h}, D_{6h}, T_h, O_h.

Type B. The first generating element of the space group is $[\mathbf{n}, \bar{t}]$ with $n = 2, 3, 4$, or 6. The dyadic $\mathbf{\phi} - \mathbf{I}$ is uniplanar, the plane being normal to the rotation axis $\bar{u}$ of $\mathbf{n}$. Space groups based upon the following point groups are of type B: C_2, D_2, C_{2v}, C_4, D_4, C_{4v}, C_3, D_3, C_{3v}, C_6, D_6, C_{6v}, T, O, T_d.

Type C. The first generating element of the space group is $[\bar{\mathbf{2}}, \bar{t}]$. The dyadic $\mathbf{\phi} - \mathbf{I}$ is unilinear, its axis being parallel to the improper rotation axis $\bar{u}$ of $\bar{\mathbf{2}}$. Only the space groups based upon the point group C_s belong to this type.

Considering now Equation 2·108, it is seen that the translation vector of the first generating element can be given the form $\bar{t} + \bar{r}_0 \cdot (\mathbf{\phi} - \mathbf{I})$. For space groups of type A we can adjust $\bar{r}_0$ so that the translation vector becomes zero, for space groups of type B we can reduce the translation vector to the form $\bar{t} \cdot \bar{u}\bar{u}$ and for space groups of type C to the form $\bar{t} - \bar{t} \cdot \bar{u}\bar{u}$. These simplifications of the translation vector for the first generating element correspond to displacements of the origin from an arbitrary point to the symmetry center, symmetry axis, or symmetry plane. (Compare Equation 2·48.) Consequently only the following representations of space groups need to be considered.

$$\text{Type } A \quad (\Gamma)(\boldsymbol{\phi})(\boldsymbol{\phi}_1, \bar{t}')(\boldsymbol{\phi}_2, \bar{t}'') \tag{2·109}$$

$$\text{Type } B \quad (\Gamma)(\boldsymbol{\phi}, \bar{t} \cdot \bar{u}\bar{u})(\boldsymbol{\phi}_1, \bar{t}')(\boldsymbol{\phi}_2, \bar{t}'') \tag{2·110}$$

$$\text{Type } C \quad (\Gamma)(\bar{\mathbf{2}}, \bar{t} - \bar{t} \cdot \bar{u}\bar{u}) \tag{2·111}$$

(The increments $\bar{r}_0 \cdot (\boldsymbol{\phi}_1 - \mathbf{I})$ and $\bar{r}_0 \cdot (\boldsymbol{\phi}_2 - \mathbf{I})$ in the translation vectors of the second and third generating elements have been incorporated in the symbols $\bar{t}'$ and $\bar{t}''$. This may, of course, be done since the restrictions on the translation vectors have not yet been considered.)

Let us next consider the conditions to be imposed upon the translation vectors in order to make the product $(\boldsymbol{\phi}, \bar{t})(\boldsymbol{\phi}_1, \bar{t}')(\boldsymbol{\phi}_2, \bar{t}'')$ an acceptable factor group. If Equations 2·105 are applied, each of the three factors, $(\boldsymbol{\phi}, \bar{t})$, $(\boldsymbol{\phi}_1, \bar{t}')$, and $(\boldsymbol{\phi}_2, \bar{t}'')$, becomes an acceptable generating subgroup, but these equations do not make the product $(\boldsymbol{\phi}, \bar{t})(\boldsymbol{\phi}_1, \bar{t}')(\boldsymbol{\phi}_2, \bar{t}'')$ a group. In a non-cyclic point group $(\boldsymbol{\phi})(\boldsymbol{\phi}_1)$ or $(\boldsymbol{\phi})(\boldsymbol{\phi}_1)(\boldsymbol{\phi}_2)$, the group nature of the product can be expressed by means of relationships between the generating elements. These relations are:

For point groups $(\boldsymbol{\phi})(\boldsymbol{\phi}_1)$:

$$\boldsymbol{\phi}_1 = \boldsymbol{\phi} \cdot \boldsymbol{\phi}_1 \cdot \boldsymbol{\phi} \tag{2·112}$$

For point groups $(\boldsymbol{\phi})(\boldsymbol{\phi}_1)(\boldsymbol{\phi}_2)$:

$$\boldsymbol{\phi}_2 = \boldsymbol{\phi}_1 \cdot \boldsymbol{\phi}_2 \cdot \boldsymbol{\phi}_1 \tag{2·113a}$$

$$\boldsymbol{\phi}_1 = \boldsymbol{\phi}^{-1} \cdot \boldsymbol{\phi}_1^j \cdot \boldsymbol{\phi}_2^k \cdot \boldsymbol{\phi}^l \tag{2·113b}$$

where j, k, and l are integers which we can specify for each point group. (For example, in the point group $(\mathbf{3}')(\mathbf{4})(\mathbf{2}'')$ we have $j = 3$, $k = 2$, $l = 2$.) Because of the isomorphism the corresponding relations must hold for the factor groups. Remembering that it is permissible to add any lattice vector $\bar{A}_p$ to the translation vector we have:

For factor groups $(\boldsymbol{\phi}, \bar{t})(\boldsymbol{\phi}_1, \bar{t}')$:

$$[\boldsymbol{\phi}_1, \bar{t}' + \bar{A}_p] = [\boldsymbol{\phi}, \bar{t}] \cdot [\boldsymbol{\phi}_1, \bar{t}'] \cdot [\boldsymbol{\phi}, \bar{t}] \tag{2·114}$$

For factor groups $(\boldsymbol{\phi}, \bar{t})(\boldsymbol{\phi}_1, \bar{t}')(\boldsymbol{\phi}_2, \bar{t}'')$:

$$[\boldsymbol{\phi}_2, \bar{t}'' + \bar{A}_p] = [\boldsymbol{\phi}_1, \bar{t}'] \cdot [\boldsymbol{\phi}_2, \bar{t}''] \cdot [\boldsymbol{\phi}_1, \bar{t}'] \tag{2·115a}$$

$$[\boldsymbol{\phi}_1, \bar{t}' + \bar{A}_p] = [\boldsymbol{\phi}, \bar{t}]^{-1} \cdot [\boldsymbol{\phi}_1, \bar{t}']^j \cdot [\boldsymbol{\phi}_2, \bar{t}'']^k \cdot [\boldsymbol{\phi}, \bar{t}]^l \tag{2·115b}$$

These equations together with Equations 2·105 represent the restrictions on the translation vectors of the generating elements.

On the basis of the preceding results the derivation of the space groups can be carried out without difficulty. Because of the great number of space groups this is, however, a tedious task. All space groups were derived fifty years ago and under these circumstances our deriving the set of space groups completely serves no useful purpose. We shall therefore list the final results but carry through the derivation in detail only for a few space groups in order to illustrate the general procedure which we have just outlined. By way of illustration we shall derive all space groups based upon the point groups C_{4h}, D_3, and C_s as examples of space groups of types A, B, and C respectively.

Type A. Space groups $(\Gamma)(\boldsymbol{\phi})(\boldsymbol{\phi}_1, \bar{t}')(\boldsymbol{\phi}_2, \bar{t}'')$, $\boldsymbol{\phi} = \bar{\mathbf{1}}, \bar{\mathbf{3}}, \bar{\mathbf{4}}$, or $\bar{\mathbf{6}}$. Since for any generating subgroup $(\boldsymbol{\psi}, \bar{t})$

$$(\Gamma)(\boldsymbol{\psi}, \bar{t}) = (\Gamma)(\boldsymbol{\psi}, \bar{t} + \bar{A}_p) \qquad [2\cdot116]$$

where $\bar{A}_p$ is any lattice vector it is permissible to add any lattice vector to the translation vectors of the generating elements of any space group. As a consequence, the two following products are equivalent representations of the same space group

$$(\Gamma)(\boldsymbol{\phi})(\boldsymbol{\phi}_1, \bar{t}')(\boldsymbol{\phi}_2, \bar{t}'') = (\Gamma)(\boldsymbol{\phi}, \bar{A}_p)(\boldsymbol{\phi}_1, \bar{t}')(\boldsymbol{\phi}_2, \bar{t}'') \qquad [2\cdot117]$$

If we shift the origin to the point $\bar{r}_0$, the three translation vectors will get increments in accordance with Equation 2·107. Since $\boldsymbol{\phi} - \mathbf{I}$ is a nonsingular dyadic in space groups of type A we may set

$$\bar{A}_p + \bar{r}_0 \cdot (\boldsymbol{\phi} - \mathbf{I}) = 0 \qquad [2\cdot118]$$

The second representation of the space group may thus again be transformed into a product in which the translation vector of the first generating element is zero, and we have the following result.

$$(\Gamma)(\boldsymbol{\phi})(\boldsymbol{\phi}_1, \bar{t}')(\boldsymbol{\phi}_2, \bar{t}'')$$
$$= (\Gamma)(\boldsymbol{\phi})(\boldsymbol{\phi}_1, \bar{t}' + \bar{r}_0 \cdot (\boldsymbol{\phi}_1 - \mathbf{I}))(\boldsymbol{\phi}_2, \bar{t}'' + \bar{r}_0 \cdot (\boldsymbol{\phi}_2 - \mathbf{I})) \qquad [2\cdot119]$$

where $\bar{r}_0$ is any solution of Equation 2·118. The increments $\bar{r}_0 \cdot (\boldsymbol{\phi}_1 - \mathbf{I})$ and $\bar{r}_0 \cdot (\boldsymbol{\phi}_2 - \mathbf{I})$ may be lattice vectors (and if so the result expressed by Equation 2·119 is trivial), but this is not necessarily true as the case below will show.

As an example we shall deduce all space groups based upon the point group $C_{4h}(\bar{\mathbf{1}})(\mathbf{4})$.

Example 1. Space groups $(\Gamma)(\bar{\mathbf{1}})(\mathbf{4}, \bar{t}')$. According to the results obtained in section 5 of this chapter and listed in Table 2·8, the translation group is either primitive or body-centered. In the former case a lattice vector $\bar{A}_p$ is of the form $\bar{A}_p = \bar{A}_L = L_1\bar{a}_1 + L_2\bar{a}_2 + L_3\bar{a}_3$, while in the latter case $\bar{A}_p = \bar{A}_L$ or $\bar{A}_p = \bar{A}_L + \frac{1}{2}(\bar{a}_1 + \bar{a}_2 + \bar{a}_3)$. Setting $\boldsymbol{\phi} = -\mathbf{I}$ in Equation 2·118 we obtain the solution $\bar{r}_0 = \frac{1}{2}\bar{A}_p$. As a consequence of Equations 2·116 and 2·119 the following representations of the space group are equivalent.

$$\begin{aligned}(\Gamma)(\bar{\mathbf{1}})(\mathbf{4}, \bar{t}') &= (\Gamma)(\bar{\mathbf{1}})(\mathbf{4}, \bar{t}' + \bar{A}_p)\\ &= (\Gamma)(\bar{\mathbf{1}})(\mathbf{4}, \bar{t}' + \tfrac{1}{2}\bar{A}_p \cdot (\mathbf{4} - \mathbf{I}))\end{aligned} \qquad [2·120]$$

where, according to Equation 2·100*a*, $\mathbf{4} - \mathbf{I} = \bar{b}_1(\bar{a}_2 - \bar{a}_1) - \bar{b}_2(\bar{a}_1 + \bar{a}_2)$. The acceptable values of the translation vector $\bar{t}'$ are given by Equations 2·105 and 2·114. Since $\{\mathbf{4}\} = 4\bar{b}_3\bar{a}_3$, the former equation gives $t_3 = 0, \frac{1}{4}, \frac{1}{2}$, or $\frac{3}{4}$, while Equation 2·114 becomes

$$[\mathbf{4}, \bar{t}' + \bar{A}_p] = [\bar{\mathbf{1}}] \cdot [\mathbf{4}, \bar{t}'] \cdot [\bar{\mathbf{1}}] = [\mathbf{4}, -\bar{t}']$$

or

$$\bar{t}' = -\tfrac{1}{2}\bar{A}_p \qquad [2·121]$$

With the aid of Equation 2·120 and our knowledge of the lattice vectors, the distinct solutions for $\bar{t}'$ are readily listed, and we find

$$\begin{aligned}(\Gamma) &= \mathcal{P}\colon\quad \bar{t}' = 0,\quad \tfrac{1}{2}\bar{a}_1,\quad \tfrac{1}{2}\bar{a}_3 \quad\text{or}\quad \tfrac{1}{2}(\bar{a}_2 + \bar{a}_3)\\ (\Gamma) &= \mathcal{J}\colon\quad \bar{t}' = 0 \quad\text{or}\quad \tfrac{1}{4}(\bar{a}_1 + \bar{a}_2 + \bar{a}_3)\end{aligned} \qquad [2·122]$$

Introducing new symbols for the generating elements according to the definitions,

$$[\mathbf{n}, \bar{t}] \equiv [\mathbf{n}, t_1\bar{a}_1 + t_2\bar{a}_2 + t_3\bar{a}_3] \equiv \mathbf{n}_{t_1t_2t_3} \qquad [2·123a]$$

$$[\bar{\mathbf{n}}, \bar{t}] \equiv [-\mathbf{n}, t_1\bar{a}_1 + t_2\bar{a}_2 + t_3\bar{a}_3] \equiv \bar{\mathbf{n}}_{t_1t_2t_3} \qquad [2·123b]$$

the space groups become

$$\begin{gathered}\mathcal{P}(\bar{\mathbf{1}})(\mathbf{4}),\quad \mathcal{P}(\bar{\mathbf{1}})(\mathbf{4}_{\frac{1}{2}00}),\quad \mathcal{P}(\bar{\mathbf{1}})(\mathbf{4}_{00\frac{1}{2}}),\quad \mathcal{P}(\bar{\mathbf{1}})(\mathbf{4}_{0\frac{1}{2}\frac{1}{2}})\\ \mathcal{J}(\bar{\mathbf{1}})(\mathbf{4}),\quad \mathcal{J}(\bar{\mathbf{1}})(\mathbf{4}_{\frac{1}{4}\frac{1}{4}\frac{1}{4}})\end{gathered} \qquad [2·124]$$

The two point space groups $\mathcal{P}(\bar{\mathbf{1}})(\mathbf{4})$ and $\mathcal{J}(\bar{\mathbf{1}})(\mathbf{4})$ were obtained earlier and are listed in Table 2·10.

Type B. Space groups $(\Gamma)(\mathbf{n}, \bar{t} \cdot \bar{u}\bar{u})(\boldsymbol{\phi}_1, \bar{t}')(\boldsymbol{\phi}_2, \bar{t}'')$. According to Equation 2·116 it is permissible to add a lattice vector to any translation vector, and hence we have

$$\begin{aligned}&(\Gamma)(\mathbf{n}, \bar{t} \cdot \bar{u}\bar{u})(\boldsymbol{\phi}_1, \bar{t}')(\boldsymbol{\phi}_2, \bar{t}'')\\ &\qquad = (\Gamma)(\mathbf{n}, \bar{t} \cdot \bar{u}\bar{u} + \bar{A}_p)(\boldsymbol{\phi}_1, \bar{t}')(\boldsymbol{\phi}_2, \bar{t}'')\end{aligned} \qquad [2·125]$$

If we shift the origin to the point $\bar{r}_0$ defined by

$$\bar{A}_p - \bar{A}_p \cdot \bar{u}\bar{u} + \bar{r}_0 \cdot (\mathbf{n} - \mathbf{I}) = 0 \qquad [2·126]$$

and transform the right side of Equation 2·125 in accordance with Equation 2·108, the following result is obtained.

$$(\Gamma)(\mathbf{n},\ \bar{t}\cdot\bar{u}\bar{u})(\boldsymbol{\phi}_1,\ \bar{t}')(\boldsymbol{\phi}_2,\ \bar{t}'') =$$
$$(\Gamma)(\mathbf{n},\ (\bar{t}+\bar{A}_p)\cdot\bar{u}\bar{u})(\boldsymbol{\phi}_1,\ \bar{t}'+\bar{r}_0\cdot(\boldsymbol{\phi}_1-\mathbf{I}))(\boldsymbol{\phi}_2,\ \bar{t}''+\bar{r}_0\cdot(\boldsymbol{\phi}_2-\mathbf{I})) \qquad [2\cdot127]$$

Since $\mathbf{n} - \mathbf{I}$ is a planar dyadic, the vector $\bar{r}_0$ as given by Equation 2·126 has an arbitrary component along the rotation axis $\bar{u}$.

According to Equation 2·30 $\{\mathbf{n}\} = n\,\bar{u}\bar{u}$ and according to Equation 2·105 $\bar{t}\cdot\{\mathbf{n}\} = j\bar{A}_u$ where j is an integer while $\bar{A}_u$ is the shortest lattice vector along the rotation axis. We have thus,

$$\bar{t}\cdot\bar{u}\bar{u} = \frac{j}{n}\bar{A}_u \qquad [2\cdot128]$$

The translation vectors $\bar{t}'$ and $\bar{t}''$ can be determined from Equations 2·115, and the distinct solutions selected with the aid of Equation 2·127.

Example 2. Space groups based upon point group D_3. According to Table 2·8 and Equation 2·128 the space groups under consideration are:

$$\mathcal{P}\left(\mathbf{3},\ \frac{j}{3}\bar{a}_3\right)(\mathbf{2}',\ \bar{t}') \qquad [2\cdot129a]$$

$$\mathcal{P}\left(\mathbf{3},\ \frac{j}{3}\bar{a}_3\right)(\mathbf{2}'',\ \bar{t}') \qquad [2\cdot129b]$$

$$\mathcal{R}\left(\mathbf{3},\ \frac{j}{3}(\bar{a}_1+\bar{a}_2+\bar{a}_3)\right)(\mathbf{2}',\ \bar{t}') \qquad [2\cdot129c]$$

The dyadics $\mathbf{3}$, $\mathbf{2}'$, and $\mathbf{2}''$ of Equations 2·129*a* and *b* are given by Equations 2·96, the dyadics $\mathbf{3}$ and $\mathbf{2}'$ of Equation 2·129*c* are given by Equation 2·99. The translation groups $\mathcal{P}$ and $\mathcal{R}$ are both primitive and we therefore set $\bar{A}_p = \bar{A}_L \equiv L_1\bar{a}_1 + L_2\bar{a}_2 + L_3\bar{a}_3$. In order to find equivalent representations of the space groups we will make use of Equation 2·127. As shown in the last column of Table 2·8 we have $\{\mathbf{3}\} = 3\bar{b}_3\bar{a}_3$ in the translation group $\mathcal{P}$, and $\{\mathbf{3}\} = (\bar{b}_1+\bar{b}_2+\bar{b}_3)(\bar{a}_1+\bar{a}_2+\bar{a}_3)$ in the translation group $\mathcal{R}$. Hence

$$(\Gamma) = \mathcal{P}:\quad \bar{A}_p\cdot\bar{u}\bar{u} = L_3 \qquad [2\cdot130a]$$

$$(\Gamma) = \mathcal{R}:\quad \bar{A}_p\cdot\bar{u}\bar{u} = \frac{L_1+L_2+L_3}{3} = -\frac{j}{3} \qquad [2\cdot130b]$$

L_1, L_2, L_3 are arbitrary integers and we may therefore in Equation

2·130*b* set $L_1 + L_2 + L_3 = -j$. The solutions $\bar{r}_0$ of Equation 2·126 become

$$(\Gamma) = \mathcal{P}: \quad \bar{r}_0 = \frac{2L_1 - L_2}{3}\bar{a}_1 + \frac{L_1 + L_2}{3}\bar{a}_2 + s\bar{a}_3 \qquad [2·131a]$$

$$(\Gamma) = \mathcal{R}: \quad \bar{r}_0 = L_1\bar{a}_1 - L_3\bar{a}_2 + s(\bar{a}_1 + \bar{a}_2 + \bar{a}_3) \qquad [2·131b]$$

The scalar s is arbitrary and we may therefore choose it so that $t_3' - 2s = 0$. With this value of s the quantities $\bar{r}_0 \cdot (\boldsymbol{\phi}_1 - \mathbf{I})$ (apart from an additive lattice vector) are readily found to be

$$(\Gamma) = \mathcal{P}, \quad \boldsymbol{\phi}_1 = \mathbf{2}': \quad \left(t_1' - \frac{k}{3}\right)\bar{a}_1 + \left(t_2' - \frac{2k}{3}\right)\bar{a}_2, \; k = 0, 1, \text{ or } 2 \qquad [2·132a]$$

$$(\Gamma) = \mathcal{P}, \quad \boldsymbol{\phi}_1 = \mathbf{2}'': \quad t_1'\bar{a}_1 + t_2'\bar{a}_2 \qquad [2·132b]$$

$$(\Gamma) = \mathcal{R}, \quad \boldsymbol{\phi}_1 = \mathbf{2}': \quad (t_1' - t_3')\bar{a}_1 + (t_2' - t_3')\bar{a}_2 \qquad [2·132c]$$

Using Equation 2·127 and the results expressed in Equations 2·130 and 2·132, the space groups of Equations 2·129 may be given in the form

$$\mathcal{P}\left(\mathbf{3}, \frac{j}{3}\bar{a}_3\right)\left(\mathbf{2}', \left(t_1' - \frac{k}{3}\right)\bar{a}_1 + \left(t_2' - \frac{2k}{3}\right)\bar{a}_2\right) \qquad [2·133a]$$

$$\mathcal{P}\left(\mathbf{3}, \frac{j}{3}\bar{a}_3\right)(\mathbf{2}'', t_1'\bar{a}_1 + t_2'\bar{a}_2) \qquad [2·133b]$$

$$\mathcal{R}(\mathbf{3})(\mathbf{2}', (t_1' - t_3')\bar{a}_1 + (t_2' - t_3')\bar{a}_2) \qquad [2·133c]$$

We shall finally determine the possible values of $\bar{t}'$ by applying Equations 2·105 and 2·114 which become

$$\bar{t}' \cdot \{\boldsymbol{\phi}_1\} = \bar{A}_L \quad \text{with} \quad \boldsymbol{\phi}_1 = \mathbf{2}' \text{ or } \mathbf{2}'' \qquad [2·134a]$$

$$\bar{t}' + \bar{A}_L = \bar{t}' \cdot \mathbf{3} \qquad [2·134b]$$

These equations are readily solved and give as result (again disregarding an additive lattice vector)

$$(\Gamma) = \mathcal{P}, \quad \boldsymbol{\phi}_1 = \mathbf{2}': \quad t_1' = \frac{k}{3}, \quad t_2' = \frac{2k}{3}, \; k = 0, 1, \text{ or } 2 \qquad [2·135a]$$

$$(\Gamma) = \mathcal{P}, \quad \boldsymbol{\phi}_1 = \mathbf{2}'': \quad t_1' = 0, \quad t_2' = 0 \qquad [2·135b]$$

$$(\Gamma) = \mathcal{R}, \quad \boldsymbol{\phi}_1 = \mathbf{2}': \quad t_1' - t_3' = 0, \quad t_2' - t_3' = 0 \qquad [2·135c]$$

Setting $j = 0$, 1, or 2, the following space groups are consequently obtained.

$$\mathcal{P}(\mathbf{3})(\mathbf{2}'), \quad \mathcal{P}(\mathbf{3}_{00\frac{1}{3}})(\mathbf{2}'), \quad \mathcal{P}(\mathbf{3}_{00\frac{2}{3}})(\mathbf{2}'), \quad \mathcal{P}(\mathbf{3})(\mathbf{2}''),$$
$$\mathcal{P}(\mathbf{3}_{00\frac{1}{3}})(\mathbf{2}''), \quad \mathcal{P}(\mathbf{3}_{00\frac{2}{3}})(\mathbf{2}''), \quad \mathcal{R}(\mathbf{3})(\mathbf{2}') \qquad [2·136]$$

In addition to the point space groups $\mathcal{P}(\mathbf{3})(\mathbf{2}')$, $\mathcal{P}(\mathbf{3})(\mathbf{2}'')$ and $\mathcal{R}(\mathbf{3})(\mathbf{2}')$ given in Table 2·10, there are thus four new space groups which are based upon the point group D_3.

Type C. Space groups $(\Gamma)(\bar{\mathbf{2}}, \bar{t} - \bar{t}\cdot\bar{u}\bar{u})$. Since the point group $(\bar{\mathbf{2}})$ is monoclinic the translation group is primitive or base-centered; furthermore, $\bar{u}\bar{u} = \bar{b}_2\bar{a}_2$ and $\{\bar{\mathbf{2}}\} = 2\bar{b}_1\bar{a}_1 + 2\bar{b}_3\bar{a}_3$. The space groups consequently have the form

$$(\Gamma)(\bar{\mathbf{2}}, t_1\bar{a}_1 + t_3\bar{a}_3), \quad (\Gamma) = \mathcal{P} \quad \text{or} \quad \mathcal{C} \tag{2·137}$$

and Equation 2·105 gives

$$t_1 = 0 \text{ or } \tfrac{1}{2}, \quad t_3 = 0 \text{ or } \tfrac{1}{2} \tag{2·138}$$

When $(\Gamma) = \mathcal{P}$ Equations 2·138 give four apparently different space groups, namely, $\mathcal{P}(\bar{\mathbf{2}})$, $\mathcal{P}(\bar{\mathbf{2}}_{\frac{1}{2}00})$, $\mathcal{P}(\bar{\mathbf{2}}_{00\frac{1}{2}})$, and $\mathcal{P}(\bar{\mathbf{2}}_{\frac{1}{2}0\frac{1}{2}})$. However, in the monoclinic system only the vector $\bar{a}_2$ of the set $\bar{a}_1, \bar{a}_2, \bar{a}_3$ has a prescribed direction so that the following primitive transformations are permissible: $\bar{a}_1, \bar{a}_2, \bar{a}_3 \longrightarrow \bar{a}_3, \bar{a}_2, \bar{a}_1$ and $\bar{a}_1, \bar{a}_2, \bar{a}_3 \longrightarrow \bar{a}_1 + \bar{a}_3, \bar{a}_2, \bar{a}_3$. Consequently the products $\mathcal{P}(\bar{\mathbf{2}}_{00\frac{1}{2}})$ and $\mathcal{P}(\bar{\mathbf{2}}_{\frac{1}{2}0\frac{1}{2}})$ can be transformed into $\mathcal{P}(\bar{\mathbf{2}}_{\frac{1}{2}00})$. When $(\Gamma) = \mathcal{C}$ we have $\bar{A}_p = \bar{A}_L$ or $\bar{A}_p = \bar{A}_L + \frac{1}{2}(\bar{a}_2 + \bar{a}_3)$, and Equation 2·116 gives $\mathcal{C}(\bar{\mathbf{2}}, t_1\bar{a}_1 + t_3\bar{a}_3) = \mathcal{C}(\bar{\mathbf{2}}, t_1\bar{a}_1 + (t_3 - \frac{1}{2})\bar{a}_3)$. Hence $\mathcal{C}(\bar{\mathbf{2}}) = \mathcal{C}(\bar{\mathbf{2}}_{00\frac{1}{2}})$ and $\mathcal{C}(\bar{\mathbf{2}}_{\frac{1}{2}00}) = \mathcal{C}(\bar{\mathbf{2}}_{\frac{1}{2}0\frac{1}{2}})$. The space groups which come into consideration are thus

$$\mathcal{P}(\bar{\mathbf{2}}), \quad \mathcal{P}(\bar{\mathbf{2}}_{\frac{1}{2}00}), \quad \mathcal{C}(\bar{\mathbf{2}}), \quad \mathcal{C}(\bar{\mathbf{2}}_{\frac{1}{2}00}) \tag{2·139}$$

The examples discussed above demonstrate that, using the general procedure which we have outlined, all space groups can be obtained with comparative ease. The complete set of 230 space groups is listed in the first column of Table 2·11. For the sake of convenience some simplifications in the nomenclature have been introduced. As in Table 2·10 Latin rather than script symbols are used for the translation groups, the inversion group $(\bar{\mathbf{1}})$ is represented as a $\pm$ sign, and the parentheses around the generating elements have been omitted. For the generating elements the notation defined by Equations 2·123 has been adopted. Accordingly a constellation of symbols like $I \pm \mathbf{4}_{\frac{1}{4}\frac{1}{4}\frac{1}{4}}\mathbf{2}'_{\frac{1}{2}00}$ is to be interpreted as follows:

$$I \pm \mathbf{4}_{\frac{1}{4}\frac{1}{4}\frac{1}{4}}\mathbf{2}'_{\frac{1}{2}00} \equiv (\Gamma_L)\cdot(E, \Gamma_{\frac{1}{2}\frac{1}{2}\frac{1}{2}})\cdot(\bar{\mathbf{1}})\cdot(\mathbf{4}, \tfrac{1}{4}(\bar{a}_1 + \bar{a}_2 + \bar{a}_3))\cdot(\mathbf{2}', \tfrac{1}{2}\bar{a}_1) \tag{2·140}$$

The nature of the operations represented by the generating elements is easily found on the basis of the discussion given in section 3 of this chapter. Consider, for example, the element $\mathbf{4}_{\frac{1}{4}\frac{1}{4}\frac{1}{4}}$. According to Table 2·1, this operation represents a fourfold screw of pitch ¼. The

TABLE 2·11

THE 230 SPACE GROUPS

Space Group	Symbols: Schoenflies	Symbols: Mauguin-Hermann
$P1$	C_1^1	$P1$
$P\bar{1}$	C_i^1	$P\bar{1}$
$P2$	C_2^1	$P2$
$P2_{0\frac{1}{2}0}$	C_2^2	$P2_1$
$A2$	C_2^3	$A2$
$P\bar{2}$	C_s^1	Pm
$P\bar{2}_{\frac{1}{2}00}$	C_s^2	Pa
$A\bar{2}$	C_s^3	Am
$A\bar{2}_{\frac{1}{2}00}$	C_s^4	Aa
$P \pm 2$	C_{2h}^1	$P2/m$
$P \pm 2_{0\frac{1}{2}0}$	C_{2h}^2	$P2_1/m$
$P \pm 2_{\frac{1}{2}00}$	C_{2h}^4	$P2/a$
$P \pm 2_{\frac{1}{2}\frac{1}{2}0}$	C_{2h}^5	$P2_1/a$
$A \pm 2$	C_{2h}^3	$A2/m$
$A \pm 2_{\frac{1}{2}00}$	C_{2h}^6	$A2/a$
$P22'$	D_2^1	$P222$
$P22'_{0\frac{1}{2}0}$	D_2^2	$P222_1$
$P22'_{\frac{1}{2}\frac{1}{2}0}$	D_2^3	$P2_12_12$
$P2_{00\frac{1}{2}}2'_{\frac{1}{2}\frac{1}{2}0}$	D_2^4	$P2_12_12_1$
$A22'$	D_2^6	$A222$
$A22'_{\frac{1}{2}00}$	D_2^5	$A2_122$
$I22'$	D_2^8	$I222$
$I2_{00\frac{1}{2}}2'_{\frac{1}{2}\frac{1}{2}0}$	D_2^9	$I2_12_12_1$
$F22'$	D_2^7	$F222$
$P2\bar{2}'$	C_{2v}^1	$Pmm2$
$P2\bar{2}'_{00\frac{1}{2}}$	C_{2v}^3	$Pcc2$
$P2\bar{2}'_{\frac{1}{2}00}$	C_{2v}^4	$Pma2$
$P2\bar{2}'_{0\frac{1}{2}\frac{1}{2}}$	C_{2v}^6	$Pnc2$
$P2\bar{2}'_{\frac{1}{2}\frac{1}{2}0}$	C_{2v}^8	$Pba2$
$P2\bar{2}'_{\frac{1}{2}\frac{1}{2}\frac{1}{2}}$	C_{2v}^{10}	$Pnn2$
$P2_{00\frac{1}{2}}\bar{2}'$	C_{2v}^2	$Pmc2_1$
$P2_{00\frac{1}{2}}\bar{2}'_{\frac{1}{2}0\frac{1}{2}}$	C_{2v}^5	$Pca2_1$
$P2_{00\frac{1}{2}}\bar{2}'_{\frac{1}{2}00}$	C_{2v}^7	$Pmn2_1$
$P2_{00\frac{1}{2}}\bar{2}'_{\frac{1}{2}\frac{1}{2}\frac{1}{2}}$	C_{2v}^9	$Pna2_1$
$C2\bar{2}'$	C_{2v}^{11}	$Cmm2$
$C2\bar{2}'_{00\frac{1}{2}}$	C_{2v}^{13}	$Ccc2$
$C2_{00\frac{1}{2}}\bar{2}'$	C_{2v}^{12}	$Cmc2_1$
$A2\bar{2}'$	C_{2v}^{14}	$Amm2$
$A2\bar{2}'_{0\frac{1}{2}0}$	C_{2v}^{15}	$Abm2$
$A2\bar{2}'_{\frac{1}{2}00}$	C_{2v}^{16}	$Ama2$
$A2\bar{2}'_{\frac{1}{2}\frac{1}{2}0}$	C_{2v}^{17}	$Aba2$
$I2\bar{2}'$	C_{2v}^{20}	$Imm2$
$I2\bar{2}'_{\frac{1}{2}00}$	C_{2v}^{22}	$Ima2$
$I2\bar{2}'_{\frac{1}{2}\frac{1}{2}0}$	C_{2v}^{21}	$Iba2$

TABLE 2·11 (*Continued*)

Space Group	Symbols: Schoenflies	Symbols: Mauguin-Hermann
$F2\bar{2}'$	C_{2v}^{18}	*Fmm*
$F2\bar{2}'_{\frac{1}{4}\frac{1}{4}\frac{1}{4}}$	C_{2v}^{19}	*Fdd*
$P \pm 22'$	D_{2h}^{1}	*Pmmm*
$P \pm 22'_{00\frac{1}{2}}$	D_{2h}^{3}	*Pccm*
$P \pm 22'_{\frac{1}{2}00}$	D_{2h}^{5}	*Pmam*
$P \pm 22'_{\frac{1}{2}0\frac{1}{2}}$	D_{2h}^{7}	*Pcnm*
$P \pm 22'_{\frac{1}{2}\frac{1}{2}0}$	D_{2h}^{9}	*Pbam*
$P \pm 22'_{\frac{1}{2}\frac{1}{2}\frac{1}{2}}$	D_{2h}^{12}	*Pnnm*
$P \pm 2_{00\frac{1}{2}}2'_{0\frac{1}{2}0}$	D_{2h}^{11}	*Pbcm*
$P \pm 2_{00\frac{1}{2}}2'_{0\frac{1}{2}\frac{1}{2}}$	D_{2h}^{13}	*Pnmm*
$P \pm 2_{00\frac{1}{2}}2'_{\frac{1}{2}\frac{1}{2}\frac{1}{2}}$	D_{2h}^{16}	*Pnam*
$P \pm 2_{\frac{1}{2}\frac{1}{2}0}2'_{0\frac{1}{2}\frac{1}{2}}$	D_{2h}^{2}	*Pnnn*
$P \pm 2_{\frac{1}{2}\frac{1}{2}0}2'_{0\frac{1}{2}0}$	D_{2h}^{4}	*Pban*
$P \pm 2_{\frac{1}{2}\frac{1}{2}0}2'_{\frac{1}{2}\frac{1}{2}\frac{1}{2}}$	D_{2h}^{6}	*Pncn*
$P \pm 2_{\frac{1}{2}\frac{1}{2}0}2'_{\frac{1}{2}0\frac{1}{2}}$	D_{2h}^{10}	*Pccn*
$P \pm 2_{\frac{1}{2}\frac{1}{2}\frac{1}{2}}2'_{\frac{1}{2}\frac{1}{2}0}$	D_{2h}^{14}	*Pbcn*
$P \pm 2_{\frac{1}{2}0\frac{1}{2}}2'_{00\frac{1}{2}}$	D_{2h}^{8}	*Pcaa*
$P \pm 2_{\frac{1}{2}0\frac{1}{2}}2'_{\frac{1}{2}\frac{1}{2}0}$	D_{2h}^{15}	*Pbca*
$A \pm 22'$	D_{2h}^{19}	*Ammm*
$A \pm 22'_{\frac{1}{2}00}$	D_{2h}^{17}	*Amam*
$A \pm 22'_{0\frac{1}{2}0}$	D_{2h}^{21}	*Abmm*
$A \pm 22'_{\frac{1}{2}\frac{1}{2}0}$	D_{2h}^{18}	*Abam*
$A \pm 2_{\frac{1}{2}00}2'$	D_{2h}^{20}	*Amaa*
$A \pm 2_{\frac{1}{2}00}2'_{0\frac{1}{2}0}$	D_{2h}^{22}	*Abaa*
$I \pm 22'$	D_{2h}^{25}	*Immm*
$I \pm 22'_{\frac{1}{2}00}$	D_{2h}^{28}	*Imam*
$I \pm 22'_{\frac{1}{2}\frac{1}{2}0}$	D_{2h}^{26}	*Ibam*
$I \pm 2_{\frac{1}{2}0\frac{1}{2}}2'_{\frac{1}{2}\frac{1}{2}0}$	D_{2h}^{27}	*Ibca*
$F \pm 22'$	D_{2h}^{23}	*Fmmm*
$F \pm 2_{\frac{1}{4}\frac{1}{4}0}2'_{0\frac{1}{4}\frac{1}{4}}$	D_{2h}^{24}	*Fddd*
$P4$	C_{4}^{1}	$P4$
$P4_{00\frac{1}{4}}$	C_{4}^{2}	$P4_1$
$P4_{00\frac{1}{2}}$	C_{4}^{3}	$P4_2$
$P4_{00\frac{3}{4}}$	C_{4}^{4}	$P4_3$
$I4$	C_{4}^{5}	$I4$
$I4_{00\frac{1}{4}}$	C_{4}^{6}	$I4_1$
$P\bar{4}$	S_{4}^{1}	$P\bar{4}$
$I\bar{4}$	S_{4}^{2}	$I\bar{4}$
$P \pm 4$	C_{4h}^{1}	$P4/m$
$P \pm 4_{00\frac{1}{2}}$	C_{4h}^{2}	$P4_2/m$
$P \pm 4_{\frac{1}{2}00}$	C_{4h}^{3}	$P4/n$
$P \pm 4_{0\frac{1}{2}\frac{1}{2}}$	C_{4h}^{4}	$P4_2/n$
$I \pm 4$	C_{4h}^{5}	$I4/m$
$I \pm 4_{\frac{1}{4}\frac{1}{4}\frac{1}{4}}$	C_{4h}^{6}	$I4_1/a$
$P\bar{4}2'$	D_{2d}^{1}	$P\bar{4}2m$
$P\bar{4}2'_{00\frac{1}{2}}$	D_{2d}^{2}	$P\bar{4}2c$

TABLE 2·11 (*Continued*)

Space Group	Symbols: Schoenflies	Symbols: Mauguin-Hermann
$P\bar{4}2'_{\frac12\frac12 0}$	D_{2d}^{3}	$P\bar{4}2_1m$
$P\bar{4}2'_{\frac12\frac12\frac12}$	D_{2d}^{4}	$P\bar{4}2_1c$
$P\bar{4}2''$	D_{2d}^{5}	$P\bar{4}m2$
$P\bar{4}2''_{00\frac12}$	D_{2d}^{6}	$P\bar{4}c2$
$P\bar{4}2''_{\frac12\frac12 0}$	D_{2d}^{7}	$P\bar{4}b2$
$P\bar{4}2''_{\frac12\frac12\frac12}$	D_{2d}^{8}	$P\bar{4}n2$
$I\bar{4}2'$	D_{2d}^{11}	$I\bar{4}2m$
$I\bar{4}2'_{0\frac12\frac14}$	D_{2d}^{12}	$I\bar{4}2d$
$I\bar{4}2''$	D_{2d}^{9}	$I\bar{4}m2$
$I\bar{4}2''_{00\frac12}$	D_{2d}^{10}	$I\bar{4}c2$
$P42'$	D_4^1	$P42$
$P42'_{\frac12\frac12 0}$	D_4^2	$P42_1$
$P4_{00\frac14}2'$	D_4^3	$P4_12$
$P4_{00\frac14}2'_{\frac12\frac12 0}$	D_4^4	$P4_12_1$
$P4_{00\frac12}2'$	D_4^5	$P4_22$
$P4_{00\frac12}2'_{\frac12\frac12 0}$	D_4^6	$P4_22_1$
$P4_{00\frac34}2'$	D_4^7	$P4_32$
$P4_{00\frac34}2'_{\frac12\frac12 0}$	D_4^8	$P4_32_1$
$I42'$	D_4^9	$I42$
$I4_{00\frac14}2'$	D_4^{10}	$I4_12$
$P4\bar{2}'$	C_{4v}^1	$P4mm$
$P4\bar{2}'_{\frac12\frac12 0}$	C_{4v}^2	$P4bm$
$P4\bar{2}'_{00\frac12}$	C_{4v}^5	$P4cc$
$P4\bar{2}'_{\frac12\frac12\frac12}$	C_{4v}^6	$P4nc$
$P4_{00\frac12}\bar{2}'$	C_{4v}^7	$P4_2mc$
$P4_{00\frac12}\bar{2}'_{\frac12\frac12 0}$	C_{4v}^8	$P4_2bc$
$P4_{00\frac12}\bar{2}'_{00\frac12}$	C_{4v}^3	$P4_2cm$
$P4_{00\frac12}\bar{2}'_{\frac12\frac12\frac12}$	C_{4v}^4	$P4_2nm$
$I4\bar{2}'$	C_{4v}^9	$I4mm$
$I4\bar{2}'_{00\frac12}$	C_{4v}^{10}	$I4cm$
$I4_{00\frac14}\bar{2}'_{\frac12 00}$	C_{4v}^{11}	$I4_1md$
$I4_{00\frac14}\bar{2}'_{\frac12 0\frac12}$	C_{4v}^{12}	$I4_1cd$
$P\pm 42'$	D_{4h}^1	$P4/mmm$
$P\pm 42'_{00\frac12}$	D_{4h}^2	$P4/mcc$
$P\pm 42'_{\frac12\frac12 0}$	D_{4h}^5	$P4/mbm$
$P\pm 42'_{\frac12\frac12\frac12}$	D_{4h}^6	$P4/mnc$
$P\pm 4_{00\frac12}2'$	D_{4h}^9	$P4/mmc$
$P\pm 4_{00\frac12}2'_{00\frac12}$	D_{4h}^{10}	$P4/mcm$
$P\pm 4_{00\frac12}2'_{\frac12\frac12 0}$	D_{4h}^{13}	$P4/mbc$
$P\pm 4_{00\frac12}2'_{\frac12\frac12\frac12}$	D_{4h}^{14}	$P4/mnm$
$P\pm 4_{\frac12 00}2'_{0\frac12 0}$	D_{4h}^3	$P4/nbm$
$P\pm 4_{\frac12 00}2'_{\frac12 00}$	D_{4h}^7	$P4/nmm$
$P\pm 4_{\frac12 00}2'_{0\frac12\frac12}$	D_{4h}^4	$P4/nnc$
$P\pm 4_{\frac12 00}2'_{\frac12 0\frac12}$	D_{4h}^8	$P4/ncc$
$P\pm 4_{0\frac12\frac12}2'_{0\frac12 0}$	D_{4h}^{11}	$P4/nbc$
$P\pm 4_{0\frac12\frac12}2'_{\frac12 00}$	D_{4h}^{15}	$P4/nmc$
$P\pm 4_{0\frac12\frac12}2'_{0\frac12\frac12}$	D_{4h}^{12}	$P4/nnm$

TABLE 2·11 (*Continued*)

Space Group	Symbols: Schoenflies	Symbols: Mauguin-Hermann
$P \pm 4_{0\frac{1}{2}\frac{1}{2}}2'_{\frac{1}{2}0\frac{1}{2}}$	D_{4h}^{16}	$P4/ncm$
$I \pm 42'$	D_{4h}^{17}	$I4/mmm$
$I \pm 42'_{00\frac{1}{2}}$	D_{4h}^{18}	$I4/mcm$
$I \pm 4_{\frac{1}{4}\frac{1}{4}\frac{1}{4}}2'_{\frac{1}{2}00}$	D_{4h}^{19}	$I4/amd$
$I \pm 4_{\frac{1}{4}\frac{1}{4}\frac{1}{4}}2'_{\frac{1}{2}0\frac{1}{2}}$	D_{4h}^{20}	$I4/acd$
$P3$	C_{3}^{1}	$C3$
$P3_{00\frac{1}{3}}$	C_{3}^{2}	$C3_1$
$P3_{00\frac{2}{3}}$	C_{3}^{3}	$C3_2$
$R3$	C_{3}^{4}	$R3$
$P\bar{3}$	C_{3i}^{1}	$C\bar{3}$
$R\bar{3}$	C_{3i}^{2}	$R\bar{3}$
$P3\bar{2}'$	C_{3v}^{1}	$C3m1$
$P3\bar{2}'_{00\frac{1}{2}}$	C_{3v}^{3}	$C3c1$
$P3\bar{2}''$	C_{3v}^{2}	$C31m$
$P3\bar{2}''_{00\frac{1}{2}}$	C_{3v}^{4}	$C31c$
$R3\bar{2}'$	C_{3v}^{5}	$R3m$
$R3\bar{2}'_{\frac{1}{2}\frac{1}{2}\frac{1}{2}}$	C_{3v}^{6}	$R3c$
$P32'$	D_{3}^{2}	$C321$
$P3_{00\frac{1}{3}}2'$	D_{3}^{4}	$C3_121$
$P3_{00\frac{2}{3}}2'$	D_{3}^{6}	$C3_221$
$P32''$	D_{3}^{1}	$C312$
$P3_{00\frac{1}{3}}2''$	D_{3}^{3}	$C3_112$
$P3_{00\frac{2}{3}}2''$	D_{3}^{5}	$C3_212$
$R32'$	D_{3}^{7}	$R32$
$P\bar{3}2'$	D_{3d}^{3}	$C\bar{3}m1$
$P\bar{3}2'_{00\frac{1}{2}}$	D_{3d}^{4}	$C\bar{3}c1$
$P\bar{3}2''$	D_{3d}^{1}	$C\bar{3}1m$
$P\bar{3}2''_{00\frac{1}{2}}$	D_{3d}^{2}	$C\bar{3}1c$
$R\bar{3}2'$	D_{3d}^{5}	$R\bar{3}m$
$R\bar{3}2'_{\frac{1}{2}\frac{1}{2}\frac{1}{2}}$	D_{3d}^{6}	$R\bar{3}c$
$P\bar{6}$	C_{3h}^{1}	$C\bar{6}$
$P6$	C_{6}^{1}	$C6$
$P6_{00\frac{1}{6}}$	C_{6}^{2}	$C6_1$
$P6_{00\frac{1}{3}}$	C_{6}^{4}	$C6_2$
$P6_{00\frac{1}{2}}$	C_{6}^{6}	$C6_3$
$P6_{00\frac{2}{3}}$	C_{6}^{5}	$C6_4$
$P6_{00\frac{5}{6}}$	C_{6}^{3}	$C6_5$
$P \pm 6$	C_{6h}^{1}	$C6/m$
$P \pm 6_{00\frac{1}{2}}$	C_{6h}^{2}	$C6_3/m$
$P\bar{6}2'$	D_{3h}^{3}	$C\bar{6}2m$
$P\bar{6}2'_{00\frac{1}{2}}$	D_{3h}^{4}	$C\bar{6}2c$
$P\bar{6}2''$	D_{3h}^{1}	$C\bar{6}m2$
$P\bar{6}2''_{00\frac{1}{2}}$	D_{3h}^{2}	$C\bar{6}c2$
$P6\bar{2}'$	C_{6v}^{1}	$C6mm$
$P6\bar{2}'_{00\frac{1}{2}}$	C_{6v}^{2}	$C6cc$
$P6_{00\frac{1}{2}}\bar{2}'$	C_{6v}^{4}	$C6_3mc$

TABLE 2·11 (*Continued*)

Space Group	Symbols: Schoenflies	Symbols: Mauguin-Hermann
$P6_{00\frac{1}{2}}\bar{2}'_{00\frac{1}{2}}$	C_{6v}^{3}	$C6_3cm$
$P62'$	D_6^1	$C62$
$P6_{00\frac{1}{6}}2'$	D_6^2	$C6_12$
$P6_{00\frac{1}{3}}2'$	D_6^4	$C6_22$
$P6_{00\frac{1}{2}}2'$	D_6^6	$C6_32$
$P6_{00\frac{2}{3}}2'$	D_6^5	$C6_42$
$P6_{00\frac{5}{6}}2'$	D_6^3	$C6_52$
$P\pm 62'$	D_{6h}^1	$C6/mmm$
$P\pm 62'_{00\frac{1}{2}}$	D_{6h}^2	$C6/mcc$
$P\pm 6_{00\frac{1}{2}}2'$	D_{6h}^4	$C6_3/mmc$
$P\pm 6_{00\frac{1}{2}}2'_{00\frac{1}{2}}$	D_{6h}^3	$C6_3/mcm$
$P3'22'$	T^1	$P23$
$P3'2_{\frac{1}{2}0\frac{1}{2}}2'_{\frac{1}{2}\frac{1}{2}0}$	T^4	$P2_13$
$I3'22'$	T^3	$I23$
$I3'2_{\frac{1}{2}0\frac{1}{2}}2'_{\frac{1}{2}\frac{1}{2}0}$	T^5	$I2_13$
$F3'22'$	T^2	$F23$
$P\bar{3}'22'$	T_h^1	$Pm3$
$P\bar{3}2_{\frac{1}{2}\frac{1}{2}0}2'_{0\frac{1}{2}\frac{1}{2}}$	T_h^2	$Pn3$
$P\bar{3}'2_{\frac{1}{2}0\frac{1}{2}}2'_{\frac{1}{2}\frac{1}{2}0}$	T_h^6	$Pa3$
$I\bar{3}'22'$	T_h^5	$Im3$
$I\bar{3}'2_{0\frac{1}{2}0}2'_{00\frac{1}{2}}$	T_h^7	$Ia3$
$F\bar{3}'22'$	T_h^3	$Fm3$
$F\bar{3}2_{\frac{1}{4}\frac{1}{4}0}2'_{0\frac{1}{4}\frac{1}{4}}$	T_h^4	$Fd3$
$P3'\bar{4}\bar{2}''$	T_d^1	$P\bar{4}3m$
$P3'\bar{4}_{\frac{1}{2}\frac{1}{2}\frac{1}{2}}\bar{2}''_{\frac{1}{2}\frac{1}{2}\frac{1}{2}}$	T_d^4	$P\bar{4}3n$
$I3'\bar{4}\bar{2}''$	T_d^3	$I\bar{4}3m$
$I3'\bar{4}_{\frac{1}{4}\frac{1}{4}\frac{1}{4}}\bar{2}''_{\frac{1}{4}\frac{1}{4}\frac{3}{4}}$	T_d^6	$I\bar{4}3d$
$F3'\bar{4}\bar{2}''$	T_d^2	$F\bar{4}3m$
$F3'\bar{4}_{00\frac{1}{2}}\bar{2}''_{00\frac{1}{2}}$	T_d^5	$F\bar{4}3c$
$P3'42''$	O^1	$P43$
$P3'4_{\frac{1}{4}\frac{3}{4}\frac{1}{4}}2''_{\frac{3}{4}\frac{1}{4}\frac{1}{4}}$	O^7	$P4_13$
$P3'4_{\frac{1}{2}\frac{1}{2}\frac{1}{2}}2''_{\frac{1}{2}\frac{1}{2}\frac{1}{2}}$	O^2	$P4_23$
$P3'4_{\frac{3}{4}\frac{1}{4}\frac{3}{4}}2''_{\frac{1}{4}\frac{3}{4}\frac{3}{4}}$	O^6	$P4_33$
$I3'42''$	O^5	$I43$
$I3'4_{\frac{1}{4}\frac{3}{4}\frac{1}{4}}2''_{\frac{3}{4}\frac{1}{4}\frac{1}{4}}$	O^8	$I4_13$
$F3'42''$	O^3	$F43$
$F3'4_{\frac{1}{4}\frac{1}{4}\frac{1}{4}}2''_{\frac{1}{4}\frac{1}{4}\frac{1}{4}}$	O^4	$F4_13$
$P\bar{3}'42''$	O_h^1	$Pm3m$
$P\bar{3}'4_{\frac{1}{2}00}2''_{00\frac{1}{2}}$	O_h^2	$Pn3n$
$P\bar{3}'4_{\frac{1}{2}\frac{1}{2}\frac{1}{2}}2''_{\frac{1}{2}\frac{1}{2}\frac{1}{2}}$	O_h^3	$Pm3n$
$P\bar{3}'4_{0\frac{1}{2}\frac{1}{2}}2''_{\frac{1}{2}\frac{1}{2}0}$	O_h^4	$Pn3m$
$I\bar{3}'42''$	O_h^9	$Im3m$
$I\bar{3}'4_{\frac{1}{4}\frac{3}{4}\frac{1}{4}}2''_{\frac{3}{4}\frac{1}{4}\frac{1}{4}}$	O_h^{10}	$Ia3d$
$F\bar{3}'42''$	O_h^5	$Fm3m$
$F\bar{3}'4_{00\frac{1}{2}}2''_{00\frac{1}{2}}$	O_h^6	$Fm3c$
$F\bar{3}'4_{0\frac{1}{4}\frac{1}{4}}2''_{\frac{1}{4}\frac{1}{4}0}$	O_h^7	$Fd3m$
$F\bar{3}'4_{\frac{1}{2}\frac{1}{4}\frac{1}{4}}2''_{\frac{1}{4}\frac{1}{4}\frac{1}{2}}$	O_h^8	$Fd3c$

screw axis is given by Equation 2·50 and becomes $\bar{r} = \frac{1}{4}\bar{a}_2 + x_3\bar{a}_3$. Since a space group (G) contains as elements all symmetry operations of the space lattice, trivial as well as non-trivial, all points equivalent to a given point $\bar{r}$ will be given by $\bar{r} \cdot (G)$. The set of equivalent points within a given unit cell can be written $\bar{r} \cdot (G/\Gamma_L)$ where $(G) = (\Gamma_L) \cdot (G/\Gamma_L)$. The coordinates of the equivalent points of a unit cell are readily obtained using the matrix forms of the generating dyadics given in Table 2·8 and remembering

$$\bar{r} \cdot \boldsymbol{\phi} \equiv \bar{r} \cdot \begin{pmatrix} \phi_{11} & \phi_{21} & \phi_{31} \\ \phi_{12} & \phi_{22} & \phi_{32} \\ \phi_{13} & \phi_{23} & \phi_{33} \end{pmatrix} \equiv \begin{aligned} &(x_1\phi_{11} + x_2\phi_{21} + x_3\phi_{31})\bar{a}_1 \\ &+ (x_1\phi_{12} + x_2\phi_{22} + x_3\phi_{32})\bar{a}_2 \\ &+ (x_1\phi_{13} + x_2\phi_{23} + x_3\phi_{33})\bar{a}_3 \end{aligned} \qquad [2{\cdot}141]$$

Let us list as an example the coordinates of the equivalent points for the space group of Equation 2·140. Since the product $(E,\ \Gamma_{\frac{1}{2}\frac{1}{2}\frac{1}{2}}) \cdot (\bar{\mathbf{1}}) \cdot (\mathbf{4},\ \frac{1}{4}(\bar{a}_1 + \bar{a}_2 + \bar{a}_3)) \cdot (\mathbf{2}',\ \frac{1}{2}\bar{a}_1)$ contains thirty-two elements, in general there will be that many equivalent points per unit cell. Expanding according to the elements in the subgroups $(E,\ \Gamma_{\frac{1}{2}\frac{1}{2}\frac{1}{2}})$ and $(\bar{\mathbf{1}})$, the thirty-two equivalent points fall into four sets of eight as follows.

$$\begin{aligned} \bar{r} \cdot (\mathbf{4},\ \tfrac{1}{4}(\bar{a}_1 + \bar{a}_2 + \bar{a}_3)) \cdot (\mathbf{2}',\ \tfrac{1}{2}\bar{a}_1) \\ -\bar{r} \cdot (\mathbf{4},\ \tfrac{1}{4}(\bar{a}_1 + \bar{a}_2 + \bar{a}_3)) \cdot (\mathbf{2}',\ \tfrac{1}{2}\bar{a}_1) \\ \bar{r} \cdot (\mathbf{4},\ \tfrac{1}{4}(\bar{a}_1 + \bar{a}_2 + \bar{a}_3)) \cdot (\mathbf{2}',\ \tfrac{1}{2}\bar{a}_1) \cdot \Gamma_{\frac{1}{2}\frac{1}{2}\frac{1}{2}} \\ -\bar{r} \cdot (\mathbf{4},\ \tfrac{1}{4}(\bar{a}_1 + \bar{a}_2 + \bar{a}_3)) \cdot (\mathbf{2}',\ \tfrac{1}{2}\bar{a}_1) \cdot \Gamma_{\frac{1}{2}\frac{1}{2}\frac{1}{2}} \end{aligned} \qquad [2{\cdot}142]$$

The second set of points is thus obtained from the first set merely by changing the signs of all coordinates, while the third and fourth sets are obtained respectively from the first and second sets by adding ½ to all coordinates. The coordinates of the first set of points become

$$\begin{aligned} &\bar{r} \cdot (\mathbf{4},\ \tfrac{1}{4}(\bar{a}_1 + \bar{a}_2 + \bar{a}_3)) \cdot (\mathbf{2}',\ \tfrac{1}{2}\bar{a}_1) = x_1, x_2, x_3; \\ &\tfrac{1}{4} - x_2, \tfrac{1}{4} + x_1, \tfrac{1}{4} + x_3;\ -x_1, \tfrac{1}{2} - x_2, \tfrac{1}{2} + x_3;\ x_2 - \tfrac{1}{4}, \tfrac{1}{4} - x_1, \tfrac{3}{4} + x_3; \\ &x_1 + \tfrac{1}{2}, -x_2, -x_3;\ \tfrac{3}{4} - x_2, \tfrac{3}{4} - x_1, \tfrac{3}{4} - x_3;\ \tfrac{1}{2} - x_1, \tfrac{1}{2} + x_2, \tfrac{1}{2} - x_3; \\ &\tfrac{1}{4} + x_2, x_1 - \tfrac{1}{4}, \tfrac{1}{4} - x_3 \end{aligned} \qquad [2{\cdot}143]$$

When $\bar{r}$ is chosen on a rotation axis, in a symmetry center or in a reflection plane, the number of distinct equivalent points in the set $\bar{r} \cdot (G/\Gamma_L)$ is only a fraction of the order of the group (G/Γ_L). One says then that $\bar{r} \cdot (G/\Gamma_L)$ represents a set of special positions.

The location of the symmetry elements, the coordinates of equivalent points (for general as well as special positions) and other useful information concerning the 230 space groups have been compiled in convenient form in *International Tables for the Determination of Crystal Structures* Vol. I, Berlin, 1935.

Columns 2 and 3 of Table 2·11 contain the space group symbols of Schoenflies and of Mauguin-Hermann.

7. THE SIGNIFICANCE OF THE SPACE GROUP THEORY

With the derivation of the 230 space groups it may be said that the problem of finding the possible symmetry groups of periodic media is completely solved. The results which have been obtained are direct consequences of the assumed periodicity and the space group theory as such must accordingly be accepted without qualification. According to the lattice hypothesis crystals represent periodic media. If the lattice hypothesis is strictly correct the space group theory thus becomes a theory of crystal symmetry and the results obtained in this chapter may be directly applied to real crystals. It is therefore important at this stage to review briefly the experimental evidence for a periodic structure in crystals.

When the space group theory was first published, fifty years ago, there was no way of directly testing the lattice hypothesis. All available measurements were of macroscopic type so that only the macroscopic consequences of the lattice hypothesis could be checked against experimental observations. The law of rational indices, the homogeneity and anisotropy, the definite chemical formulas, and the sharp melting points are some of the physical properties of macroscopic crystals which we have already cited as either explained or readily understood by means of an assumed periodic structure. The most impressive evidence of indirect nature in support of the lattice hypothesis is, however, the agreement between the empirically observed and the theoretically deduced symmetry groups of macroscopic crystals. As long as crystals have been studied it has been recognized that most crystals have non-trivial symmetry. The symmetry was particularly apparent in the orientation and distribution of crystal faces, but it manifested itself in a great many other physical properties as well. Since a symmetry operation by definition is an invariance operation with respect to all physical properties of the crystal, it is not in general justifiable to deduce the symmetry group from a study of one isolated property. However, it was empirically demonstrated that the symmetry group of the set of unit face normals as a rule is the symmetry group of the macroscopic crystal with respect to the sum total of all physical properties, and it is for this reason that the study of crystal faces has played such a significant role in the development of crystallography.

With the aid of the results of the space group theory it is easy to deduce the possible symmetry groups of the macroscopic physical properties of media which are periodic on a submicroscopic scale. The symmetry of the periodic medium is described by one of the 230 space groups which we customarily write as the product of the translation group and its factor group. Any element of the factor group other than the identity represents a non-trivial symmetry operation and it consists of a dyadic and a vector part. The vector part $\bar{t}$ may always be so chosen that $0 \leq t_j < 1$ and the length of this vector is therefore comparable to or smaller than the shortest lattice period. In macroscopic measurements the smallest volume elements with which we are concerned are still large enough to contain a great many unit cells. The uncertainty of linear measurements is therefore large compared to the smallest lattice period. Macroscopically it is thus impossible to detect the vector parts of the elements in the factor group so that the factor group becomes indistinguishable from its isomorphic point group. For the same reason the discrete translation group will, from the macroscopic viewpoint, be indistinguishable from the continuous group formed by all conceivable translations in much the same way as the individual lines of a band spectrum by insufficient resolving power appear to form a continuous band. A medium which is periodic submicroscopically consequently will have macroscopically a symmetry which corresponds to the product of the continuous translation group and a point group. Obviously the continuous translation group merely expresses the fact that the macroscopic medium is homogeneous. By leaving the translation group out of consideration as trivial we have thus found that the only possible macroscopic symmetry groups are the thirty-two point groups. This consequence of the space group theory is in complete agreement with the results of empirical studies of the symmetry of macroscopic crystals.

With the development of x-ray diffraction methods direct tests of the validity of the lattice hypothesis could be made. In anticipation of results to be discussed in subsequent chapters it may be stated that x-ray diffraction experiments prove the existence of periodic structure in crystals. The periodicity of real crystals is, however, of a less perfect type than is assumed by the lattice hypothesis. For one thing the real crystal medium is dynamic in character because of the heat motion of the atoms, whereas the lattice hypothesis deals with a static medium. Thus the periodicity of real crystals is to be associated with the time average rather than with the instantaneous structure. The periodic structure of actual crystals may be in other respects also less sharply defined, and it is therefore convenient to speak of real crystals as distinct from ideal crystals. By definition an ideal crystal is a static, solid medium for which the periodicity requirement of Equation 1·17 is exactly fulfilled. In the next chapter we shall develop the theory of x-ray diffraction for ideal crystals. The diffraction phenomena predicted on the basis of ideal crystals agree closely with those observed for real crystals although there are small but significant differences. These differences are not at once apparent and to begin with we shall do well to disregard them. At a later stage when we have become thoroughly familiar with the theory of x-ray diffraction for ideal crystals we shall be in a better position to give a worth-while discussion of the differences between real and ideal crystals.

If for the present the lattice hypothesis is assumed to be correct, the space group theory may be regarded as a theory of crystal symmetry. It must be emphasized that the space group theory contains no physical principles, and the predictions to which it leads are therefore of purely formal nature. Thus the theory cannot predict the specific symmetry of any given crystal, but provides an exhaustive list of the symmetry groups which come into consideration. If we have no information beyond the fact that the sample under investigation is a crystal, the correct space group must be sought among the 230 possible ones. With the knowledge of the point group describing the macroscopic symmetry of the crystal the choice is narrowed to a considerable extent since the possible space groups are isomorphic with the point group. Similarly the number of possible space groups is greatly reduced when the translation group is known. A discussion of the methods which are used for space group determination will not be given in this book, but it may be stated that the space group theory provides the theoretical basis for all systematic studies of the symmetry of crystal lattices. The knowledge of the space group represents valuable information about the crystal lattice, and the space group determination forms an important step in all crystal structure investigations.

LITERATURE

A. Bravais, *Journ. de l'école polytechnique Paris*, **19**, 1 (1850).

L. Sohnke, *Entwicklung einer Theorie der Kristallstruktur*, Leipzig, 1879.

E. v. Fedorow, *Verh. d. Miner. Gesell. St. Petersburg*, **27**, 448 (1891); *Zeitschr. f. Krist.*, **20**, 28 (1892); **37**, 22 (1903).

A. Schoenflies, *Krystallsysteme und Krystallstruktur*, Leipzig, 1891; *Theorie der Kristallstruktur*, Berlin, 1923.

F. Seitz, *Zeitschr. f. Krist.*, **88**, 413 (1934); **90**, 289 (1935); **91**, 336 (1935); **94**, 100 (1936).

International Tables for the Determination of Crystal Structures, I, Berlin, Gebrüder Borntraeger, 1935.

CHAPTER III

THEORY OF X-RAY DIFFRACTION IN IDEAL CRYSTALS

The complete space group theory was published in 1891 and four years later Röntgen discovered the x rays. In the following years great efforts were made to determine the nature of this radiation. By 1912 the advocates of the wave nature could claim considerable experimental evidence in support of their viewpoint. The polarization of x rays had been demonstrated and it was observed that a beam of x rays passing through a narrow slit suffered a small broadening leading to a wavelength estimate of 10^{-8} cm. This reported value was only slightly smaller than the fairly reliable estimates of interatomic distances in solids from the density, the molecular weight, and Avogadro's number. The possibility of using crystals as natural diffraction gratings for x rays was suggested by von Laue in 1912, and the subsequent experiments immediately proved that the idea was correct. von Laue was able to show that the observed effects could be interpreted as due to diffraction of electromagnetic waves in a three-dimensional grating.[1] Thus von Laue's discovery gave convincing proof both of the wave nature of x rays and of the periodic structure of crystals. Accordingly the foundation was laid for two important fields of scientific research: the study of x rays and the study of crystal structure. The improved experimental technique due to W. H. and W. L. Bragg[2] contributed greatly to the rapid development of both fields, and their early work demonstrated clearly the far-reaching consequences of von Laue's fundamental discovery.

In this chapter the theory of x-ray interference in ideal crystals will be developed in detail. The purely geometrical part of the diffraction problem is concerned only with the directions of the diffraction maxima, and the detailed intensity distribution of the scattered x rays is left out of consideration. The geometry of x-ray interference in crystals can be satisfactorily discussed on a quite elementary basis, but treatment of the intensity questions requires extensive theoretical consideration. It is therefore convenient to begin this chapter with a discussion of the geometry of x-ray diffraction effects in crystals.

[1] M. von Laue, *Münchener Sitzungsberichte,* **1912**, 363; *Ann. der Phys.*, **41**, 989 (1913).

[2] W. H. Bragg and W. L. Bragg, *Proc. Roy. Soc. London,* **88**, 428 (1913); **89**, 246 (1913).

1. THE LAUE AND BRAGG EQUATIONS

A linear diffraction grating may conveniently be defined as a straight line along which the scattering power is a periodic function of position, i.e., $\psi(\bar{r}) = \psi(\bar{r} + L_1\bar{a}_1)$, where L_1 is any integer. $\bar{a}_1$ is the period or grating space and measures the vector separation of neighboring equivalent points. A plane wave of monochromatic electromagnetic radiation incident upon the grating will be scattered in all directions by a line element. Because of the periodic nature of the scattering power per unit length of the grating diffraction maxima occur in the directions corresponding to path differences equal to an integral number of wavelengths. This elementary formulation of the diffraction problem leads to the familiar grating equation

$$\bar{a}_1 \cdot (\bar{k}_{H_1} - \bar{k}_0) = H_1 \qquad [3\cdot1]$$

$\bar{k}_0$ is the wave vector of the incident x-ray beam and $\bar{k}_{H_1}$ that of the diffracted beam, i.e.,

$$\bar{k}_0 \equiv \frac{1}{\lambda}\bar{u}_0, \quad \bar{k}_{H_1} \equiv \frac{1}{\lambda}\bar{u}_{H_1} \qquad [3\cdot2]$$

where $\bar{u}_0$ and $\bar{u}_{H_1}$ are unit vectors along the direction of incidence and of maximum diffraction and λ is the wavelength.

The linear grating can be considered as a special case of one in three dimensions. A three-dimensional grating corresponds to a spatial distribution of matter for which the scattering power is a triply periodic function of position, i.e., $\psi(\bar{r}) = \psi(\bar{r} + L_1\bar{a}_1 + L_2\bar{a}_2 + L_3\bar{a}_3)$. It is of no consequence whether we consider the function ψ to be continuous or discrete. In the preceding chapters we have learned that all physical properties of crystals are represented by periodic functions of this type, and the crystal lattice may accordingly serve as a three-dimensional diffraction grating. When two of the three integers L_1, L_2, L_3 are held constant while the third is allowed to assume all possible integral values, a linear grating is obtained. The three-dimensional grating may thus be considered as consisting of three sets of component linear gratings with grating spaces $\bar{a}_1$, $\bar{a}_2$, and $\bar{a}_3$. In order to find the diffraction maxima for such a three-dimensional grating we require that the wave vectors simultaneously satisfy Equation 3·1 for each of the component linear gratings. Accordingly we have

$$\begin{aligned} \bar{a}_1 \cdot (\bar{k}_{H_1H_2H_3} - \bar{k}_0) &= H_1 \\ \bar{a}_2 \cdot (\bar{k}_{H_1H_2H_3} - \bar{k}_0) &= H_2 \\ \bar{a}_3 \cdot (\bar{k}_{H_1H_2H_3} - \bar{k}_0) &= H_3 \end{aligned} \qquad [3\cdot3]$$

Three integers H_1, H_2, H_3 are thus associated with each diffraction maximum. It is convenient to use these integers as subscripts for the wave vector representing a diffraction maximum. When we are not dealing with any particular diffraction maximum the abbreviated form $\bar{k}_H (\equiv \bar{k}_{H_1H_2H_3})$ will be used. Equations 3·3 are the three Laue equations. The three scalar equations can be written in more convenient form as a single vector equation. By making use of the identity given in Equation A·14, one finds readily

$$\bar{k}_H - \bar{k}_0 = \bar{B}_H \qquad [3\cdot4]$$

In this equation $\bar{B}_H = \bar{B}_{H_1H_2H_3} = H_1\bar{b}_1 + H_2\bar{b}_2 + H_3\bar{b}_3$, where $\bar{b}_1$, $\bar{b}_2$, $\bar{b}_3$ is the vector set reciprocal to $\bar{a}_1$, $\bar{a}_2$, $\bar{a}_3$. Equation 3·4 is, of course, entirely equivalent to the three scalar Equations 3·3 and may hence properly be called the Laue vector equation. According to Equation 3·4 a vector $\bar{B}_H$ of the reciprocal lattice is associated with each diffraction maximum. It was shown earlier (in Chapter I, section 9) that the vector $\bar{B}_H$ is normal to a sequence of planes in the space lattice and that the magnitude of $\bar{B}_H$ is equal to the reciprocal spacing for the sequence. The quantities H_1, H_2, H_3 which in Equations 3·3 have significance only as integers may accordingly be interpreted as Miller indices of a family of lattice planes. The formal correlation which we have found between a diffraction maximum and a sequence of planes in the space lattice permits a simple physical interpretation of Equation 3·4. Since $|\bar{k}_H| = |\bar{k}_0| = 1/\lambda$, the Laue vector equation expresses the fact that the vectors $\bar{k}_H$ and $\bar{k}_0$ are edges of a rhomb of which $\bar{B}_H$ is a diagonal as shown in Fig. 3·1. The sequence of planes in the space lattice represented by $\bar{B}_H$ accordingly makes equal angles with vectors $\bar{k}_0$ and $\bar{k}_H$. In other words, one may consider the diffracted beam to be produced by a reflection of the incident beam in the family of planes normal to $\bar{B}_H$. Of course, it is not a reflection in the usual sense for the reflected beam is produced only for specific values of the incident wave vector. These discrete values are readily found by equating the magnitudes of the two sides of Equation 3·4. The magnitude of the left side of the equation is $2 \sin \theta_B/\lambda$, where $2\theta_B$ is the scattering angle. The angle θ_B is thus complementary to the angle of incidence or reflection and is called the

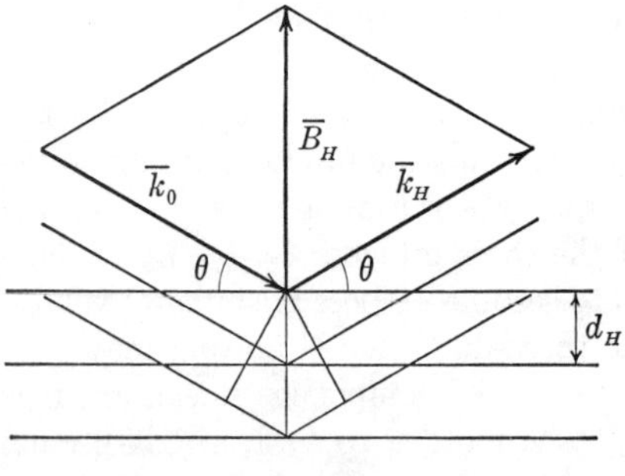

FIG. 3·1.

Bragg glancing angle. The magnitude of the right side of Equation 3·4 is $1/d_{H_1H_2H_3}$ or, using Equation 1·23, $n/d_{h_1h_2h_3}$ when H_1, H_2, H_3 have a common integral factor n. Accordingly we have

$$\frac{2 \sin \theta_B}{\lambda} = \frac{1}{d_H} = \frac{n}{d_h} \qquad [3{\cdot}5]$$

This is the Bragg equation.

The spacings d_H are (for numerically small values of H_1, H_2, H_3) of the same order of magnitude as the smallest lattice periods. Because of the atomic nature of matter these periods must be greater than the smallest interatomic distances, while we, on the other hand, know that they are of submicroscopic order of magnitude since crystals appear homogeneous in a high-power microscope. The wavelength of x rays is of the order of 10^{-8} cm., whereas the smallest lattice periods according to the considerations given above may be expected to lie in the range $10^{-8} - 10^{-5}$ cm. Accordingly it may be expected that the scattering angles for the diffraction maxima are large enough to be measured conveniently.

2. CONSTRUCTION OF THE DIFFRACTED WAVE VECTORS IN THE RECIPROCAL LATTICE

Bragg's formulation of the diffraction phenomenon as a reflection of the incident beam in a lattice plane is convenient for many purposes, but a simple construction in the reciprocal lattice of the diffracted wave vectors associated with a given direction of incidence and a given wavelength is more directly useful for a general discussion of the various experimental methods.[3] Let Fig. 3·2 represent a section of the reciprocal lattice with the origin at the point O. The point P is so chosen that the line PO corresponds in direction and magnitude to the incident wave vector $\bar{k}_0$. Since $|\bar{k}_H| = |\bar{k}_0| = 1/\lambda$, it is possible to represent the vector $\bar{k}_H$ as a radius vector in a sphere of radius $1/\lambda$ constructed with the point P as center. This sphere, which obviously passes through the point O, is called the sphere of reflection. According to the Laue vector equation the three vectors $\bar{k}_0$, $\bar{k}_H$, and $\bar{B}_H$ form a closed triangle. A vector $\bar{B}_H$ which satisfies the Laue vector equation, in other words, must have its terminus on the sphere of reflection. It is clear that the sphere of reflection in general will not pass through any reciprocal lattice point, if the incident wave vector $\bar{k}_0$ is chosen entirely at random. In order to satisfy the Laue vector equation and thus produce diffraction maxima, it becomes necessary to adjust the wavelength

[3] P. P. Ewald, *Phys. Zeitschr.*, **14**, 465 (1913).

or the direction of incidence in such a way that one or more of the reciprocal lattice points, i.e., in addition to the point O, fall on the sphere of reflection. Since the incident wave vector is a function of three scalar variables, there are different ways of making this adjustment. We have thus been led to a general discussion of the various experimental methods which are being used to produce x-ray diffraction maxima.

When the wavelength or the direction of incidence is varied continuously there will be a corresponding variation in the radius or in the orientation of the sphere of reflection in the reciprocal lattice. In either case the surface of the sphere of reflection moves through the reciprocal

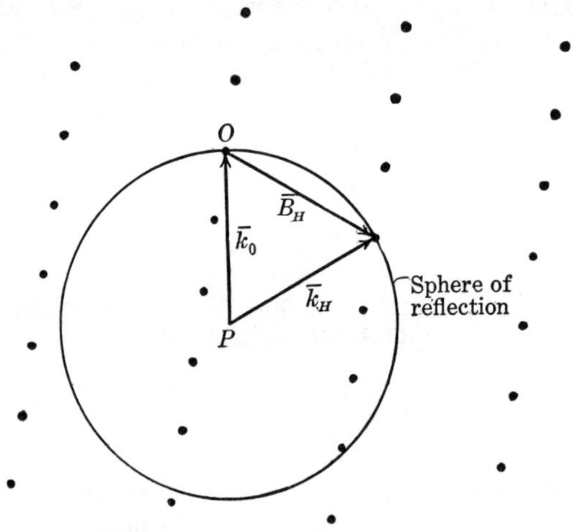

FIG. 3·2.

lattice. Any reciprocal lattice point lying in a region which is swept through by the spherical surface as $\bar{k}_0$ is varied must at some instant during the variation have been located on the instantaneous sphere of reflection. At that instant the Laue vector equation was satisfied and a diffraction maximum produced. It is readily seen that in order to produce diffraction maxima it is sufficient to vary only one of the three variables in the incident wave vector while the other two are held fixed, but two or all three variables may be varied simultaneously.

It is not difficult to prepare an exhaustive list of all conceivable methods for the production of diffraction maxima. For this purpose let λ, μ, ν be the three scalar variables of the incident wave vector. λ, the wavelength, measures the reciprocal length of $\bar{k}_0$, while μ and ν are two suitably chosen parameters describing the direction of incidence. According to the Laue vector equation any diffracted wave vector $\bar{k}_H$

which come into consideration, the Laue method, the rotating crystal method, and the powder method.

The determination of the atomic arrangement in crystals is the basic problem of crystal structure, and it is therefore proper to ask what a study of the geometry of the diffraction effects can contribute towards the solution of this problem. This question is readily answered, since the vectors $\bar{B}_H$ are the only quantities of the Laue vector equation which are related to the structure of the crystal. We may, in other words, expect to be able to determine the vectors $\bar{a}_1$, $\bar{a}_2$, $\bar{a}_3$, i.e., the translation group, and the three integers H_1, H_2, H_3 which characterize the various diffraction maxima. In order to find out how the atoms are distributed in the lattice it is necessary, however, to go beyond the purely geometrical properties of the diffraction phenomena and investigate their intensity as well.

The detailed geometry of the x-ray diffraction field for the three principal methods is easily deduced from the Laue vector equation by means of the reciprocal lattice construction discussed above. The geometry of the x-ray diffraction effects, including the procedure for determining the lattice constants $\bar{a}_1$, $\bar{a}_2$, $\bar{a}_3$ and for the assignment of indices H_1, H_2, H_3 to the diffraction maxima, has been thoroughly treated in several books on crystal structure.[4] In order to avoid unnecessary repetition we shall therefore omit further discussion of the geometrical part of the diffraction problem.

3. ELEMENTARY THEORY OF X-RAY SCATTERING BY A SINGLE ELECTRON AND BY A SINGLE ATOM

The x-ray interference pattern of a crystal may be described in terms of the intensity of scattering as function of scattering direction. The intensity distribution depends upon the incident beam, its direction relative to the crystal, and upon the crystal structure. It is the object of the theory of x-ray interference in crystals to find the specific form of this intensity function, thereby laying the theoretical foundation for the determination of the structure of crystals from experimentally measured intensities of scattering. The intensity function exhibits sharp maxima for certain scattering directions, but the considerations of the preceding sections have shown that an experimental study of only the directions of the diffraction maxima does not suffice for a determination of the crystal structure. A more profound theoretical treatment of the interference phenomena is accordingly needed. As an intro-

[4] See: *International Tables for the Determination of Crystal Structures*, II, Berlin, Borntraeger, 1935.

M. J. Buerger, *X-Ray Crystallography*, John Wiley and Sons, New York, 1942.

duction to the general theory of x-ray diffraction in crystals we shall first discuss the classical theory of the scattering of x rays by single electrons and by single atoms.

A. **Scattering by a Single Electron.** Consider an electron of charge $-\mathrm{e}$ and mass m to be held at the origin with a small restoring force. A plane wave of monochromatic x rays

$$\bar{E}_0\, e^{i\omega_0 t - i2\pi \bar{k}_0\cdot\bar{r}} \qquad [3\cdot6]$$

acts on the electron. $\bar{E}_0$ is the electric vector, $\bar{k}_0$ is the wave vector, while $\omega_0 = 2\pi\nu_0$, where ν_0 is the frequencey. We shall assume that the natural frequency of the electron is small compared with the x-ray frequency. The force on the electron due to the electric field of the wave is $-\mathrm{e}\,\bar{E}_0\, e^{i\omega_0 t}$. Since the restoring force by assumption is negligible, the impressed force equals $m\dfrac{d^2\bar{x}}{dt^2}$ where $\bar{x}$ is the displacement of the electron. The steady state solution of the equation of motion is

$$\bar{x} = \frac{\mathrm{e}}{m\omega_0^2}\bar{E}_0\, e^{i\omega_0 t} \qquad [3\cdot7]$$

The electric moment of the electron is $-\mathrm{e}\,\bar{x}$ for which we may write

$$-\mathrm{e}\,\bar{x} = \bar{p}_e\, e^{i\omega_0 t}, \quad \bar{p}_e = -\frac{\mathrm{e}^2}{m\omega_0^2}\bar{E}_0 \qquad [3\cdot8]$$

The polarizability, α_e, is by definition the dipole moment induced by unit field and hence

$$\alpha_e = -\frac{\mathrm{e}^2}{m\omega_0^2} \qquad [3\cdot9]$$

According to electromagnetic theory an oscillating dipole $\bar{p}_e\, e^{i\omega_0 t}$ gives rise to an electromagnetic field. At distances from the dipole large compared with the wavelength the electric and magnetic fields are given by

$$\begin{aligned} e^{i\omega_0 t}\bar{H}_e &= \bar{u}\times\bar{p}_e\frac{\omega_0^2}{c^2R}\, e^{i\omega_0 t - i2\pi\bar{k}\cdot\bar{R}} \\ e^{i\omega_0 t}\bar{E}_e &= (\bar{u}\times\bar{p}_e)\times\bar{u}\frac{\omega_0^2}{c^2R}\, e^{i\omega_0 t - i2\pi\bar{k}\cdot\bar{R}} \end{aligned} \qquad [3\cdot10]$$

$\bar{R} = R\bar{u}$ is the radius vector from the dipole to the point of observation and $\bar{k} = \dfrac{1}{\lambda}\bar{u}$.

Equations 3·10 represent spherical waves originating at the dipole.

The average intensity of the radiation at the point of observation $\bar{R}$ is $I_e = \frac{c}{8\pi} E_e^2$, while the intensity of the incident wave given in Equation 3·6 is $I_0 = \frac{c}{8\pi} E_0^2$. Using Equations 3·8 and 3·10, the intensity of scattering from a single electron becomes

$$I_e = I_0 \left(\frac{e^2 \sin \varphi}{mc^2 R} \right)^2 \qquad [3\cdot 11]$$

where φ is the angle between $\bar{E}_0$ and $\bar{u}$.

If the incident wave is unpolarized the angle φ becomes indeterminate and the term $\sin^2 \varphi$ occurring in Equation 3·11 must be replaced by its average value. From Fig. 3·3 we have obviously

$$\overline{\sin^2 \varphi} = 1 - \sin^2 2\theta\, \overline{\cos^2 \psi} = \frac{1 + \cos^2 2\theta}{2} \qquad [3\cdot 12]$$

where 2θ is the scattering angle, i.e., the angle between the direction of incidence and direction of scattering.

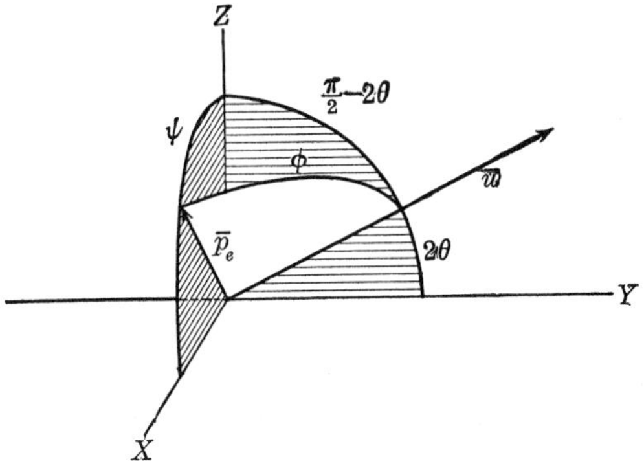

FIG. 3·3.

The result given in Equation 3·11 is the familiar J. J. Thomson scattering formula. It shows that the intensity of scattering is independent of the frequency of the x rays.

***B.* Scattering by an Atom.** We imagine next that the nucleus of an atom containing z electrons is placed at the origin. At a given instant the positions of the various electrons may be described by means of vectors $\bar{r}_1 \cdots \bar{r}_j \cdots \bar{r}_z$. Under the action of the field of the wave given in Equation 3·6 the electrons will be displaced by amounts $\bar{x}_j$ from their instantaneous rest positions. If we neglect the restoring forces and the interaction between the electrons, we find the following steady state solution for the displacement of the jth electron

$$\bar{x}_j = \frac{\mathrm{e}^2}{m\omega_0^2} \bar{E}_0 \, e^{i\omega_0 t - i2\pi \bar{k}_0 \cdot \bar{r}_j} \qquad [3\cdot13]$$

The dipole moment $\bar{p}_j$ of the jth electron becomes

$$-\mathrm{e}\bar{x}_j = \bar{p}_j \, e^{i\omega_0 t}, \quad \bar{p}_j = \bar{p}_e \, e^{-i2\pi \bar{k}_0 \cdot \bar{r}_j} \qquad [3\cdot14]$$

The field strengths at a point of observation $\bar{R}$, where R is large compared with the wavelength and atomic dimensions, are obtained by superposition of the fields due to the various electrons. Using Equations 3·10 and 3·14 the electric field at point $\bar{R}$ becomes

$$\bar{E}_{\text{at.}} \, e^{i\omega_0 t} = \sum_j (\bar{u}_j \times \bar{p}_j) \times \bar{u}_j \frac{\omega_0^2}{c^2 R_j} \, e^{i\omega_0 t - i2\pi \bar{k}_j \cdot \bar{R}_j} \qquad [3\cdot15]$$

with a similar expression for the magnetic field. $\bar{R}_j$ is the radius vector from the jth electron to the field point so that $\bar{R}_j = \bar{R} - \bar{r}_j$, where $\bar{R}_j = R_j \bar{u}_j$ and $\bar{R} = R\bar{u}$. In Equation 3·15 it is justifiable to replace R_j by R and $\bar{k}_j$ by $\bar{k}$ without making appreciable errors. Accordingly we have

$$\bar{E}_{\text{at.}} = \bar{E}_e \sum_j e^{i\bar{s} \cdot \bar{r}_j} \qquad [3\cdot16]$$

where the symbol $\bar{s}$ denotes the vector $2\pi(\bar{k} - \bar{k}_0)$. Equation 3·16 represents the instantaneous amplitude of scattering at the point $\bar{R}$; the instantaneous intensity is obtained upon multiplying by the complex conjugate and by the factor $c/8\pi$. The quantity $\bar{s} \cdot \bar{r}_j$ measures the phase difference between the radiation scattered by the jth electron and that scattered by an electron at the origin. Since x-ray wavelengths are comparable to the distances between the electrons, these phase differences are appreciable and cannot be neglected. The electrons in an atom are changing positions so rapidly that it is quite impossible to measure the instantaneous amplitude and intensity of the scattered radiation. Accordingly we must deal with average rather than instantaneous values for these quantities, and then the question arises of how these average values are to be obtained. In this connection it becomes important to distinguish sharply between coherent and incoherent radiation. It is our object to study x-ray diffraction effects in crystal lattices. We are therefore primarily interested in the coherent part of the scattering by an atom, i.e., in the part of the scattering which can give rise to interference effects.

Let the motion of the various electrons be represented by distribution functions $\sigma_1 \cdots \sigma_j \cdots \sigma_z$ such that $\sigma_j\,dv$ is the probability of finding the jth electron in the volume element dv. Furthermore, let it be assumed that all functions σ_j are independent of one another. In order to obtain the coherent scattering we average the instantaneous amplitude of Equation 3·16 over the variable positions of the electrons. From the mean amplitude so obtained we find the intensity of the coherent radiation in the usual manner, namely, by multiplying the amplitude by its complex conjugate and the factor $c/8\pi$. The expression for the mean amplitude is thus

$$E_e \sum_j \varphi_j \tag{3·17}$$

where the symbol φ_j is defined by

$$\varphi_j \equiv \int \sigma_j\, e^{i\bar{s}\cdot\bar{r}_j}\, dv \tag{3·18}$$

while the intensity of the coherent scattering becomes

$$I_{\text{coh.}} = I_e \Big|\sum_j \varphi_j\Big|^2 \tag{3·19}$$

The total scattering is obtained by averaging the instantaneous intensity expression, i.e.,

$$I_{\text{tot.}} = I_e \int\int \sum_j \sum_k \sigma_j \sigma_k\, e^{i\bar{s}\cdot(\bar{r}_j - \bar{r}_k)}\, dv_j dv_k{}' = I_e\Big(z + \sum_{j \neq k}\sum \varphi_j \varphi_k^*\Big) \tag{3·20}$$

Since the total scattering represents the sum of coherent and incoherent scattering, we have

$$I_{\text{inc.}} = I_e\Big(z + \sum_{j \neq k}\sum \varphi_j\varphi_k^* - \Big|\sum_j \varphi_j\Big|^2\Big) = I_e\Big(z - \sum_j |\varphi_j|^2\Big) \tag{3·21}$$

The incoherent scattering is, in other words, equal to $c/8\pi$ times the difference between the mean square and the squared mean amplitude.

The results obtained above can be accepted only as long as they are confirmed by more rigorous quantum mechanical treatments of the scattering problem. According to quantum mechanics x rays scattered by an atom are partly coherent and partly incoherent. As far as the coherent part is concerned classical and quantum mechanical methods lead to the same formulas for amplitude and intensity. The classical formula for the incoherent radiation as given in Equation 3·21 is but an approximation to the quantum mechanical expression. Moreover, according to quantum mechanics the coherent and the incoherent parts of the radiation are due to two distinct scattering processes. The incoherent, or Compton, scattering represents a distinct quantum process and involves a small frequency shift. Because of its incoherence the intensity of the Compton scattering from a crystal is represented by the sum of the intensities of the Compton scattering from the individual atoms composing the crystal. Since the Compton scattering thus is independent of the crystal structure it is of no further interest to us.

According to Equation 3·17 the coherent scattering can be interpreted as due to an atom in which the individual electrons are smeared into continuous distributions represented by the probability functions. The number of electrons per unit volume in this smeared atom will be denoted by ρ, and we have obviously $\rho = \sum_j \sigma_j$. The atomic scattering power f^0 is defined as the ratio between the amplitudes of the radiation scattered by an atom and by an electron under the same conditions. Hence

$$f^0 = \sum_j \varphi_j = \int \rho\, e^{i\bar{s}\cdot\bar{r}}\, dv \qquad [3\cdot22]$$

When the electron distribution function ρ has spherical symmetry it is possible to express the atomic scattering power in a simpler form. For this purpose we shall introduce the radial distribution function $U(r)$ defined by

$$U(r) = 4\pi r^2 \rho(r) \qquad [3\cdot23]$$

so that $U\,dr$ represents the number of electrons between spherical shells of radii r and $r + dr$. Using spherical coordinates with $\bar{s}$ as the unique axis we have $dv = 2\pi r^2 \sin\varphi\, dr\, d\varphi$ and $\bar{s}\cdot\bar{r} = s\,r\,\cos\varphi$ where φ is the angle between $\bar{s}$ and $\bar{r}$. Hence

$$f^0(s) = \int_0^\infty \int_0 \tfrac{1}{2} U(r)\, e^{isr\cos\varphi} \sin\varphi\, dr\, d\varphi = \int_0^\infty U(r) \frac{\sin sr}{sr}\, dr \qquad [3\cdot24]$$

In order to obtain numerical values for the atomic scattering power one must know the electron distribution functions σ_j or the function ρ. The electron distribution for many atoms has been calculated with considerable accuracy by means of Hartree's method of selfconsistent fields, and it is known with fair approximation for all atoms. Conversely, if the atomic scattering power is known from experimental data the electron distribution function can be found. This is readily seen from Equation 3·24 which may be solved for $U(r)$ with the aid of the Fourier reciprocity theorem. The solution is

$$U(r) = \frac{2r}{\pi} \int_0^\infty s f^0(s) \sin sr\, ds \qquad [3\cdot25]$$

4. ATOMIC SCATTERING POWER AND ANOMALOUS DISPERSION

The results of the preceding section do not apply when the x-ray frequency approaches the characteristic frequencies of the electrons, and resonance phenomena occur. It is the purpose of this section to consider the modifications which must be introduced into our equations when the electronic binding forces are taken into account.

The amplitude of the coherent scattering from the atom may again be expressed in terms of the amplitude of scattering from a free (Thomson) electron, i.e.,

$$f\, E_e \qquad [3\cdot26]$$

where f again is called the atomic scattering power. The more rigorous treatment of the problem will lead to a somewhat different expression for the amplitude of coherent scattering than was obtained in Equation 3·17, and hence the atomic scattering power defined by Equation 3·26 is somewhat different from the quantity f^0 given by Equation 3·22. f^0 is in other words the limiting value of f for high x-ray frequencies.

Clearly a satisfactory theory of the scattering problem must be developed on quantum mechanical basis. It is possible, however, to modify the classical viewpoint in a formal manner to such an extent that the quantum mechanical results may be reinterpreted in terms of such a flexible classical picture.

If we include the binding force of the electron $-m\omega_j^2\bar{x}_j$ and a damping term $-m\kappa_j\dfrac{d\bar{x}_j}{dt}$ (in order to include the radiation damping formally) the equation of motion of the jth electron under the action of the electric field of the incident wave becomes

$$\frac{d^2\bar{x}_j}{dt^2} + \kappa_j\frac{d\bar{x}_j}{dt} + \omega_j^2\bar{x}_j = -\frac{e}{m}\bar{E}_0\, e^{i\omega_0 t - i2\pi\bar{k}_0\cdot\bar{r}_j} \qquad [3\cdot27]$$

The steady state solution is

$$\bar{x}_j = \frac{e}{m\omega_0^2}\,\frac{1}{1-\left(\dfrac{\omega_j}{\omega_0}\right)^2 - i\dfrac{\kappa_j}{\omega_0}}\,\bar{E}_0\, e^{i\omega_0 t - i2\pi\bar{k}_0\cdot\bar{r}_j} \qquad [3\cdot28]$$

A comparison with the derivations of the preceding section shows that the revised expression for the atomic scattering power becomes

$$f = \sum_j \frac{\varphi_j}{1-\left(\dfrac{\omega_j}{\omega_0}\right)^2 - i\dfrac{\kappa_j}{\omega_0}} \qquad [3\cdot29]$$

In order to modify this classical formula so as to agree with the quantum mechanical picture of the atom, the electrons will be replaced by continuous bands of virtual classical oscillators. Consider the jth electron in an atom in which all levels are completely occupied so that transitions to these levels are forbidden by the Pauli principle. The characteristic frequency of the electron must then be associated with a transition from the normal state to an excited state of the continuum. Accordingly we assume a frequency distribution of the corresponding oscillators between ω_j and ∞, the specific form of the distribution function being determined by the transition probabilities.

Let $w_j(\omega)$ be the distribution function so that $w_j\, d\omega$ is the number of virtual oscillators (associated with the jth electron) in the range ω to $\omega + d\omega$. In accordance with the suggested modification the terms $1/\left[1 - \left(\frac{\omega_j}{\omega_0}\right)^2 - i\frac{\kappa_j}{\omega_0}\right]$ are to be replaced by integrals giving for the atomic scattering power

$$f = \sum_j \varphi_j \int_{\omega_j}^{\infty} \frac{w_j\, d\omega}{1 - \left(\frac{\omega}{\omega_0}\right)^2 - i\frac{\kappa_j}{\omega_0}} \qquad [3\cdot30]$$

It is to be noted that according to the quantum mechanical calculations the integral $\int w_j\, d\omega = g_j$ (the oscillator strength of the jth electron) is in general different from unity, but the total oscillator strength is equal to the total number of electrons in the atom, i.e., $\sum_j g_j = z$.

As we expect f to approach f^0 at high frequencies, we shall assume that the integral in Equation 3·30 may be given in the form $1 + \xi_j + i\eta_j$. Hence

$$f = f^0 + \sum_j \varphi_j(\xi_j + i\eta_j) \qquad [3\cdot31]$$

The term $\varphi_j(\xi_j + i\eta_j)$ is called the anomalous contribution to the atomic scattering power due to the jth electron.

A detailed study of the application of quantum mechanical dispersion theory to the problem of the atomic scattering power has been given in articles by H. Hönl[5] to which the reader is referred. Numerical computations of the anomalous contributions will be discussed in section 12.

5. THE STRUCTURE FACTOR

In this section we shall go one step farther and consider the scattering from a single unit cell of a crystal lattice. Placing the origin of our

[5] H. Hönl, *Zeitschr. f. Phys.*, **84**, 1 (1933); *Ann. der Phys.*, [5], **18**, 625 (1933).

reference frame at a corner of the unit cell under consideration any point within the unit cell is represented by a vector $\bar{r} = \sum x_i \bar{a}_i$ where $0 \leq x_i < 1$. Let there be n atoms in the unit cell, the nuclear positions being $\bar{r}_1 \cdots \bar{r}_k \cdots \bar{r}_n$. Since we are interested only in the coherent part of the scattering it may be assumed that the electrons have been smeared into continuous distributions. The amplitude of scattering from a single atom, as we have seen, can be expressed in terms of the amplitude of scattering from a free electron. The ratio between the two amplitudes was called the atomic scattering power and was denoted by f (or by f^0 when anomalous dispersion was neglected). The amplitude of scattering from a single unit cell may in a similar manner be written as $F\,E_e$. F may be called the scattering power of the unit cell, but we shall use the more common term *structure factor*. When anomalous dispersion is neglected we shall use the symbol F^0 instead of F.

A. **No Anomalous Dispersion.** In an x-ray frequency range where anomalous dispersion can be neglected it is not necessary to distinguish between different types of electrons. Hence the electron distribution throughout the crystal medium may be represented by means of the single function $\Omega(\bar{r})$ so that $\Omega\,dv$ is the number of electrons contained in a volume element dv at position $\bar{r}$. The distribution function Ω must of necessity possess the periodicity of the crystal lattice. According to the discussion given in section 10 of Chapter I the distribution function may thus be expressed as a Fourier series.

$$\begin{aligned} \Omega(\bar{r}) &= \sum \Omega_H \, e^{-i2\pi \bar{B}_H \cdot \bar{r}} \\ \Omega_H &= V^{-1} \int \Omega \, e^{i2\pi \bar{B}_H \cdot \bar{r}} \, dv \end{aligned} \qquad [3{\cdot}32]$$

The constant term in the series, Ω_{000}, represents the average electron density, i.e.,

$$\Omega_{000} = \frac{Z}{V} \qquad [3{\cdot}33]$$

where Z is the total number of electrons per unit cell and V the volume of the unit cell.

Consider a volume element dv at $\bar{r}$ containing $\Omega\,dv$ electrons, having a charge $-\mathrm{e}\,\Omega\,dv$ and a mass $m\,\Omega\,dv$. The equation of motion of this volume element under the action of the electric field of the wave given in Equation 3·6 becomes

$$\frac{d^2\bar{x}}{dt^2} = -\frac{\mathrm{e}}{m}\bar{E}_0 \, e^{i\omega_0 t - i2\pi \bar{k}_0 \cdot \bar{r}} \qquad [3{\cdot}34]$$

By comparison with the results obtained in section 3A, the polarizability of the volume element is seen to be

$$\alpha\, dv = -\frac{e^2\Omega}{m\omega_0^2}\, dv \qquad [3\cdot35]$$

while the contribution from the volume element to the amplitude of scattering at an observation point $\bar{R}$ becomes $E_e\, e^{i\bar{s}\cdot\bar{r}}\Omega\, dv$. The expression for the structure factor is therefore

$$F^0 = \int \Omega\, e^{i\bar{s}\cdot\bar{r}}\, dv \qquad [3\cdot36]$$

Usually it has physical significance to distribute the electrons between the various atomic nuclei contained in the unit cell. The number of electrons belonging to the kth nucleus will be denoted by z_k so that $\sum z_k = Z$. The electron density function for the crystal lattice, i.e., the function Ω, may thus be considered as the superposition of the electron distribution functions for the various atoms. Hence we write

$$\Omega(\bar{r}) = \sum_k \rho_k(\bar{r} - \bar{r}_k) \qquad [3\cdot37]$$

Combining Equations 3·36 and 3·37 and using the identity

$$e^{i\bar{s}\cdot\bar{r}} = e^{i\bar{s}\cdot\bar{r}_k}\, e^{i\bar{s}\cdot(\bar{r}-\bar{r}_k)}$$

we find readily

$$F^0 = \sum_k f_k^0\, e^{i\bar{s}\cdot\bar{r}_k} \qquad [3\cdot38]$$

where f_k^0 is the scattering power of the kth atom. Because of the interaction between the atoms in the crystal lattice, the distribution function ρ_k for the kth atom is somewhat different from the electron distribution function for the same atom in free space. The interaction will primarily affect the loosely bound electrons, i.e., the electron distribution at relatively large distances from the nucleus. The effect of the interaction on the scattering power is therefore negligible except for small s and for light atoms where the number of the outer electrons represents a major fraction of all electrons.

***B.* Anomalous Dispersion.** When anomalous dispersion is no longer neglected the results obtained in part A of this section need to be modified. It is necessary to distinguish between the different kinds of electrons in the unit cell. Let the subscript j indicate a specific type of electrons (for instance, a K electron of a sodium atom). The distribution of electrons of type j in the unit cell will be represented by a function $\Omega_j(\bar{r})$. The electrons of a given type may belong to different atoms and we write therefore

$$\Omega_j(\bar{r}) = \sum_k \sigma_j^{(k)} (\bar{r} - \bar{r}_k) \tag{3·39}$$

where $\sigma_j^{(k)}$ is the distribution function for electrons of type j in the kth atom. In accordance with the procedure of section 4 the electrons are replaced by continuous distributions of virtual oscillators. The number of virtual oscillators associated with electrons of type j, having frequencies in the range ω to $\omega + d\omega$ and contained in a volume element dv becomes

$$\Omega_j(\bar{r}) w_j(\omega)\, dv\, d\omega \tag{3·40}$$

By comparison with the derivations given in the two preceding sections, it is readily seen that the polarizability is no longer given by Equation 3·35 but by

$$\alpha = -\frac{e^2}{m\omega_0^2} \sum_j (1 + \xi_j + i\eta_j)\Omega_j \tag{3·41}$$

Similarly the amplitude of scattering due to the entire unit cell becomes $F\, E_e$ with

$$F = \sum_j (1 + \xi_j + i\eta_j) \int \Omega_j\, e^{i\bar{s}\cdot\bar{r}}\, dv \tag{3·42}$$

Using Equation 3·39 the expression for the structure factor may be rewritten in the form

$$F = \sum_k \Big[\sum_j (1 + \xi_j + i\eta_j)\varphi_j^{(k)} \Big] e^{i\bar{s}\cdot\bar{r}_k} \tag{3·43}$$

where

$$\varphi_j^{(k)} = \int \sigma_j^{(k)} (\bar{r} - \bar{r}_k)\, e^{i\bar{s}\cdot(\bar{r}-\bar{r}_k)}\, dv \tag{3·43a}$$

According to Equation 3·31 the expression $\sum_j (1 + \xi_j + i\eta_j)\varphi_j^{(k)}$ is simply the scattering power of the kth atom and we have thus

$$F = \sum_k f_k\, e^{i\bar{s}\cdot\bar{r}_k} \tag{3·44}$$

6. SCATTERING FROM A SMALL CRYSTAL

Having now discussed the scattering from an electron, from an atom, and from a single unit cell, we shall next consider the scattering due to a single ideal crystal. We shall assume that the dimensions of the crystal are small compared with the distance R from the crystal to the point of observation. If the origin is chosen at a corner of one unit cell the location of any other unit cell in the crystal is described by means of a lattice vector $\bar{A}_L = L_1\bar{a}_1 + L_2\bar{a}_2 + L_3\bar{a}_3$. The problem of finding the amplitude of scattering due to the entire crystal is seemingly a simple one. It might be expected that the resultant amplitude is merely the sum of the contributions from the various unit cells with the phase differences taken into account. If we assume for the present that this reasoning is correct, the contribution to the total amplitude from the unit cell located at $\bar{A}_L$ is $F\,E_e\,e^{i\bar{s}\cdot\bar{A}_L}$ since $\bar{s} \cdot \bar{A}_L$ is the phase difference with respect to the radiation scattered by the unit cell at the origin. Accordingly the total amplitude becomes

$$E_{\text{xl.}} = E_e F \sum_L e^{i\bar{s}\cdot\bar{A}_L} \tag{3·45}$$

where the summation is to be extended over all the unit cells composing the crystal. For the sake of convenience we shall assume that the crystal has the shape of a parallelopiped with edges $N_1\bar{a}_1$, $N_2\bar{a}_2$, and $N_3\bar{a}_3$. The number of unit cells contained in the crystal is thus $N_1N_2N_3 = N$. The detailed form of the sum contained in Equation 3·45 becomes

$$\sum_L e^{i\bar{s}\cdot\bar{A}_L} = \sum_0^{N_1-1} e^{iL_1\bar{s}\cdot\bar{a}_1} \sum_0^{N_2-1} e^{iL_2\bar{s}\cdot\bar{a}_2} \sum_0^{N_3-1} e^{iL_3\bar{s}\cdot\bar{a}_3} \tag{3·46}$$

The summation is the familiar one of a geometric series and hence Equation 3·45 may be given in the form

$$\frac{E_{\text{xl.}}}{E_e} = F \prod_i \frac{e^{iN_i\bar{s}\cdot\bar{a}_i} - 1}{e^{i\bar{s}\cdot\bar{a}_i} - 1} \tag{3·47}$$

The intensity ratio is obtained from the amplitude ratio by multiplication with the complex conjugate and we have thus

$$\frac{I_{\text{xl.}}}{I_e} = |F|^2 \prod_i \frac{\sin^2 \frac{1}{2}N_i\bar{s} \cdot \bar{a}_i}{\sin^2 \frac{1}{2}\bar{s} \cdot \bar{a}_i} \tag{3·48}$$

It is to be recalled that $\bar{s} = 2\pi(\bar{k} - \bar{k}_0)$ where $\bar{k}_0$ and $\bar{k}$ are the incident and scattered wave vectors respectively. Accordingly Equation 3·48 gives the intensity of scattering as a function of the scattering direction expressed in terms of the direction of incidence and the structure of the crystal. The maximum values of the intensity ratio occur for such values $\bar{s}_H$ of $\bar{s}$ that

$$\begin{aligned} \bar{s}_H \cdot \bar{a}_1 &= 2\pi H_1 \\ \bar{s}_H \cdot \bar{a}_2 &= 2\pi H_2 \\ \bar{s}_H \cdot \bar{a}_3 &= 2\pi H_3 \end{aligned} \tag{3·49}$$

where H_1, H_2, and H_3 are three integers entirely independent of one another. Solving Equations 3·49 for the vector $\bar{s}_H$ the following result is obtained.

$$\bar{s}_H = 2\pi \bar{B}_H = 2\pi(H_1\bar{b}_1 + H_2\bar{b}_2 + H_3\bar{b}_3) \qquad [3\cdot50]$$

Obviously Equations 3·49 and 3·50 are identical with Equations 3·3 and 3·4, i.e., with the scalar Laue equations and the Laue vector equation respectively. The elementary method for the determination of the diffraction directions described in section 1 is thus properly justified.

When the Laue equations are satisfied the intensity of scattering becomes

$$I_e|F_H|^2N^2 \qquad [3\cdot51]$$

where N is the number of unit cells in the crystal and where F_H is the value of the structure factor for $\bar{s} = \bar{s}_H$, i.e.,

$$F_H = \sum_k f_k\, e^{i2\pi\bar{B}_H\cdot\bar{r}_k} \qquad [3\cdot52]$$

It is seen from Equation 3·48 that the scattered radiation is concentrated at or very near to the intensity maxima, while the radiation is quite negligible between the maxima except when N_1, N_2, or N_3 is very small. It is not difficult to obtain an approximate expression for the half width of the diffraction maxima. When the Laue equation is satisfied we have $s_H = 4\pi \sin\theta_B/\lambda$ where $2\theta_B$ is the scattering angle. Let the direction of incidence be unchanged, but consider a direction of scattering in the plane of incidence slightly different from the diffraction direction and thus corresponding to a scattering angle of $2\theta_B + \varepsilon$. The corresponding value of $\bar{s}$ may be written as $\bar{s} = \bar{s}_H + \bar{\delta}$, and a simple geometrical consideration shows that

$$\delta = \frac{2\pi}{\lambda}\,\varepsilon\cos\theta_B \qquad [3\cdot53]$$

The intensity of scattering close to a maximum will be denoted by I_H and may be given in the form

$$I_H = I_e|F_H|^2\prod_i \frac{\sin^2 \frac{1}{2}N_i\bar{\delta}\cdot\bar{a}_i}{\sin^2 \frac{1}{2}\bar{\delta}\cdot\bar{a}_i} \qquad [3\cdot54]$$

We shall next smooth out the oscillations in I_H by replacing each of the three factors $\dfrac{\sin^2 \frac{1}{2}N_ix_i}{\sin^2 \frac{1}{2}x_i}$ by an appropriate smoothing function $N_i^2e^{-\frac{N_i^2x_i^2}{4\pi}}$ which has the same maximum value and the same area. In this manner

Equation 3·54 is transformed into

$$I_H \approx I_e|F_H|^2 N^2\, e^{-\frac{1}{4\pi}(\bar{\delta}\cdot\bar{A}_N)^2} \qquad [3\cdot55]$$

where $\bar{A}_N = N_1\bar{a}_1 + N_2\bar{a}_2 + N_3\bar{a}_3$ is the diagonal of our crystal block. Within the limit of the desired accuracy we may set $\bar{\delta}\cdot\bar{A}_N = \delta D$ where D is the average linear dimension of the crystal. Hence we have

$$I_H(\varepsilon) \approx I_e|F_H|^2 N^2\, e^{-\frac{\pi}{\lambda^2}\varepsilon^2 D^2 \cos^2\theta_B} \qquad [3\cdot56]$$

The half width value $\varepsilon_{\frac{1}{2}}$ becomes

$$\varepsilon_{\frac{1}{2}} \approx \sqrt{\frac{\log 2}{\pi}}\,\frac{\lambda}{D\cos\theta_B} \qquad [3\cdot57]$$

Although this equation is to be considered only as an approximation it shows that the diffraction maxima are exceedingly sharp. Indeed they attain a measurable width only when the scattering crystal approaches colloidal size.

Further discussion of Equation 3·48 will be postponed until we have examined the validity of our derivations. Equation 3·48 was obtained on the assumption that the incident wave anywhere in the crystal is given by Equation 3·6, i.e., it was tacitly assumed that the incident wave is not affected by the presence of the crystal medium. This assumption is clearly untenable. A beam of x rays traversing matter will suffer absorption, i.e., there will occur a diversion of energy from the incident beam. There are two main types of absorption processes. In the first type, the photoelectric or true absorption process, part of the incident radiation energy is converted into the kinetic energy of an ejected electron plus the potential energy of an excited atom. The second type of absorption corresponds to an energy transfer from the incident to the scattered radiation. There are two distinct scattering processes which divert energy from the incident wave, the Compton scattering and the coherent scattering. According to Equation 3·48 the intensity of the coherent scattering from a crystal is negligible unless the Laue vector equation is exactly or very nearly satisfied. When the Laue equation is not fulfilled we may speak of normal absorption, i.e., absorption due to the ejection of photoelectrons and to Compton scattering. The additional absorption which arises when the Laue equation is exactly or nearly satisfied and strong diffracted waves are produced will be called *extinction*. Normal absorption is quantitatively described by means of the linear absorption coefficient μ which is defined as the fractional intensity decrease per unit length of path through the medium, i.e.,

$$\frac{dI}{I} = -\mu\, dx \qquad I = I_0\, e^{-\mu x} \tag{3·58}$$

where I_0 is the intensity of the incident radiation at the crystal surface and I the intensity at a depth of penetration x. Clearly normal absorption becomes negligible for sufficiently small crystals, namely, when $\mu D \ll 1$, where D is the average linear dimension of the crystal. Equation 3·48 shows that the intensity associated with the diffracted wave decreases with decreasing crystal size. In the limit of very small crystals it is thus justifiable to neglect both normal absorption and extinction. Later investigations will show that extinction in an average case must be taken into account when the linear dimension of the crystal is of the order of 10^{-4} cm. or greater. The intensity formula given in Equation 3·48 consequently represents an asymptotic solution which is valid only for crystals with linear dimensions of 10^{-4} cm. or smaller.

Before we attempt to develop a general theory of x-ray diffraction in an ideal crystal of any size the results obtained for a small crystal will be discussed further in the next section.

7. INTEGRATED INTENSITY FOR A SMALL CRYSTAL

According to Equation 3·48 the intensity of coherent scattering from a small crystal is negligible unless the Laue vector equation is exactly or very nearly satisfied. In other words if we set $\bar{s} = \bar{s}_H + \bar{\Delta} \equiv 2\pi \bar{B}_H + \bar{\Delta}$, the intensity of scattering may be taken to be zero unless $\bar{\Delta}$ is nil or very small. Setting

$$\bar{\Delta} = p_1\bar{b}_1 + p_2\bar{b}_2 + p_3\bar{b}_3 \tag{3·59}$$

Equation 3·48 takes the form

$$I_H(\bar{\Delta}) = I_e|F_H|^2 \prod_i \frac{\sin^2 \frac{1}{2}N_i p_i}{\sin^2 \frac{1}{2}p_i} \tag{3·60}$$

The particular values for the directions of incidence and scattering and for the wavelength which satisfy the Laue vector equation will be denoted by $\bar{u}_0^B$, $\bar{u}_H^B$ and λ_H^B respectively, so that

$$\bar{s}_H = \frac{2\pi}{\lambda_H^B}(\bar{u}_H^B - \bar{u}_0^B) = 2\pi(\bar{k}_H^B - \bar{k}_0^B) \tag{3·61}$$

In order to satisfy the Laue vector equation it is necessary experimentally to provide for a continuous variation of the incident wave vector as discussed in section 2. In the Laue method only the wavelength is varied, while in the rotating crystal method the direction of incidence is varied with one degree of freedom by means of a relative rotation of incident beam and crystal.

Experimentally one cannot measure the intensity for a sharply defined scattering direction. The best one can do is to measure the average intensity for scattering directions lying within a finite solid angle. The intensity function I_H has very sharp maxima and it cannot be considered a constant throughout a solid angle of the order of magnitude used in experiments. Hence experimental data cannot be directly compared with the formula given in Equation 3·60. Suppose that the measurements are made with an ionization chamber and that the axis of the chamber coincides with an ideal diffraction direction $\bar{u}_H^B$. Let dS be an element of area in the aperture of the ionization chamber. We may then measure the power P_H defined by

$$P_H = \iint_S I_H \, dS \tag{3·62}$$

where the integration is to be extended over the area S of the entire aperture. The intensity I_H goes to zero as the scattering direction deviates more and more from the diffraction direction $\bar{u}_H^B$. It will therefore be assumed that the aperture of the ionization chamber is sufficiently large so as to receive all radiation scattered in the diffraction direction and in neighboring directions. In other words the integral of Equation 3·62 approaches a limiting value as the area of the ionization chamber slit increases, and it is this limiting value of P_H in which we are interested. Since the diffraction maximum is very sharp the limiting value of P_H is quickly reached.

In the Laue method and the rotating crystal method the incident wave vector $\bar{k}_0$ is varied with one degree of freedom. We therefore set $\bar{k}_0 = \bar{k}_0(\varepsilon_1)$ where the parameter ε_1 is so chosen that $\bar{k}_0 = \bar{k}_0^B$ for $\varepsilon_1 = 0$. Clearly the power P_H received by the ionization chamber becomes a function of the parameter ε_1 and if this functional relationship is plotted we will get a curve with a sharp maximum at $\varepsilon_1 = 0$. The area under this curve will be denoted by $\mathfrak{J}_H$, i.e.,

$$\mathfrak{J}_H = \int P_H \, d\varepsilon_1 = \iiint I_H \, dS \, d\varepsilon_1 \tag{3·63}$$

The quantity $\mathfrak{J}_H$ may logically be called the *integrated power*, but *integrated intensity* is the common name. We shall find the explicit form of the integrated intensity for the Laue method and the rotating crystal method.

A. **The Laue Method.** We shall let the parameter ε_1 represent the difference between the actual wavelength and the ideal wavelength, i.e.,

$$\lambda_H = \lambda_H^B + \varepsilon_1 \quad [3\cdot64]$$

A direction of scattering near a diffraction direction $\bar{u}_H^B$ will be described by means of the two parameters ε_2 and ε_3 shown in Fig. 3·4. From the figure we have $dS = R^2\, d\varepsilon_2\, d\varepsilon_3$ where R is the distance from the crystal to the observation point, i.e., to the aperture of the ionization chamber or to the photographic plate. With the aid of simple geometrical considerations based on Fig. 3·4 the vector $\bar{\Delta} \equiv \bar{s} - \bar{s}_H$ is readily expressed in terms of the three parameters ε_1, ε_2, and ε_3. The result is

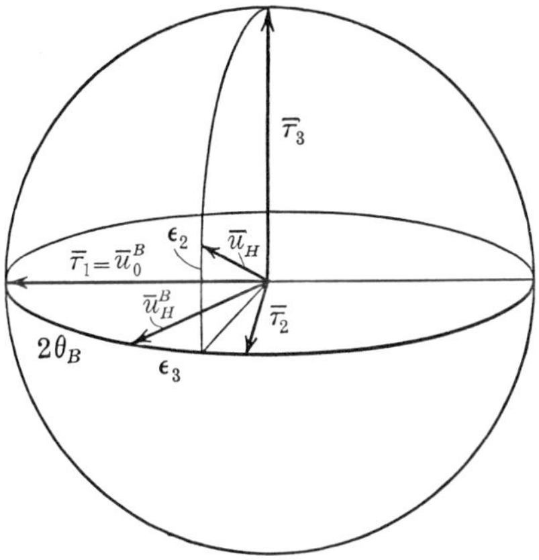

FIG. 3·4.

$$\bar{\Delta} = \frac{2\pi\,\varepsilon_1}{\lambda_B^2}\{(1 - \cos 2\theta_B)\bar{\tau}_1 - \sin 2\theta_B\,\bar{\tau}_2\} + \frac{2\pi\,\varepsilon_2}{\lambda_B}\bar{\tau}_3 + \frac{2\pi\,\varepsilon_3}{\lambda_B}\{-\sin 2\theta_B\,\bar{\tau}_1 + \cos 2\theta_B\,\bar{\tau}_2\} \quad [3\cdot65]$$

$\bar{\tau}_1$, $\bar{\tau}_2$, $\bar{\tau}_3$ are three unit vectors forming an orthogonal set as shown in the figure.

The expression for $\mathfrak{I}_H$ is

$$\mathfrak{I}_H = R^2 \int\!\!\int\!\!\int I_H(\bar{\Delta})\, d\varepsilon_1\, d\varepsilon_2\, d\varepsilon_3 \quad [3\cdot66]$$

The vector $\bar{\Delta}$ may be given either in terms of p_1, p_2, p_3 as in Equation 3·59 or in terms of ε_1, ε_2, ε_3 as in Equation 3·65. For the triple integral of Equation 3·66 we may therefore write

$$\int\!\!\int\!\!\int I_H(\bar{\Delta})\, d\varepsilon_1\, d\varepsilon_2\, d\varepsilon_3 = \int\!\!\int\!\!\int I_H(\bar{\Delta}) \frac{J\left(\dfrac{\partial\bar{\Delta}}{\partial p_i}\right)}{J\left(\dfrac{\partial\bar{\Delta}}{\partial\varepsilon_i}\right)}\, dp_1\, dp_2\, dp_3 \quad [3\cdot67]$$

where $J\left(\dfrac{\partial\bar{\Delta}}{\partial p_i}\right)$ and $J\left(\dfrac{\partial\bar{\Delta}}{\partial\varepsilon_i}\right)$ are the two Jacobians. Using Equations

3·59 and 3·60 we have

$$J\left(\frac{\partial \bar{\Delta}}{\partial p_i}\right) \equiv \frac{\partial \bar{\Delta}}{\partial p_1} \cdot \frac{\partial \bar{\Delta}}{\partial p_2} \times \frac{\partial \bar{\Delta}}{\partial p_3} = \bar{b}_1 \cdot \bar{b}_2 \times \bar{b}_3 = \frac{1}{V} \qquad [3{\cdot}68a]$$

$$J\left(\frac{\partial \bar{\Delta}}{\partial \varepsilon_i}\right) \equiv \frac{\partial \bar{\Delta}}{\partial \varepsilon_1} \cdot \frac{\partial \bar{\Delta}}{\partial \varepsilon_2} \times \frac{\partial \bar{\Delta}}{\partial \varepsilon_3} = \frac{16\pi^3 \sin^2 \theta_B}{\lambda_B^4} \qquad [3{\cdot}68b]$$

where V is the volume of the unit cell. Hence Equation 3·66 becomes

$$\mathfrak{J}_H = \frac{R^2\, I_e\, \lambda_B^4\, |F_H|^2}{16\pi^3 V \sin^2 \theta_B} \prod_i \int_{-\delta_i}^{+\delta_i} \frac{\sin^2 \frac{1}{2} N_i p_i}{\sin^2 \frac{1}{2} p_i}\, dp_i \qquad [3{\cdot}69]$$

The integration limits $\pm\delta_i$ are to be chosen large enough to make the integrand negligibly small in agreement with the requirement that all radiation associated with the diffracted beam is to be received by the ionization chamber. Since N_i may be considered a large number (except for crystals of colloidal size) the limit δ_i is still small compared with $\pi/2$ and the following approximation may therefore be used

$$\int_{-\delta_i}^{+\delta_i} \frac{\sin^2 \frac{1}{2} N_i p_i}{\sin^2 \frac{1}{2} p_i}\, dp_i \approx \int_{-\infty}^{\infty} \frac{\sin^2 \frac{1}{2} N_i p_i}{(\frac{1}{2} p_i)^2}\, dp_i = 2\pi\, N_i \qquad [3{\cdot}70]$$

Hence we have

$$\prod_i \int_{-\delta_i}^{+\delta_i} \frac{\sin^2 \frac{1}{2} N_i p_i}{\sin^2 \frac{1}{2} p_i}\, dp_i = \frac{(2\pi)^3}{V}\, \delta V \qquad [3{\cdot}71]$$

where $\delta V = N_1 N_2 N_3 V$ is the volume of the crystal. Remembering Equation 3·11 the final result for the integrated intensity becomes

$$\mathfrak{J}_H = I_0 Q\, \delta V$$

$$Q = \left(\frac{e^2}{mc^2 V}\right)^2 \frac{1 + \cos^2 2\theta_B}{2}\, \frac{|F_H|^2 \lambda_B^4}{2 \sin^2 \theta_B} \qquad [3{\cdot}72]$$

Instead of defining the parameter ε_1 by means of Equation 3·64 we could have defined it by $\dfrac{1}{\lambda} = \dfrac{1}{\lambda_B} + \varepsilon_1$ in which case the factor λ_B^4 in the expression for Q would have to be replaced by λ_B^2.

B. **The Rotating Crystal Method.** In this method the wavelength is fixed, i.e., $\lambda = \lambda_B$, while the incident beam is rotated relative to the crystal. Let the constant angle between the incident beam and the rotation axis be $\dfrac{\pi}{2} - \chi$ and let the parameter ε_1 describe the rotation angle as shown in Fig. 3·5. Hence we have

$$\bar{u}_0 = \bar{u}_0^B + \varepsilon_1 \bar{\tau}_3 \times \bar{u}_0^B = \bar{u}_0^B + \varepsilon_1 \cos \chi\, \bar{\tau}_2 \qquad [3{\cdot}73]$$

where $\bar{\tau}_3$ is a unit vector along the rotation axis and $\bar{\tau}_2$ another unit vector normal to the plane containing $\bar{\tau}_3$ and $\bar{u}_0^B$. We shall introduce a third unit vector $\bar{\tau}_1$ defined by $\bar{\tau}_1 \equiv \bar{\tau}_2 \times \bar{\tau}_3$ so that $\bar{\tau}_1$, $\bar{\tau}_2$, $\bar{\tau}_3$ form an

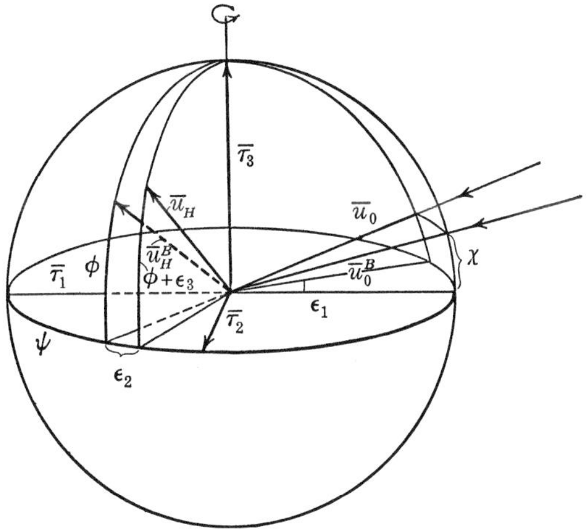

FIG. 3·5.

orthogonal set. The diffraction direction $\bar{u}_H^B$ will be described by means of its longitude ψ and its latitude φ in the system $\bar{\tau}_1, \bar{\tau}_2, \bar{\tau}_3$, while ε_2 and ε_3 are the increments in ψ and φ respectively which correspond to a neighboring direction $\bar{u}_H$. With the aid of Fig. 3·5 we find

$$dS = R^2 \cos \varphi \, d\varepsilon_2 \, d\varepsilon_3 \qquad [3\cdot74]$$

and

$$\bar{\Delta} = \frac{2\pi \, \varepsilon_1}{\lambda} \cos \chi \, \bar{\tau}_2 + \frac{2\pi \, \varepsilon_2 \cos \varphi}{\lambda} \{-\sin \psi \, \bar{\tau}_1 + \cos \psi \, \bar{\tau}_2\}$$

$$+ \frac{2\pi \, \varepsilon_3}{\lambda} \{-\sin \varphi \cos \psi \, \bar{\tau}_1 - \sin \varphi \sin \psi \, \bar{\tau}_2 + \cos \varphi \, \bar{\tau}_3\} \qquad [3\cdot75]$$

The integrated intensity becomes

$$\mathfrak{I}_H = R^2 \cos \varphi \int\!\!\int\!\!\int I_H(\bar{\Delta}) \frac{J\left(\dfrac{\partial \bar{\Delta}}{\partial p_i}\right)}{J\left(\dfrac{\partial \bar{\Delta}}{\partial \varepsilon_i}\right)} dp_1 \, dp_2 \, dp_3 \qquad [3\cdot76]$$

The Jacobian $J\left(\frac{\partial \bar{\Delta}}{\partial \varepsilon_i}\right)$ is readily evaluated from Equation 3·75. We find

$$J\left(\frac{\partial \bar{\Delta}}{\partial \varepsilon_i}\right) \equiv \frac{\partial \bar{\Delta}}{\partial \varepsilon_1} \cdot \frac{\partial \bar{\Delta}}{\partial \varepsilon_2} \times \frac{\partial \bar{\Delta}}{\partial \varepsilon_3} = \frac{8\pi^3 \cos \chi \sin \psi \cos^2 \varphi}{\lambda^3} \qquad [3·77]$$

Using results obtained in part A of this section we have therefore

$$\mathfrak{J}_H = I_0 Q\, \delta V$$

$$Q = \left(\frac{e^2}{mc^2 V}\right)^2 \frac{1 + \cos^2 2\theta_B}{2} \frac{|F_H|^2 \lambda^3}{\sin \psi \cos \varphi \cos \chi} \qquad [3·78]$$

The relation between ψ, φ, χ and the scattering angle $2\theta_B$ is

$$\cos 2\theta_B = \cos \psi \cos \varphi \cos \chi + \sin \psi \sin \chi \qquad [3·79]$$

***C.* The Powder Method.** For the sake of completeness we shall also consider the third principal experimental method in which the vector $\bar{u}_0$ is varied with two degrees of freedom in such a way that all directions of incidence become equally probable. We are interested in the scattering associated with a reciprocal vector $\bar{B}_H$ of the crystal. This scattering is negligible unless the glancing angle of incidence is $\theta_B + \varepsilon_1$ where ε_1 is a small quantity. The directions of incidence which correspond to a glancing angle $\theta_B + \varepsilon_1$ are the generatrices of a circular cone.

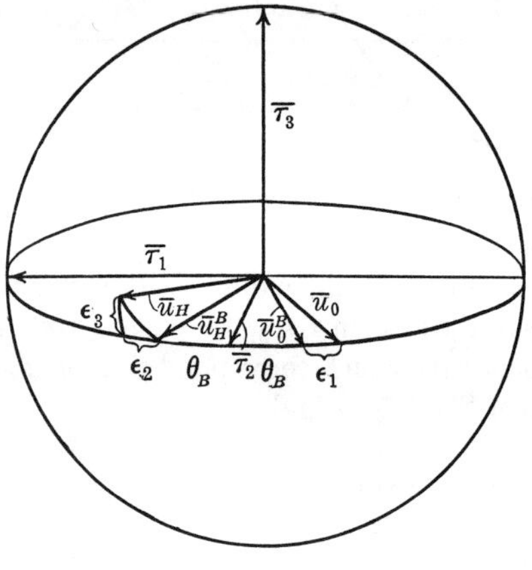

FIG. 3·6.

The axis of this cone is $\bar{B}_H$ and the semi-apex angle is $\frac{\pi}{2} - (\theta_B + \varepsilon_1)$. The probability $w\, d\varepsilon_1$ of finding an incident glancing angle in the range $\theta_B + \varepsilon_1$ to $\theta_B + \varepsilon_1 + d\varepsilon_1$ is therefore

$$w\, d\varepsilon_1 = \tfrac{1}{2} \cos (\theta_B + \varepsilon_1)\, d\varepsilon_1 \approx \tfrac{1}{2} \cos \theta_B\, d\varepsilon_1 \qquad [3·80]$$

Consider any one of these directions of incidence $\bar{u}_0$, its associated diffraction direction $\bar{u}_H^B$ and a neighboring scattering direction $\bar{u}_H$. Let ε_2 and ε_3 be the angular separations between $\bar{u}_H$ and $\bar{u}_H^B$ parallel and normal to the plane of incidence as shown in Fig. 3·6. The power reaching the ionization chamber is $P(\varepsilon_1) = \iint I_H \, dS$ where $dS = R^2 \, d\varepsilon_2 \, d\varepsilon_3$. The integrated intensity is the total power of the diffracted beam as the incident beam is varied, i.e.,

$$\mathfrak{J}_H = \int wP \, d\varepsilon_1 = \frac{R^2}{2} \cos \theta_B \iiint I_H \, d\varepsilon_1 \, d\varepsilon_2 \, d\varepsilon_3 \qquad [3\cdot81]$$

From Fig. 3·6 we find

$$\bar{\Delta} = \frac{2\pi \, \varepsilon_1}{\lambda} (\cos \theta_B \, \bar{\tau}_1 + \sin \theta_B \, \bar{\tau}_2) + \frac{2\pi \, \varepsilon_2}{\lambda} (\cos \theta_B \, \bar{\tau}_1 - \sin \theta_B \, \bar{\tau}_2) + \frac{2\pi \, \varepsilon_3}{\lambda} \bar{\tau}_3 \qquad [3\cdot82]$$

where $\bar{\tau}_1$ is the unit vector along $\bar{B}_H$, $\bar{\tau}_3$ the unit normal to the plane of incidence and $\bar{\tau}_2 \equiv \bar{\tau}_3 \times \bar{\tau}_1$.

The integrated intensity may be written in the form

$$\mathfrak{J}_H = \frac{R^2 \cos \theta_B}{2} \iiint I_H \frac{J\left(\dfrac{\partial \bar{\Delta}}{\partial p_i}\right)}{J\left(\dfrac{\partial \bar{\Delta}}{\partial \varepsilon_i}\right)} dp_1 \, dp_2 \, dp_3 \qquad [3\cdot83]$$

With the aid of Equation 3·82 we obtain

$$J\left(\frac{\partial \bar{\Delta}}{\partial \varepsilon_i}\right) = -\frac{8\pi^3 \sin 2\theta_B}{\lambda^3} \qquad [3\cdot84]$$

and the formula for the integrated intensity becomes

$$\mathfrak{J}_H = I_0 Q \, \delta V$$

$$Q = \left(\frac{e^2}{mc^2 V}\right)^2 \frac{1 + \cos^2 2\theta_B}{2} \frac{|F_H|^2 \lambda^3}{4 \sin \theta_B} \qquad [3\cdot85]$$

We have been speaking of a variation of the incident direction and a fixed vector $\bar{B}_H$. However, we are concerned only with the relative orientation of incident beam and crystal, and it is therefore immaterial whether we consider the crystal fixed and the direction of incidence variable or the direction of incidence fixed and the crystal orientation variable. Adopting the latter viewpoint the diffraction directions $\bar{u}_H^B$ appear as generatrices of a circular cone of semi-apex angle $2\theta_B$ about the direction of incidence as shown in Fig. 3·7. Equation 3·85 represents the total power associated with this and with neighboring cones. The diffraction cone intersects a plane normal to the incident beam in a circle of radius $R \sin 2\theta_B$. Experimentally it is customary to measure the integrated intensity per unit length of this circle, i.e.,

$$\frac{\mathfrak{I}_H}{2\pi R \sin 2\theta_B} = I_0 \left(\frac{e^2}{mc^2 V}\right)^2 \frac{1 + \cos^2 2\theta_B}{2} \frac{|F_H|^2 \lambda^3}{16\pi R \sin^2 \theta_B \cos \theta_B} \delta V \quad [3\cdot86]$$

When the crystal has symmetry there are in general other reciprocal vectors equivalent to $\bar{B}_H$. Two equivalent vectors $\bar{B}_H$ and $\bar{B}_{H'} = \bar{B}_H \cdot \boldsymbol{\phi}$ (where $\boldsymbol{\phi}$ is a symmetry dyadic of the crystal) correspond to the same glancing angle and to the same integrated intensity.

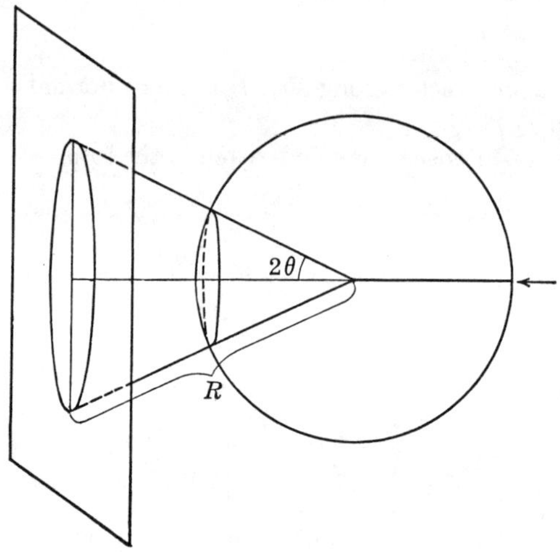

FIG. 3·7.

A given diffraction cone is therefore to be associated with the total set of equivalent vectors $\bar{B}_H$. If there are j equivalent vectors in the set the observed integrated intensity will obviously be j times greater than the expression given in Equation 3·85.

As mentioned in section 2 a random relative orientation of crystal and incident beam is statistically realized if a sample of finely divided crystal powder is placed in the incident beam. The integrated intensity from such a powder sample is evidently given by Equation 3·85 provided δV now stands for the aggregate volume of all crystallites. (It is, of course, assumed that the powder sample is sufficiently small so that absorption and extinction may be neglected.)

8. THE DYNAMICAL THEORY OF X-RAY DIFFRACTION

The theory of x-ray diffraction in ideal crystals presented in section 6 neglected both normal absorption and extinction. This theory is therefore valid only in the limiting case of small crystals. In the remaining sections of this chapter we will develop a general theory of x-ray diffraction in which normal absorption as well as the interaction between incident and scattered radiation are taken into account. The theory given in section 6 could easily be modified so as to take care of normal absorption. Indeed, the effect of normal absorption on the intensity of scattering can be represented by means of the factor $\overline{e^{-\mu_0 x}}$ where μ_0 is the normal linear absorption coefficient, x the path through the crystal and where the averaging is to be performed over all paths which come into consideration. Normal absorption occurs for all directions of incidence while extinction is important only when the incident wave vector has such a value that the Laue vector equation is exactly or very nearly satisfied for one or more reciprocal lattice vectors $\bar{B}_H$. It is clear therefore that the general theory will not greatly affect our earlier results concerning the *directions* of the diffraction maxima, but the results we have obtained for the *intensity* at or near these diffraction maxima may have to be radically changed.

In the simplified theory it was assumed that the incident x-ray wave suffers no change when it enters the crystal medium, i.e., that the expression

$$\bar{E}_0^e\, e^{i\omega_0 t - i2\pi \bar{k}^e \cdot \bar{r}} \qquad [3\cdot 87]$$

represents the incident wave within as well as outside the crystal. In Equation 3·87 $\bar{k}_0^e = \dfrac{1}{\lambda_0}\, \bar{u}_0^e$ where λ_0 is the wavelength in vacuum and $\bar{u}_0^e$ the propagation direction outside the crystal. The contribution to the electric field inside the crystal medium coming from the diffracted waves was in other words neglected. The diffracted waves depend upon the internal incident wave which in turn depend upon the diffracted waves. Hence the incident and the diffracted waves form a coupled system. The general theory of x-ray diffraction in crystals accordingly becomes a problem in dispersion theory and is therefore commonly referred to as the dynamical theory of x-ray diffraction, while the simplified theory presented in section 6 is called the wave kinematical theory. Clearly the wave kinematical theory is the first approximation to the dynamical theory in the limit of small crystals.

Due to the interaction between incident and scattered radiation inside the crystal medium Equation 3·87 will no longer represent the internal incident wave. Let us for convenience suppose that the wave of Equation 3·87 enters the crystal through a plane boundary. The orientation of the boundary plane will be described by means of a unit normal $\bar{n}$ pointing into the crystal medium. If the origin is chosen in the boundary plane the equation of this plane consequently becomes $\bar{n} \cdot \bar{r} = 0$. Within the crystal medium the incident wave will be represented by the expression

$$\bar{D}_0 \, e^{i\omega_0 t - i2\pi \bar{\beta}_0 \cdot \bar{r}} \qquad [3{\cdot}88]$$

where the amplitude $\bar{D}_0$ and the wave vector $\bar{\beta}_0$ have to be determined from the following considerations. (1) At the boundary $\bar{n} \cdot \bar{r} = 0$ the external incident wave (Equation 3·87) must be joined to the internal incident wave (Equation 3·88). (2) The internal incident wave and the internal diffracted waves with which it is coupled must form a self-consistent set.

When considering the boundary conditions at $\bar{n} \cdot \bar{r} = 0$ it is useful to remember that the dielectric constant in the x-ray region is only slightly different from unity (in the next section we will show this to be true). For the refractive index of the incident wave we may accordingly set $1 + \delta_0$ where δ_0 is a small quantity. Hence we have

$$\beta_0^2 = k_0^2(1 + \delta_0)^2 \approx k_0^2(1 + 2\delta_0) \qquad [3{\cdot}89]$$

At the boundary the exponential functions of Equations 3·87 and 3·88 must agree. This requirement is fulfilled if $\bar{\beta}_0 = \bar{k}_0^e + \Delta\bar{n}$. By using Equation 3·89 one finds readily $\Delta = \dfrac{k_0\delta_0}{\bar{n} \cdot \bar{u}_0^e} = \dfrac{k_0\delta_0}{\gamma_0}$, and hence

$$\bar{\beta}_0 = \bar{k}_0^e + \frac{k_0\delta_0}{\gamma_0}\bar{n} \qquad [3{\cdot}90]$$

The normal components of the displacement vectors and the tangential components of the electric vectors are continuous at the boundary. Since the dielectric constant is so nearly unity these boundary conditions may be given approximately as

$$\bar{D}_0 \approx \bar{E}_0^e \qquad [3{\cdot}91]$$

The internal incident wave is not yet completely determined since the refractive index $1 + \delta_0$ is unknown. The refractive index is variable and depends upon the strength of interaction between the incident and diffracted waves.

It was stated earlier in this section that the results of the kinematical theory as regards the directions of the diffracted waves must hold with great accuracy also for the dynamical theory. According to the kinematical theory each diffracted wave is associated with a different reciprocal lattice vector $\bar{B}_H$ such that the diffracted wave vector is $\bar{k}_0 + \bar{B}_H$. The amplitude of scattering is, however, negligible unless $|\bar{k}_0 + \bar{B}_H| \approx k_0$, i.e., unless the Laue vector equation is exactly or very nearly satisfied. By analogy we write $\bar{\beta}_0 + \bar{B}_H$ for the wave vector of a diffracted wave in the dynamical theory and expect the amplitude of this wave to be negligibly small except when the Laue vector equation is accurately or very nearly fulfilled. The wave field in the interior of the crystal, corresponding to the incident wave and any number of diffracted waves, may thus be represented by the expression

$$\bar{\mathfrak{D}} = \sum_H \bar{D}_H \, e^{i\omega_0 t - i2\pi \bar{\beta}_H \cdot \bar{r}}$$
$$\bar{\beta}_H = \bar{\beta}_0 + \bar{B}_H \qquad [3\cdot92]$$

If the Laue vector equation is far from satisfied for any vector $\bar{B}_H$ we may set $\bar{D}_0 \neq 0$ and $\bar{D}_H \approx 0$ for $H \neq 0$. In order to find which amplitudes $\bar{D}_H$ may have appreciable values, it is convenient to make use of the reciprocal lattice construction discussed in section 2. If a reciprocal lattice point $\bar{B}_H$ lies relatively far from the surface of the sphere of reflection one may set $\bar{D}_H \approx 0$. In our discussions we shall specifically treat the case in which all amplitudes except $\bar{D}_0$ and one $\bar{D}_H$ are negligibly small, i.e., the case in which the incident beam produces just one diffracted beam at a time. Of course, by proper adjustment of the incident wave vector $\bar{k}_0^e$ it is possible to make two or more reciprocal lattice points fall very nearly on the sphere of reflection so that two or more diffracted waves are produced simultaneously. Such cases are, however, rarely encountered under the usual experimental conditions and they will therefore not be discussed in detail.

The wave field given in Equation 3·92 represents a set of coupled plane waves. Accordingly the amplitudes $\bar{D}_H$ are not independent and the requirement of selfconsistency leads, as we shall learn in the next section, to a system of linear and homogeneous relations between them while the secular equation of this homogeneous system determines the possible values for the refractive index $1 + \delta_0$.

9. THE FUNDAMENTAL EQUATIONS OF THE DYNAMICAL THEORY

In order to find the conditions of selfconsistency for the coupled system of incident and diffracted waves in a crystal we shall require the internal wave field (as given in Equations 3·92) to satisfy the electromagnetic field equations. Before trying to solve this problem it is useful to discuss in detail the nature of the dielectric constant of the crystal medium.

A. **The Dielectric Constant of the Crystal Lattice.** The dielectric constant ε and the polarizability per unit volume α are connected by the well-known relation

$$\varepsilon = 1 + \frac{4\pi\,\alpha}{1 - \dfrac{4\pi}{3}\alpha} \approx 1 + 4\pi\,\alpha \qquad [3\cdot93]$$

The suggested approximation $\varepsilon \approx 1 + 4\pi\,\alpha$ is justifiable since α according to Equation 3·41 is small compared with unity. In the x-ray region it is thus not necessary to distinguish between the polarizability per unit volume and the electric susceptibility. The dielectric constant has, furthermore, scalar rather than tensor character. However, it is not a constant but a function of position having the periodicity of the crystal lattice. We shall introduce the symbol ψ for the function $4\pi\,\alpha$. Since ψ is periodic it may be written as a Fourier series, i.e.,

$$\psi = 4\pi\,\alpha = \sum_H \psi_H\, e^{-i2\pi\bar{B}_H\cdot\bar{r}}$$

$$\psi_H = \frac{1}{V}\int_V \psi\, e^{i2\pi\bar{B}_H\cdot\bar{r}}\, dv \qquad [3\cdot94]$$

Using Equations 3·41 and 3·42 we find

$$\psi_H = -\frac{4\pi\,e^2F_H}{m\omega_0^2V} \qquad [3\cdot95]$$

where F_H is the value of the structure factor for $\bar{s} = 2\pi\,\bar{B}_H$.

The square of the refractive index n is equal to the dielectric constant. Hence, since ψ is a small quantity,

$$n = 1 + \tfrac{1}{2}\psi \qquad [3\cdot96]$$

According to Equation 3·41 the refractive index becomes a complex and periodic function of position. The complex character of the refractive index implies that the scattering is accompanied by an absorption (scattering taking place with a phase shift). This absorption process corresponds to the ejection of photoelectrons, i.e., to true absorption. We shall separate real and imaginary parts of the function ψ and obtain by definition

$$\psi' = -\frac{4\pi\,e^2}{m\omega_0^2}\sum_j(1 + \xi_j)\Omega_j \qquad [3\cdot97a]$$

$$\psi'' = -\frac{4\pi\,e^2}{m\omega_0^2}\sum_j\eta_j\Omega_j \qquad [3\cdot97b]$$

where $\psi = \psi' + i\psi''$. The imaginary part of the refractive index, $\frac{1}{2}\psi''$, is called the absorption index and, as we shall see from a simple consideration given in section 12, it is related to the linear absorption coefficient μ (for true absorption) by the following equation

$$\mu = -\frac{2\pi\,\psi''}{\lambda_0} \qquad [3\cdot98]$$

Thus the true absorption coefficient is a periodic function of position also and can be expanded in a Fourier series

$$\mu = \sum_H \mu_H\, e^{-i2\pi \bar{B}_H\cdot\bar{r}}$$
$$\mu_H = \frac{2e^2\lambda_0}{mc^2 V}\sum_j \eta_j \int_V \Omega_j\, e^{i2\pi \bar{B}_H\cdot\bar{r}}\, dv \qquad [3\cdot99]$$

The average true absorption coefficient throughout the crystal medium is

$$\bar{\mu} = \mu_0 = -2\pi\, k_0\psi_0'' = \frac{2e^2\lambda_0}{mc^2 V}\sum_j \eta_j Z_j \qquad [3\cdot100]$$

where Z_j is the number of electrons of type j per unit cell. Similarly the average real refractive index is $1 + \frac{1}{2}\overline{\psi'}$ where

$$\overline{\psi'} = \psi_0' = -\frac{e^2\lambda_0^2}{\pi mc^2 V}\sum_j (1 + \xi_j) Z_j \qquad [3\cdot101]$$

***B.* The Fundamental Equations for the General Case.** The dielectric constant of the crystal medium for x-ray frequencies is $\varepsilon = 1 + \psi$, where ψ is a small quantity, and we shall assume the magnetic permeability to be unity and the current density to be zero. Maxwell's equations lead to the following differential equation for the displacement vector

$$\bar{\nabla}\times[\bar{\nabla}\times(1-\psi)\mathfrak{D}] = -\frac{1}{c^2}\frac{\partial^2\mathfrak{D}}{\partial t^2} \qquad [3\cdot102]$$

where we have set $\frac{1}{\varepsilon} = 1 - \psi$. For the displacement vector $\mathfrak{D}$ we shall use the wave field given in Equations 3·92. Expanding the function ψ in Fourier series gives

$$(1-\psi)\mathfrak{D} = e^{i\omega_0 t}\Big[\sum_H \bar{D}_H\, e^{-i2\pi\bar{\beta}_H\cdot\bar{r}} - \sum_K\sum_L \psi_K \bar{D}_L\, e^{-i2\pi(\bar{B}_K+\bar{\beta}_L)\cdot\bar{r}}\Big] \qquad [3\cdot103]$$

This equation can be simplified. In the first place $\bar{B}_K + \bar{\beta}_L = \bar{\beta}_{K+L}$ according to the definition of $\bar{\beta}_L$ given in Equation 3·92. Secondly we shall let $K + L = H$ in the double sum and obtain thus

$$(1-\psi)\mathfrak{D} = e^{i\omega_0 t}\sum_H (\bar{D}_H - \bar{C}_H)\, e^{-i2\pi\bar{\beta}_H\cdot\bar{r}} \qquad [3\cdot104]$$

where

$$\bar{C}_H \equiv \sum_L \psi_{H-L}\bar{D}_L \qquad [3\cdot104a]$$

By inserting the expressions for $\mathfrak{D}$ and for $(1 - \psi)\mathfrak{D}$ in Equation 3·102 and comparing coefficients the following set of equations is obtained

$$-\bar{\beta}_H \times [\bar{\beta}_H \times (\bar{D}_H - \bar{C}_H)] = k_0^2\bar{D}_H \qquad [3\cdot105a]$$

or

$$\sum_L \{\psi_{H-L}(\bar{\beta}_H \cdot \bar{D}_L)\bar{\beta}_H - \psi_{H-L}\,\beta_H^2\bar{D}_L\} = (k_0^2 - \beta_H^2)\bar{D}_H \qquad [3\cdot105b]$$

This is the fundamental system of equations of the dynamical theory upon which our study of the interference phenomena will be based. It is seen from Equation 3·105*a* that $\bar{D}_H \cdot \bar{\beta}_H = 0$ so that all waves are of the transverse type. Accordingly our wave field satisfies the equation $\bar{\nabla} \cdot \mathfrak{D} = 0$. This result requires discussion. A priori it might have been expected that $\mathfrak{D}$ would satisfy the equation $\bar{\nabla} \cdot \mathfrak{D} = 4\pi\, e(\Omega' - \Omega)$ where Ω' and Ω are the distribution functions for positive and negative charges respectively, and where $\overline{\Omega' - \Omega} = 0$ since the net charge is zero for every unit cell. However, we have been dealing only with the oscillating part of the electric displacement while the static part is left out of consideration. The apparent discrepancy is explained when we recall that the divergence of the static part of the electric displacement does not vanish.

Let us assume at first that the Laue vector equation is far from satisfied for any vector $\bar{B}_H$. The incident wave will in that case produce diffracted waves of negligibly small amplitude. We set then $\bar{D}_0 \neq 0$ and $\bar{D}_H \approx 0$ (for $H \neq 0$). The system of Equations 3·105 reduces to

$$\beta_0^2 = \frac{k_0^2}{1 - \psi_0} \quad \text{or} \quad \beta_0 \approx k_0(1 + \tfrac{1}{2}\psi_0) \qquad [3\cdot106]$$

showing that the refractive index for the incident wave must be equal to the average refractive index for the crystal medium. The internal incident wave is completely determined by means of the condition of selfconsistency (Equation 3·106) and the boundary conditions (Equations 3·90 and 3·91).

We are particularly interested in the case for which the incident wave produces only one diffracted wave of appreciable amplitude.

C. Solution of the Fundamental System of Equations for the Case of Two Internal Waves. Suppose that the direction of incidence is so chosen that only one reciprocal lattice point $\bar{B}_H$ lies near the surface of the sphere of reflection. In accordance with the arguments given in part A of this section we may then set $\bar{D}_0 \neq 0$, $\bar{D}_H \neq 0$ and $\bar{D}_L \approx 0$ (for $L \neq H$ or 0). Equations 3·105 become

$$\begin{aligned} \psi_{\bar{H}}(\bar{\beta}_0 \cdot \bar{D}_H)\bar{\beta}_0 - \psi_{\bar{H}}\beta_0^2\bar{D}_H &= [k_0^2 - \beta_0^2(1 - \psi_0)]\bar{D}_0 \\ \psi_H(\bar{\beta}_H \cdot \bar{D}_0)\bar{\beta}_H - \psi_H\beta_H^2\bar{D}_0 &= [k_0^2 - \beta_H^2(1 - \psi_0)]\bar{D}_H \end{aligned} \qquad [3\cdot107]$$

The second of the two equations shows that $\bar{D}_H$ lies in the same plane as $\bar{\beta}_H$ and $\bar{D}_0$ and normal to $\bar{\beta}_H$.

We shall set

$$\beta_0^2 = k_0^2(1 + 2\delta_0), \quad \beta_H^2 = k_0^2(1 + 2\delta_H) \qquad [3\cdot108]$$

so that $1 + \delta_0$ and $1 + \delta_H$ are the refractive indices of the incident and diffracted waves respectively. Now multiplying the first of the two Equations 3·107 scalarly with $\bar{D}_0$ and the second scalarly with $\bar{D}_H$ we find

$$\begin{aligned} (2\delta_0 - \psi_0)D_0 - \psi_{\bar{H}} \sin\chi\, D_H &= 0 \\ -\psi_H \sin\chi\, D_0 + (2\delta_H - \psi_0)D_H &= 0 \end{aligned} \qquad [3\cdot109]$$

where χ is the angle between $\bar{D}_0$ and $\bar{\beta}_H$. These linear and homogeneous equations represent the selfconsistency conditions and they have a non-trivial solution only if the determinant vanishes, i.e., if

$$(2\delta_0 - \psi_0)(2\delta_H - \psi_0) = \psi_H\psi_{\bar{H}} \sin^2\chi \qquad [3\cdot110]$$

and this non-trivial solution is

$$x \equiv \frac{D_H}{D_0} = \frac{2\delta_0 - \psi_0}{\psi_{\bar{H}} \sin\chi} \qquad [3\cdot111]$$

It is convenient to introduce the two principal polarization directions of the incident wave. In normal polarization $\bar{D}_0$ is normal to the plane containing $\bar{\beta}_0$ and $\bar{\beta}_H$ so that $\chi = \pi/2$. In parallel polarization $\bar{D}_0$ lies in the plane of $\bar{\beta}_0$ and $\bar{\beta}_H$, and consequently $\chi = (\pi/2) - 2\theta$ where 2θ is the scattering angle. If the incident wave is unpolarized the intensity of the scattered wave is given by the average value of the intensity for the two principal polarization directions (compare Equation 3·12). Setting $\sin\chi = 1$ in Equations 3·110 and 3·111 corresponds to the normal component of polarization, while the value $\sin\chi = \cos 2\theta$ corresponds to the parallel component. It is seen that it will be sufficient in the following to deal with the normal component, for the corresponding result applying to the parallel component is obtained by the simple procedure of replacing ψ_H and $\psi_{\bar{H}}$ everywhere by $\psi_H \cos 2\theta$ and $\psi_{\bar{H}} \cos 2\theta$.

Remembering that $\bar{\beta}_H = \bar{\beta}_0 + \bar{B}_H$ and using Equation 3·90 we find

$$\bar{\beta}_H = \bar{k}_0^e + \frac{k_0\delta_0}{\gamma_0}\bar{n} + \bar{B}_H \qquad [3\cdot112]$$

Combining Equations 3·108 and 3·112 the quantity δ_H may be expressed as follows.

$$\delta_H = \frac{1}{b}\,\delta_0 + \frac{1}{2}\,\alpha \qquad [3\cdot113]$$

where

$$\frac{1}{b} = 1 + \frac{\bar{n}\cdot\bar{B}_H}{\bar{n}\cdot\bar{k}_0^e} \qquad [3\cdot114a]$$

$$\alpha = \frac{1}{k_0^2}\,\{B_H^2 + 2\bar{k}_0^e\cdot\bar{B}_H\} \qquad [3\cdot114b]$$

It is useful to remember that our considerations are limited to the case where the Laue vector equation is exactly or very nearly satisfied for one reciprocal lattice vector $\bar{B}_H$. Let $\bar{k}_0^B$ and $\bar{k}_H^B$ be the particular values of the incident and diffracted wave vectors for which the Laue vector equation is satisfied, i.e., $\bar{k}_H^B - \bar{k}_0^B = \bar{B}_H$. The quantity b may then be written as

$$b = \frac{\bar{n}\cdot\bar{k}_0^e}{\bar{n}\cdot[\bar{k}_0^e + \bar{k}_H^B - \bar{k}_0^B]} \approx \frac{\gamma_0}{\gamma_H} \qquad [3\cdot115]$$

where $\gamma_0 \equiv \bar{n}\cdot\bar{u}_0^B$ and $\gamma_H \equiv \bar{n}\cdot\bar{u}_H^B$ are the direction cosines of the incident and diffracted wave respectively.

Let us next consider the detailed expression for the quantity α. In the rotating crystal method the wavelength is constant while the direction of incidence is varied. Hence we find

$$\text{Rotating crystal method} \quad \alpha \approx 2(\theta_B - \theta)\sin 2\theta_B \qquad [3\cdot116]$$

where θ_B is the Bragg glancing angle and θ the actual glancing angle of incidence. In our discussion of the rotating crystal method (see Fig. 3·5 and part B of section 7) we introduced a set of angles χ, ε_1, ψ, and φ to describe the direction of incidence and of scattering. When the parameter ε_1 is zero the Laue equation is satisfied and a simple consideration shows that the deviation from the Bragg angle $(\theta_B - \theta)$ can be expressed in terms of the parameter ε_1 as follows.

$$(\theta_B - \theta)\sin 2\theta_B = \varepsilon_1 \cos\chi \sin\psi \cos\varphi \qquad [3\cdot117]$$

In the Laue method the direction of incidence is fixed, i.e., $\theta = \theta_B$, but the wavelength is varied. Let λ_B be the particular wavelength for which the Laue equation is exactly satisfied and let λ_0 be a neighboring wavelength. In this case we find

$$\text{Laue method} \quad \alpha \approx 4\,\frac{\lambda_0 - \lambda_B}{\lambda_B}\sin^2\theta_B \qquad [3\cdot118]$$

In using Equation 3·113 Equation 3·110 becomes a quadratic equation in δ_0. Since Equation 3·110 thus determines the possible values for the refractive index of the incident and the diffracted wave as functions of the incident wave vector, we shall call this equation the dispersion equation. The dispersion equation (for normal polarization) becomes

$$(2\delta_0 - \psi_0)\left(\frac{2}{b}\,\delta_0 - \psi_0 + \alpha\right) = \psi_H\psi_{\bar{H}} \qquad [3·119]$$

Introducing the amplitude ratio x defined by Equation 3·111 the dispersion equation may also be written as a quadratic equation in x, namely,

$$x^2 + x\left[(1 - b)\frac{\psi_0}{\psi_{\bar{H}}} + \frac{b}{\psi_{\bar{H}}}\alpha\right] - b\frac{\psi_H}{\psi_{\bar{H}}} = 0 \qquad [3·120]$$

The solutions of Equations 3·119 and 3·120 are:

$$\left.\begin{matrix}\delta_0' \\ \delta_0''\end{matrix}\right\} = \tfrac{1}{2}\{\psi_0 - z \pm \sqrt{q + z^2}\} \qquad [3·121]$$

$$\left.\begin{matrix}x_1 \\ x_2\end{matrix}\right\} = \frac{-z \pm \sqrt{q + z^2}}{\psi_{\bar{H}}} \qquad [3·122]$$

with the following abbreviations

$$z \equiv \frac{1 - b}{2}\,\psi_0 + \frac{b}{2}\,\alpha, \quad q = b\psi_H\psi_{\bar{H}} \qquad [3·123]$$

Since there are two possible values for δ_0 and for the amplitude ratio x, there are two internal incident waves and two internal diffracted waves in the general case. The general form of the incident beam inside the crystal medium is thus

$$e^{i\omega_0 t - i2\pi\bar{k}_0^e\cdot\bar{r}}\,[D_0'\,e^{-i\varphi_1 t} + D_0''\,e^{-i\varphi_2 t}] \qquad [3·124]$$

and for the diffracted beam

$$e^{i\omega_0 t - i2\pi(\bar{k}_0^e + \bar{B}_H)\cdot\bar{r}}\,[x_1 D_0'\,e^{-i\varphi_1 t} + x_2 D_0''\,e^{-i\varphi_2 t}] \qquad [3·125]$$

where

$$\varphi_1 \equiv 2\pi\,\frac{k_0\delta_0'}{\gamma_0}, \quad \varphi_2 \equiv 2\pi\,\frac{k_0\delta_0''}{\gamma_0}, \quad t \equiv \bar{n}\cdot\bar{r} \qquad [3·126]$$

The external incident wave enters the crystal medium through the plane boundary $\bar{n}\cdot\bar{r} = \cdot 0$ where it must be joined to the internal incident wave. This requires

$$D_0' + D_0'' = E_0^e \qquad [3·127]$$

This boundary condition alone does not, however, uniquely determine the internal incident and diffracted waves, since the ratio $D_0' : D_0''$ is arbitrary and additional boundary conditions must accordingly be imposed.

10. GENERAL SOLUTION FOR PLANE PARALLEL CRYSTAL PLATES

In the preceding section we found a general expression for a self-consistent internal x-ray wave field in a crystal medium. It was assumed that an incident wave entered the crystal through a plane boundary and produced a diffracted wave in the interior. In order to obtain a unique solution to the problem it becomes necessary to deal with a bounded crystal which obviously must be presupposed if the interference phenomena are to be observed. We shall assume the crystal to

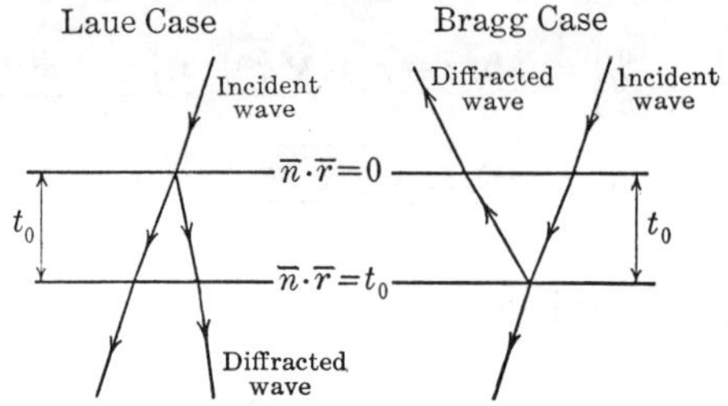

FIG. 3·8.

be a plane parallel plate of thickness t_0 with unlimited lateral extension. The equations of the two boundary planes are thus $\bar{n} \cdot \bar{r} = 0$ and $\bar{n} \cdot \bar{r} = t_0$. Although the incident wave enters the crystal through the plane $\bar{n} \cdot \bar{r} = 0$, the diffracted wave may emerge either through the plane $\bar{n} \cdot \bar{r} = 0$ or through the plane $\bar{n} \cdot \bar{r} = t_0$. Since the boundary conditions are different for the two cases it becomes necessary to distinguish sharply between them, and this is conveniently done by means of the quantity b of Equation 3·115. When b is positive the diffracted wave emerges through the boundary $\bar{n} \cdot \bar{r} = t_0$. We will refer to this case as the Laue case. When b is negative, the Bragg case, the diffracted wave leaves the crystal through the boundary $\bar{n} \cdot \bar{r} = 0$.

A. **The Laue Case.** The directions of the incident and diffracted waves for the Laue case are shown schematically in Fig. 3·8. The boundary conditions for the incident wave at the surface $\bar{n} \cdot \bar{r} = 0$ have been discussed earlier, and the condition for the amplitudes is expressed by Equation 3·127. No diffracted wave enters the crystal medium through the boundary $\bar{n} \cdot \bar{r} = 0$, and it must therefore be required that the internal diffracted beam shall vanish at this surface. This requirement gives

$$x_1 D_0' + x_2 D_0'' = 0 \tag{3·128}$$

Accordingly we have

$$D_0' = \frac{x_2}{x_2 - x_1} E_0^e, \quad D_0'' = -\frac{x_1}{x_2 - x_1} E_0^e \tag{3·129}$$

and the internal incident and diffracted beams are thus completely determined.

Let I_e^0 and I_H be the intensities of the transmitted incident wave and of the external diffracted wave. These quantities are readily found, for they may be set equal to the intensities of the corresponding internal waves at the boundary $\bar{n} \cdot \bar{r} = t_0$. By setting $t = t_0$ in Equations 3·124 and 3·125 and using Equation 3·129 we find

$$\frac{I_H}{I_0^e} = \left| \frac{x_1 x_2 (c_1 - c_2)}{x_2 - x_1} \right|^2 \tag{3·130}$$

$$\frac{I_e^0}{I_0^e} = \left| \frac{x_2 c_1 - x_1 c_2}{x_2 - x_1} \right|^2 \tag{3·131}$$

where

$$c_1 \equiv e^{-i\varphi_1 t_0}, \quad c_2 \equiv e^{-i\varphi_2 t_0} \tag{3·132}$$

and where I_0^e is the intensity of the external incident wave.

Since the result given in Equation 3·130 will be extensively used in the following paragraphs we shall rewrite it in more explicit form. One finds after some manipulation that

$$\frac{I_H}{I_0^e} = b^2 |\psi_H|^2 \, e^{-\mu_0 t} \, \frac{\sin^2 (av) + \sinh^2 (aw)}{|q + z^2|} \tag{3·133}$$

where the following abbreviations are used

$$v + iw \equiv \sqrt{q + z^2}, \quad a \equiv \pi k_0 \frac{t_0}{\gamma_0}, \quad t \equiv \tfrac{1}{2} \left(\frac{1}{\gamma_0} + \frac{1}{\gamma_H} \right) t_0 \tag{3·134}$$

The quantity t is obviously the average length of path through the crystal plate, while μ_0 is the average absorption coefficient given in Equation 3·100.

***B.* The Bragg Case.** If b is negative the diffracted wave emerges through the boundary $\bar{n} \cdot \bar{r} = 0$ as shown in Fig. 3·8, while it must vanish at the boundary $\bar{n} \cdot \bar{r} = t_0$. Instead of the boundary condition given in Equation 3·128 we get therefore

$$c_1 x_1 D_0' + c_2 x_2 D_0'' = 0 \tag{3·135}$$

which with Equation 3·127 gives

$$D_0' = \frac{c_2 x_2}{c_2 x_2 - c_1 x_1} E_0^e, \quad D_0'' = -\frac{c_1 x_1}{c_2 x_2 - c_1 x_1} E_0^e \qquad [3\cdot136]$$

Using Equations 3·125 and 3·136, we find the following result for the intensity of the diffracted wave at $\bar{n} \cdot \bar{r} = 0$

$$\frac{I_H}{I_0^e} = \left| \frac{x_1 x_2 (c_1 - c_2)}{c_2 x_2 - c_1 x_1} \right|^2 \qquad [3\cdot137]$$

The intensity I_e^0, which as in the Laue case must be evaluated at $\bar{n} \cdot \bar{r} = t_0$, is obtained from Equations 3·124 and 3·136 and becomes

$$\frac{I_e^0}{I_0^e} = \left| \frac{c_1 c_2 (x_2 - x_1)}{c_2 x_2 - c_1 x_1} \right|^2 \qquad [3\cdot138]$$

Equation 3·137 may be written in more explicit form as follows.

$$\frac{I_H}{I_0^e} = \frac{b^2|\psi_H|^2}{|q+z^2| + \{|q+z^2| + |z|^2\}\sinh^2 aw - \{|q+z^2| - |z|^2\}\sin^2 av}$$
$$\frac{\{\sin^2 av + \sinh^2 aw\}}{+ \frac{1}{2}|\{|q+z^2| + |z|^2\}^2 - |q|^2|^{1/2}\sinh|2aw| + \frac{1}{2}|\{|q+z^2| - |z|^2\}^2 - |q|^2|^{1/2}\sin|2av|} \qquad [3\cdot139]$$

We have now obtained the general solutions for the plane parallel plate. The formulas for the intensity of the diffracted wave, as given in Equations 3·133 and 3·139, are, however, fairly complicated. It must also be remembered that the expressions we have obtained apply to normal polarization, while the corresponding results for parallel polarization are obtained by everywhere replacing ψ_H and $\psi_{\bar{H}}$ by $\psi_H \cos 2\theta_B$ and $\psi_{\bar{H}} \cos 2\theta_B$. Because of the complexity of the intensity formulas it becomes a laborious task to make detailed numerical calculations of the diffraction patterns for the general case of absorbing crystal plates of arbitrary thickness. We shall therefore limit detailed discussions to special cases for which the intensity expressions are greatly simplified.

Let S_H represent the cross section and $P_H = S_H I_H$ the power of the diffracted beam. Similarly, S_0 and $P_0 = S_0 I_0^e$ denote the cross section and power of the incident beam. If the linear width of the incident beam is large compared with the depth of penetration in the crystal plate we may set $\dfrac{S_H}{S_0} = \left|\dfrac{\gamma_H}{\gamma_0}\right| = \dfrac{1}{|b|}$. The power ratio (the reflecting power), $\dfrac{P_H}{P_0} = \dfrac{1}{|b|}\dfrac{I_H}{I_0^e}$, is a function of the quantity α which can be expressed in terms of some convenient variable. The power ratio plotted as function of this variable gives the diffraction pattern. The area under the diffraction pattern will be called the integrated power ratio or the integrated reflecting power and denoted by the symbol R_H. The integrated reflecting power is related to the integrated intensity $\mathfrak{I}_H$, introduced in section 7, as follows: $R_H P_0 = \mathfrak{I}_H$.

11. SOLUTIONS FOR ZERO ABSORPTION

In this section we shall discuss the nature of the diffraction phenomena in the plane parallel plate on the basis of the assumption that no true absorption processes occur. The assumption of zero absorption is equivalent to the statement that the polarizability per unit volume is real rather than complex. The Fourier coefficients ψ_H must then satisfy the condition $\psi_{\bar{H}} = \psi_H^*$ so that $\psi_H \psi_{\bar{H}} = |\psi_H|^2$.

Laue Case. Since ψ is assumed to be real also the quantities q and z (as defined in the preceding section) must be real. Moreover $\sqrt{q + z^2}$ is real since b is positive in the Laue case. A consideration of Equation 3·133 will show that $\mu_0 = 0$, $w = 0$, and $v = \sqrt{q + z^2} = \sqrt{b|\psi_H|^2 + z^2}$. We shall introduce two new quantities A and y defined by

$$A = a\sqrt{|b|}K|\psi_H| = \pi k_0 K|\psi_H| \frac{t_0}{\sqrt{|\gamma_0 \gamma_H|}} \qquad [3\cdot140]$$

$$y = \frac{z}{\sqrt{|b|}K|\psi_H|} = \frac{\frac{1-b}{2}\psi_0 + \frac{b}{2}\alpha}{\sqrt{|b|}K|\psi_H|} \qquad [3\cdot141]$$

where $K = 1$ for normal and $K = |\cos 2\theta_B|$ for parallel polarization. Using these quantities, Equation 3·133 assumes the following simple form for zero absorption

$$\frac{P_H}{P_0} = \frac{\sin^2 [A\sqrt{1 + y^2}\,]}{1 + y^2} \qquad [3\cdot142]$$

This equation gives the power ratio as function of the variable y which is a linear function of the variable α. As shown by Equations 3·116–3·118, α can be expressed as a linear function of the glancing angle, the rotation angle, or the wavelength. Accordingly we may consider the power ratio as expressed by Equation 3·142 as a function of one of these variables. In studying the diffraction pattern we shall, however, make use chiefly of the more convenient y-scale.

Bragg Case. Since b is negative in the Bragg case the quantity $\sqrt{q + z^2}$ is real for $q + z^2 > 0$ and imaginary for $q + z^2 < 0$. Let us therefore consider the two possibilities separately.

(1) $q + z^2 > 0$. Then $w = 0$ and Equation 3·139 simplifies to

$$\frac{P_H}{P_0} = \frac{\sin^2 [A\sqrt{y^2 - 1}]}{y^2 - 1 + \sin^2 [A\sqrt{y^2 - 1}]}$$

$$= \frac{1}{y^2 + (y^2 - 1) \cot^2 [A\sqrt{y^2 - 1}]} \qquad [3\cdot143]$$

(2) $q + z^2 < 0$. Now $v = 0$ and Equation 3·139 may be written in the form

$$\frac{P_H}{P_0} = \frac{\sinh^2 [A\sqrt{1 - y^2}]}{1 - y^2 + \sinh^2 [A\sqrt{1 - y^2}]}$$

$$= \frac{1}{y^2 + (1 - y^2) \coth^2 [A\sqrt{1 - y^2}]} \qquad [3\cdot144]$$

Remembering that $\sinh^2 \varphi = -\sin^2 (i\varphi)$ and that $\coth^2 \varphi = -\cot^2 (i\varphi)$, it will be seen that the two equations given above actually may be written as a single equation.

Equations 3·142–3·144 represent the diffraction patterns for zero absorption as functions of the parameter y which again may be expressed in terms of the glancing angle or of the wavelength. It is seen from the equations that the diffraction patterns are symmetrical with respect to the value $y = 0$. On the glancing angle and wavelength scales the center of the diffraction pattern becomes

$$\theta_B + \frac{1 - b}{2b \sin 2\theta_B} \psi_0 \qquad [3\cdot145a]$$

$$\lambda_B - \lambda_B \frac{1 - b}{4b \sin^2 \theta_B} \psi_0 \qquad [3\cdot145b]$$

Thus the center of the diffraction pattern does not coincide with the ideal Bragg angle θ_B or the ideal Bragg wavelength unless $b = +1$. In other words Equation 3·145 show that Bragg's equation is not exactly satisfied at the center of the diffraction pattern (except for the symmetrical Laue case, i.e., $b = +1$). The deviation from the Bragg law may be positive or negative depending upon the value of b. In the Bragg case, b is negative and the glancing angle for the center of the diffraction pattern is thus always greater than the Bragg angle (remember that ψ_0 is negative). In the Laue case the theoretical glancing angle is greater than the Bragg angle for $b > 1$ and less than the Bragg angle for $b < 1$. The greatest deviation from Bragg's law occurs when $|b|$ is small, i.e., for grazing direction of incidence.

It is of interest to consider the intensity I_e^0 of the transmitted incident beam. The general expressions for the intensity ratio $I_e^0 : I_0^e$ are given in Equations 3·131 and 3·138. For zero absorption these equations can be written in the form

$$\frac{I_e^0}{I_0^e} = 1 - \frac{1}{|b|}\frac{I_H}{I_0^e} \qquad [3\cdot146a]$$

or

$$P_e^0 + P_H = P_0 \qquad [3\cdot146b]$$

This relation is clearly a statement of energy conservation, and it is an immediate consequence of our assumption of zero normal absorption which implies no energy dissipation within the crystal plate. The decrease in the intensity of the incident beam as it traverses the crystal plate is thus due only to energy transfer to the diffracted wave, i.e., Equation 3·146a illustrates the phenomenon of extinction which was briefly mentioned at the close of section 6.

In the rotating crystal method and in the Laue method the incident wave vector has one degree of freedom. The diffracted power is a function of this variable. In Equations 3·142–3·144 the power of the diffracted wave is expressed in terms of a parameter y, which in the rotating crystal method is a linear function of the glancing angle or of the rotation angle and which in the Laue method is a linear function of the wavelength. Hence we may plot the power ratio P_H/P_0 as function of y, glancing angle, rotation angle or wavelength. The numerical value for the integrated reflecting power (which is defined as the area under the diffraction pattern) will depend upon which quantity is chosen as independent variable, and we shall therefore indicate the abscissa scale which is used by an appropriate superscript as follows.

$$\begin{aligned}
&y\text{-scale} && R_H^y = \int \frac{P_H}{P_0}\,dy \\
&\text{Glancing angle scale} && R_H^\theta = \int \frac{P_H}{P_0}\,d(\theta - \theta_B) \\
&\text{Rotation angle scale} && R_H^{\varepsilon_1} = \int \frac{P_H}{P_0}\,d\varepsilon_1 \\
&\text{Wavelength scale} && R_H^\lambda = \int \frac{P_H}{P_0}\,d(\lambda - \lambda_B)
\end{aligned} \qquad [3\cdot147]$$

Since the integrand is different from zero only in a narrow range, the limits of integration may conveniently be taken as $\pm\infty$. According to earlier results (see Equations 3·116–3·118 and 3·141), the relationship between y and the other variables is

$$y = \frac{\frac{1-b}{2}\psi_0 + b(\theta_B - \theta)\sin 2\theta_B}{\sqrt{|b|}\,|K\psi_H|} = \frac{\frac{1-b}{2}\psi_0 + b\varepsilon_1 \cos\chi \sin\psi \cos\varphi}{\sqrt{|b|}\,|K\psi_H|}$$

$$y = \frac{\frac{1-b}{2}\psi_0 + 2b\frac{\lambda - \lambda_B}{\lambda_B}\sin^2\theta_B}{\sqrt{|b|}\,|K\psi_H|} \qquad [3\cdot148]$$

Hence we have

$$R_H^\theta = \frac{|K\psi_H|}{\sqrt{|b|}\sin 2\theta_B} R_H^y$$

$$R_H^\lambda = \frac{|K\psi_H|\lambda_B}{\sqrt{|b|}\,2\sin^2\theta_B} R_H^y \qquad [3\cdot149]$$

$$R_H^{\varepsilon_1} = \frac{|K\psi_H|}{\sqrt{|b|}\cos\chi \sin\psi \cos\varphi} R_H^y$$

Equations 3·142–3·144 show that the nature of the diffraction pattern depends upon the value of the quantity A which is proportional to the product of the structure factor and the crystal thickness. It is convenient to say that the crystal is "thick" with respect to the diffracted beam if $A \gg 1$, and that it is "thin" if $A \ll 1$. The terms "thick" and "thin" as used in this sense must be treated with some caution since a crystal plate of given thickness t_0 may be "thick" with respect to a strong diffracted beam and "thin" with respect to a weak diffracted beam. In the following we shall discuss the nature of the diffraction pattern for $A \gg 1$, for $A \ll 1$, and for $A \approx 1$.

A. **Diffraction in Thick Crystals.** *Laue Case.* Because of the presence of the term $\sin^2[A\sqrt{1+y^2}]$ in the numerator on the right side of Equation 3·142, the diffraction pattern will exhibit interference fringes. As the thickness t_0 — and hence also A — increases, these interference fringes come closer together, but the diffraction pattern does not approach any definite limit. At a given value of y the power ratio P_H/P_0 will oscillate between zero and $1/(1+y^2)$ as A is allowed to go to infinity. When A becomes very great one may reasonably suppose that its value is no longer sharply defined, i.e., one may expect the thickness to vary somewhat throughout the crystal plate. If the uncertainty ΔA is greater than $\pi/2$ (for a strong diffracted beam this would correspond to an uncertainty in the thickness t_0 of about 10^{-3} cm.) the term $\sin^2 [A\sqrt{1 + y^2}]$ may be replaced by its average value of ½ and the mean diffraction pattern becomes

$$\frac{\overline{P_H}}{P_0} = \frac{1}{2(1 + y^2)} \qquad [3\cdot150]$$

The mean diffraction pattern is shown in Fig. 3·9. The power ratio P_H/P_0 has a maximum value of ½ at the center of the diffraction

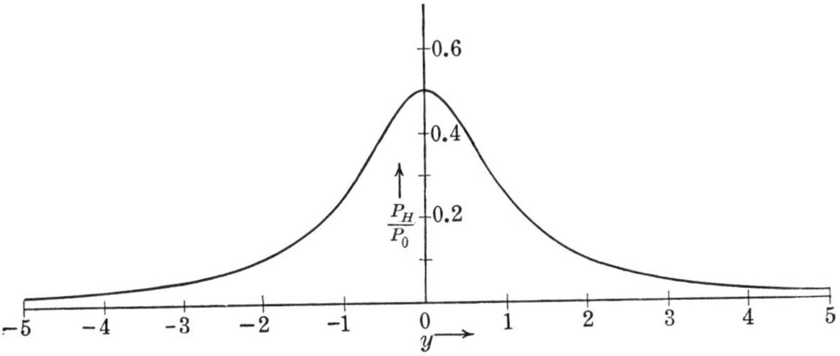

FIG. 3·9. The diffraction pattern in the Laue case for zero absorption and a thick crystal.

pattern. The half width at half maximum is seen to be 1 on the y-scale. Thus the half-width values on glancing angle and wavelength scales, w_θ and w_λ become

$$w_\theta = \frac{|K\psi_H|}{\sqrt{b}\sin 2\theta_B}, \quad w_\lambda = \frac{|K\psi_H|\lambda_B}{2\sqrt{b}\sin^2 \theta_B} \qquad [3\cdot151]$$

It is of interest to note that the parallel component has a smaller half width than the normal component.

Since $\int_{-\infty}^{+\infty} \frac{dy}{1 + y^2} = \pi$, the formulas for the integrated reflecting power are readily obtained. We find

$$R_H^y = \frac{\pi}{2}$$

$$R_H^\theta = \frac{\pi|\psi_H|K}{2\sqrt{b}\sin 2\theta_B}$$

$$R_H^{\varepsilon_1} = \frac{\pi|\psi_H|K}{2\sqrt{b}\cos\chi\sin\psi\cos\varphi} \qquad [3\cdot152]$$

$$R_H^\lambda = \frac{\pi|\psi_H|\lambda_B K}{4\sqrt{b}\sin^2\theta_B}$$

If the incident wave is unpolarized we must form the mean $\bar{R}_H = \frac{1}{2}\{{}^nR_H + {}^pR_H\}$, i.e., K in the above expressions must be replaced by its average value $\bar{K}$ which is

$$\bar{K} = \frac{1 + |\cos 2\theta_B|}{2} = \begin{cases} \cos^2\theta_B \text{ for } \theta_B < \dfrac{\pi}{4} \\ \sin^2\theta_B \text{ for } \theta_B > \dfrac{\pi}{4} \end{cases} \qquad [3\cdot153]$$

Bragg Case. Considering first the range $|y| < 1$ in which Equation 3·144 holds, it is seen that P_H/P_0 approaches the constant value 1 as A increases, i.e.,

$$\frac{P_H}{P_0} = 1 \quad \text{for} \quad \begin{matrix} |y| < 1 \\ A \gg 1 \end{matrix} \qquad [3\cdot154]$$

This equation may be written in the form $\gamma_0 I_0^e + \gamma_H I_H = 0$, showing that the inward energy flux across the boundary $\bar{n} \cdot \bar{r} = 0$ equals the outward flux. There is, in other words, total reflection in the range $|y| < 1$.

In the ranges $|y| > 1$ the power ratio approaches no definite limit as A increases because of the presence of trigonometric functions in Equation 3·143. Following the procedure in the Laue case we shall therefore represent the diffraction pattern by the average function for large values of A. The appropriate smoothing function is readily found by integrating Equation 3·143 with respect to A over a range of uncertainty $\Delta A > \frac{\pi}{2}$. One finds

$$\frac{P_H}{P_0} = \{1 - \sqrt{1 - y^{-2}}\} \quad \text{for} \quad \begin{matrix} |y| > 1 \\ A \gg 1 \end{matrix} \qquad [3\cdot155]$$

The half width at half maximum is $W_y = \frac{2}{3}\sqrt{3} = 1.15$ on the y-scale as compared with the value $W_y = 1$ which we found in the Laue case.

The contribution to the integrated reflecting power coming from the range $|y| < 1$ is obviously 2. Since $\int_1^\infty [1 - \sqrt{1 - y^{-2}}]\,dy = \frac{\pi}{2} - 1$ we have therefore

$$R_H^y = \pi$$

$$\tfrac{1}{2}\{{}^nR_H^\theta + {}^pR_H^\theta\} = \frac{\pi|\psi_H|}{\sqrt{|b|}\sin 2\theta_B}\,\frac{1 + |\cos 2\theta_B|}{2}$$

$$\tfrac{1}{2}\{{}^nR_H^\lambda + {}^pR_H^\lambda\} = \frac{\pi|\psi_H|\lambda_B}{2\sqrt{|b|}\sin^2\theta_B}\,\frac{1 + |\cos 2\theta_B|}{2} \qquad [3\cdot156]$$

The integrated reflecting power of a thick crystal is thus exactly twice as great for the Bragg case as for the Laue case. The diffraction pattern is shown in Fig. 3·10.

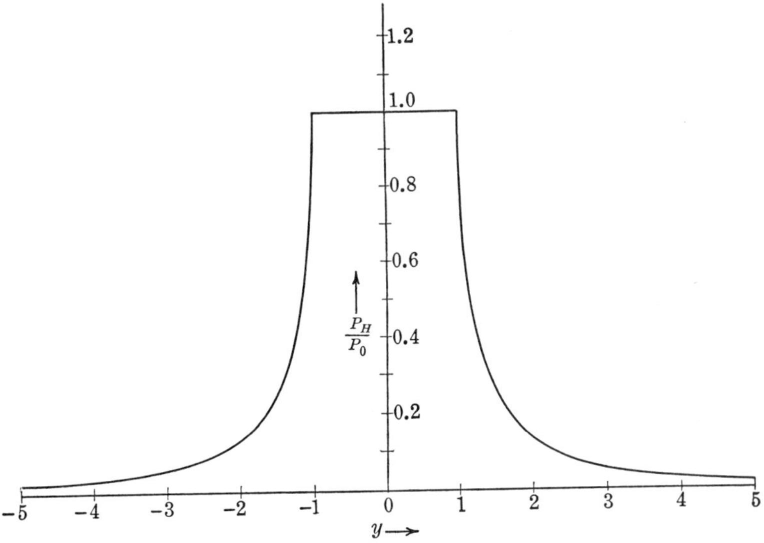

FIG. 3·10. The diffraction pattern in the Bragg case for zero absorption and a thick crystal.

B. Thin Crystals. The Kinematical Theory. According to our definition a crystal is thin with respect to a given reflection $\overline{B}_H$ if $A \ll 1$. It is seen from Equations 3·142–3·144 that the power ratio for $A \ll 1$ in the Laue case as well as in the Bragg case may be represented by the following equation

$$\frac{P_H}{P_0} \approx \frac{\sin^2 Ay}{y^2} \quad \text{for} \quad A \ll 1 \qquad [3\cdot157]$$

In order to assign a half-width value to the diffraction pattern we shall smear out the interference fringes. This may be done by replacing the diffraction pattern by a smoothing function having the same area and the same maximum value. The sought smoothing function is clearly

$$A^2 e^{-A^2 y^2/\pi} \tag{3·158}$$

For the half width at half maximum of the smoothing function we have thus

$$\begin{aligned} w_y &= \frac{\sqrt{\pi \log 2}}{A} = \sqrt{\frac{\log 2}{\pi}} \frac{\lambda\sqrt{|\gamma_0 \gamma_H|}}{|\psi_H| K t_0}, \\ w_\theta &= \sqrt{\frac{\log 2}{\pi}} \frac{\lambda |\gamma_H|}{t_0 \sin 2\theta_B}, \quad w_\lambda = \sqrt{\frac{\log 2}{\pi}} \frac{\lambda^2 |\gamma_H|}{t_0\, 2 \sin^2 \theta_B} \end{aligned} \tag{3·159}$$

In Equation 3·57 we gave an expression for the half-width value deduced from the kinematical theory. The two results agree if the average thickness D of Equation 3·57 is given by $D = t_0 \sin \theta_B / |\gamma_H|$. For the symmetrical Bragg case ($b = -1$) we have $|\gamma_H| = \sin \theta_B$ and hence $D = t_0$. For the symmetrical Laue case, on the other hand, $\gamma_H = \cos \theta_B$ and $D = t_0 \tan \theta_B$.

If we remember that $\int_0^\infty \left(\frac{\sin Ay}{y}\right)^2 dy = \frac{\pi}{2} A$, the expression for the integrated reflecting power is readily obtained

$$\begin{aligned} R_H^y &= \pi A \\ R_H^\theta &= \frac{\pi A |\psi_H| K}{\sqrt{|b|} \sin 2\theta_B} \\ R_H^{\epsilon_1} &= \frac{\pi A |\psi_H| K}{\sqrt{|b|} \cos \varphi \sin \psi \cos \chi} \\ R_H^\lambda &= \frac{\pi A |\psi_H| K \lambda}{\sqrt{|b|}\, 2 \sin^2 \theta_B} \end{aligned} \tag{3·160}$$

Taking the mean integrated reflecting power for normal and parallel polarization and introducing the quantity Q defined by Equations 3·72 and 3·78 results in the following.

$$R_H = Q \frac{t_0}{\gamma_0} = \frac{Q\, \delta V}{S_0} \tag{3·161}$$

where $\delta V = S_0 \dfrac{t_0}{\gamma_0}$ is the irradiated section of the crystal plate. This formula is, however, identical with Equations 3·72 and 3·78 which were deduced using the kinematical theory of x-ray diffraction. The kinematical theory is thus merely the limiting form of the dynamical theory for $A \ll 1$. For such small values of A the power ratio P_H/P_0 is small compared with unity. According to Equation 3·146*a* any decrease in the intensity of the incident beam due to extinction is thus negligibly small in agreement with the basic assumption of the kinematical theory. The results for $A \ll 1$ differ from those obtained in sections 6 and 7 as regards the location of the center of the diffraction pattern. In the kinematical theory the center of the diffraction pattern is given by $\theta = \theta_B$ rather than by Equation 3·145*a*. This difference is due to our treatment of the kinematical theory in which we assumed the refractive index of the crystal medium to be unity.

C. Crystals of Intermediate Thickness. In the two preceding parts of this section we have discussed the diffraction pattern for the limiting cases $A \gg 1$ and $A \ll 1$. The equations for the power ratio are radically different for the two extreme cases. It is therefore of interest to consider the intermediate range of values $A \approx 1$ where neither approximation is valid. In this range Equations 3·142–3·144 must be used. The shape of the diffraction pattern for intermediate values of A is shown in Figs. 3·11 and 3·12.

Laue Case. The change in the diffraction pattern as A increases is readily followed. We have seen that the power ratio P_H/P_0 for very small values of A may be represented by the function $\left(\dfrac{\sin Ay}{y}\right)^2$, which is a sufficiently good approximation to the correct function $\dfrac{\sin^2 [A\sqrt{1+y^2}]}{1+y^2}$. The value of the power ratio at the center of the diffraction pattern is $\sin^2 A$. As A approaches the value $\pi/2$, the power ratio at the center consequently approaches the value 1 corresponding to total reflection. For $A < \dfrac{\pi}{2}$ the center of the diffraction pattern is thus also the maximum. As A increases towards $\pi/2$, there is simultaneously a corresponding decrease in the width of the central interference fringe and in the separation of the secondary fringes. The squeezing together of the interference fringes continues as A increases beyond the value $\pi/2$, while the power ratio at the center of the diffraction pattern begins to oscillate between 1 and zero.

It is particularly important to study the variation of the integrated

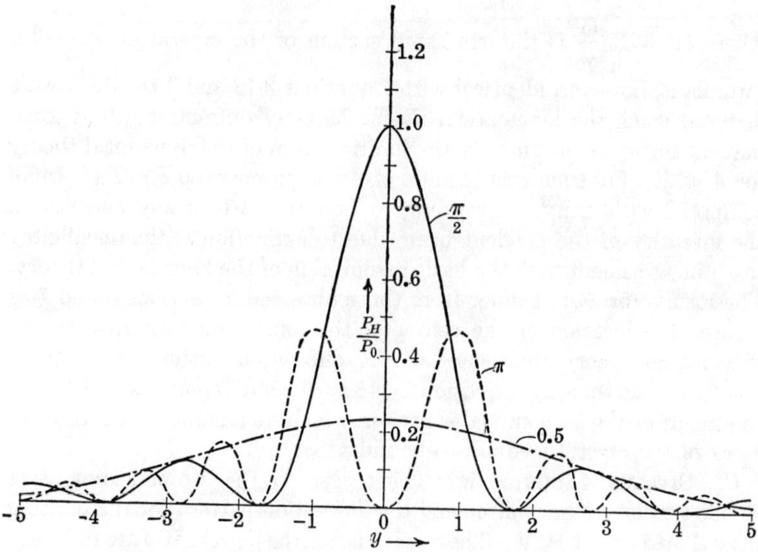

FIG. 3·11. Diffraction patterns in the Laue case for zero absorption and crystals of intermediate thickness. The three diffraction patterns shown in the figure correspond to $A = 0.5, \pi/2$, and π.

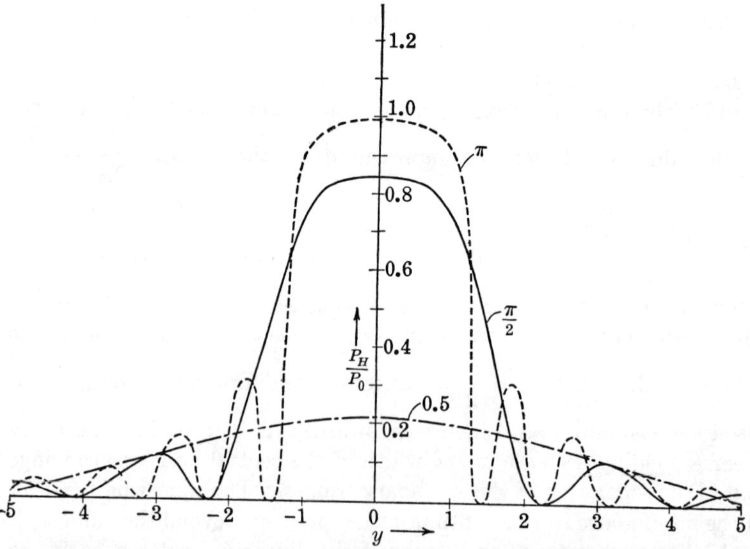

FIG. 3·12. Diffraction patterns in the Bragg case for zero absorption and crystals of intermediate thickness. The three diffraction patterns shown in the figure correspond to $A = 0.5, \pi/2$, and π.

power ratio as function of A since the integrated reflecting power may be found experimentally with less difficulty than the detailed diffraction pattern. The integrated reflecting power is given by the integral

$$R_H^y = \int_{-\infty}^{\infty} \frac{\sin^2 [A\sqrt{1+y^2}]}{1+y^2}\, dy \qquad [3\cdot162]$$

As shown by Waller[6] this integral may be rewritten in the form

$$R_H^y = \int_0^{\pi/2} \frac{\sin [2A \sin \varphi]}{\sin \varphi}\, d\varphi \qquad [3\cdot163]$$

The Bessel function of order zero, J_0, may be defined as

$$J_0(\rho) \equiv \frac{2}{\pi} \int_0^{\pi/2} \cos (\rho \sin \varphi)\, d\varphi \qquad [3\cdot164]$$

Setting $2A = \rho$ in Equation 3·163 and differentiating we find

$$\frac{dR_H^y}{d\rho} = \frac{\pi}{2} J_0(\rho)$$

and hence

$$R_H^y = \frac{\pi}{2} \int_0^{2A} J_0(\rho)\, d\rho = \pi \sum_{n=0}^{n=\infty} J_{2n+1}(2A) \qquad [3\cdot165]$$

In agreement with earlier results we have

$$\sum_{n=0}^{n=\infty} J_{2n+1}(2A) = \begin{cases} A \text{ for } A \ll 1 \\ \frac{1}{2} \text{ for } A \gg 1 \end{cases} \qquad [3\cdot166]$$

The integrated reflecting power as function of A is shown in Fig. 3·13. At first R_H^y increases linearly with A, i.e., with the thickness of the crystal plate or with the volume of the irradiated part of the crystal plate. This first portion of the curve consequently represents the range in which extinction is negligible and the assumptions of the kinematical theory are valid. R_H^y reaches its maximum value of 2.38 for $A = 1.202$, and as A increases towards infinity R_H^y oscillates with steadily diminishing amplitude about a mean value of $\pi/2$.

Bragg Case. Diffraction patterns calculated for some intermediate values of A are shown in Fig. 3·12 from which we see that the limiting value $P_H/P_0 \approx 1$ in the range $|y| < 1$ is rather rapidly approached as A increases.

[6] I. Waller, *Ann. der Phys.*, **79**, 261 (1926).

The integrated reflecting power is given by the integral[7]

$$R_H^y = \int_{-\infty}^{\infty} \frac{dy}{y^2 + (1 - y^2)\coth^2 [A\sqrt{1 - y^2}]} = \pi \tanh A \qquad [3\cdot167]$$

In accordance with previous results (Equations 3·156 and 3·160) we have $\tanh A \approx A$ for $A \ll 1$ and $\tanh A \approx 1$ for $A \gg 1$. With an accuracy of 5 per cent one may set

$$R_H^y = \begin{cases} \pi A & \text{for } A < 0.4 \\ \pi & \text{for } A > 1.8 \end{cases} \qquad [3\cdot168]$$

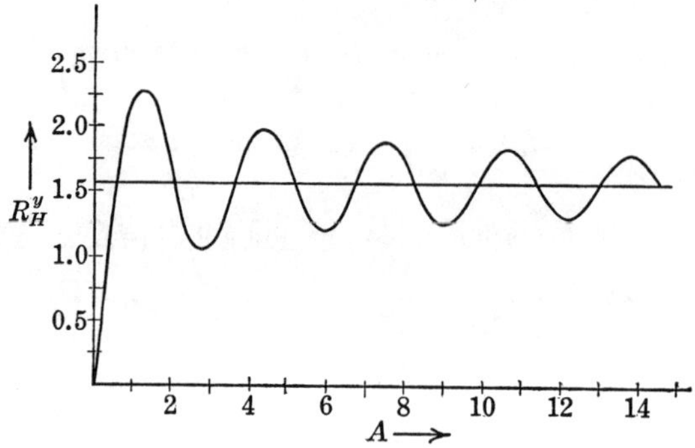

FIG. 3·13. The integrated reflecting power in the Laue case as function of A.

Thus in contrast with the Laue case there is in the Bragg case only a very narrow range of values $0.4 < A < 1.8$ where neither the thick crystal solution (Equation 3·156) nor the thin crystal solution (Equation 3·160) may be applied. Figure 3·14 shows the integrated reflecting power plotted as function of A.

According to our definition a crystal is thin if $A \ll 1$ and thick if $A \gg 1$. The quantity A is directly proportional to the thickness of the crystal plate and to the structure factor of the reflection. The detailed expression for A is

$$A = \frac{e^2\lambda|F_H|Kt_0}{mc^2V\sqrt{|\gamma_0\gamma_H|}} \qquad [3\cdot169]$$

For a strong reflection like the first-order reflection from the cleavage plane of calcite using $\lambda = 1.54$ A the numerical value becomes

$$A = 1.7 \times 10^3 \frac{Kt_0}{\sqrt{|\gamma_0\gamma_H|}}$$

[7] C. G. Darwin, *Phil. Mag.*, **43**, 800 (1922).

In order to be able to use the "thin" crystal approximation (requiring an accuracy of 5 per cent) we must thus have $Kt_0/\sqrt{|\gamma_0\gamma_H|} < 2 \times 10^{-4}$ cm. For a weak reflection this critical thickness is correspondingly greater. The quantity $t_0/\sqrt{|\gamma_0\gamma_H|}$ may conveniently be interpreted as the effective linear dimension of a crystal block. Our results show that intensity measurements made with the powder method

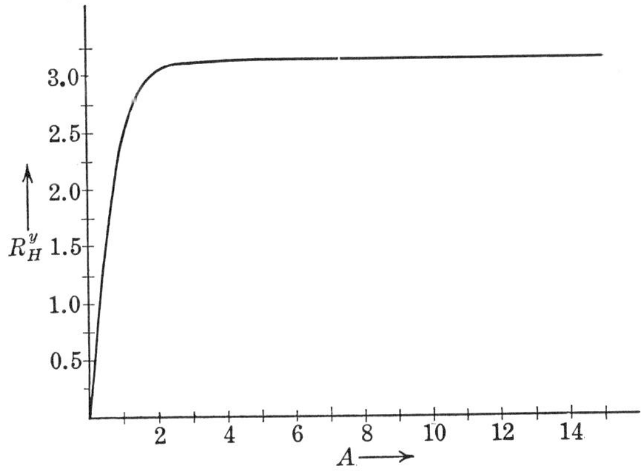

FIG. 3·14. The integrated reflecting power in the Bragg case as function of A.

may safely be interpreted by means of the kinematical approximation provided the average linear particle size is of the order 10^{-4} cm. or smaller. If the particle size is greater than this value, say of the order of 10^{-2} cm., the thin crystal formula may still hold for the weakest reflections, but cannot be used for the strong reflections.

The considerations of this section are based on the assumption that normal absorption is zero. The intensity formulas which have been obtained may therefore be used only for crystal plates for which $\mu_0 t_0 \ll 1$.

12. ABSORBING CRYSTALS

In this section true absorption phenomena will be taken into account, and our considerations must accordingly be based upon the most general solutions for a plane parallel crystal plate, namely, Equation 3·133 for the Laue case and Equation 3·139 for the Bragg case.

When true absorption is different from zero the polarizability per unit volume is complex as shown by Equation 3·97, i.e., $\psi = \psi' + i\psi''$. Each of the two functions ψ' and ψ'' is real and periodic and may hence be represented as a Fourier series

$$\psi' = \sum \psi'_H \, e^{-i2\pi \bar{B}_H \cdot \bar{r}}$$
$$\psi'' = \sum \psi''_H \, e^{-i2\pi \bar{B}_H \cdot \bar{r}} \qquad [3\cdot170]$$

where $\psi'_{\bar{H}} = (\psi'_H)^*$ and $\psi''_{\bar{H}} = (\psi''_H)^*$. The average refractive index is

$$n = 1 + \tfrac{1}{2}\psi'_0 + i\tfrac{1}{2}\psi''_0 \qquad [3\cdot171]$$

and is thus complex. The imaginary part, $\frac{1}{2}\psi''_0$ (the absorption index), is related to the true linear absorption coefficient μ_0 by the equation

$$\mu_0 = -\frac{2\pi}{\lambda}\psi''_0 \qquad [3\cdot172]$$

which we shall now deduce. Experimentally the linear absorption coefficient is determined in the following manner. A homogeneous x-ray beam is passed through a crystal plate of thickness t_0 and the ratio of transmitted to incident intensity is measured. It is to be assumed that the direction of incidence is such that no diffracted wave is produced. The linear absorption coefficient is defined as the fractional decrease in intensity per unit length of path, i.e., $dI/I = -\mu_0 \, dx$. The ratio of transmitted to incident intensity for a crystal plate of thickness t_0 is thus

$$\frac{I_e^0}{I_0^e} = e^{-\mu_0 \frac{t_0}{\gamma_0}} \qquad [3\cdot173]$$

where t_0/γ_0 is the length of path through the crystal. Since there is only one wave in the interior its refractive index is $1 + \frac{1}{2}\psi'_0 + i\frac{1}{2}\psi''_0$ as shown by Equation 3·106. Using the boundary condition of Equation 3·90 this internal wave becomes

$$\bar{D}_0 \, e^{i\omega_0 t - i2\pi[\bar{k}_0 + k_0 \frac{\psi_0}{2\gamma_0}\bar{n}]\cdot} \qquad [3\cdot174]$$

The ratio of the intensities at $\bar{n}\cdot\bar{r} = t_0$ and $\bar{n}\cdot\bar{r} = 0$ is thus

$$\frac{I_e^0}{I_0^e} = e^{2\pi k_0 \psi''_0 \frac{t_0}{\gamma_0}} \qquad [3\cdot175]$$

By comparing Equations 3·173 and 3·175, the sought relationship of Equation 3·172 follows directly. Let

$$\psi'_H \equiv (\psi'_H)_r + i(\psi'_H)_i, \quad \psi''_H \equiv (\psi''_H)_r + i(\psi''_H)_i \qquad [3\cdot176]$$

where subscripts r and i are used to indicate real and imaginary parts respectively. In contrast with the case of zero absorption the three quantities $\psi_H\psi_{\bar{H}}$, $|\psi_H|^2$ and $|\psi_{\bar{H}}|^2$ in general are different from one another as shown by the following expressions.

$$|\psi_H|^2 = |\psi'_H|^2 + |\psi''_H|^2 + 2[(\psi'_H)_i(\psi''_H)_r - (\psi'_H)_r(\psi''_H)_i]$$
$$|\psi_{\bar{H}}|^2 = |\psi'_H|^2 + |\psi''_H|^2 - 2[(\psi'_H)_i(\psi''_H)_r - (\psi'_H)_r(\psi''_H)_i] \quad [3\cdot177]$$
$$\psi_H\psi_{\bar{H}} = |\psi'_H|^2 - |\psi''_H|^2 + i2[(\psi'_H)_r(\psi''_H)_r + (\psi'_H)_i(\psi''_H)_i]$$

If the inversion operation is an element of the space group (and if the origin is chosen in an inversion center) the function ψ must satisfy the condition $\psi(\bar{r}) = \psi(-\bar{r})$ for any $\bar{r}$. For crystals with inversion center we have thus $\psi_H = \psi_{\bar{H}}$.

Unless we are dealing with a very weak reflection and unless the incident wavelength is very close to a critical absorption edge $|\psi''_H|$ is very small compared with $|\psi'_H|$ and the three quantities of Equations 3·177 are then very nearly equal. This is the theoretical explanation of the empirical rule due to G. Friedel.[8] Friedel's rule states that the x-ray diffraction phenomena are invariant under an inversion of the crystal with respect to the incident beam. The rule will obviously hold for crystals with an inversion center, but according to Friedel the rule has general validity. The inversion of the crystal corresponds analytically to a change of sign for the Miller indices. Thus a reflection which before the inversion was associated with a reciprocal lattice vector $\bar{B}_H$ will after the inversion be associated with the vector $\bar{B}_{\bar{H}} \equiv -\bar{B}_H$. From Equations 3·133 and 3·139 we find

$$\frac{I_H}{I_{\bar{H}}} = \frac{R_H}{R_{\bar{H}}} = \left|\frac{\psi_H}{\psi_{\bar{H}}}\right|^2 \quad [3\cdot178]$$

Friedel's rule will accordingly break down when ψ''_H is no longer negligibly small compared with ψ'_H. Deviations from Friedel's rule have indeed been demonstrated experimentally for the (111) reflection of sphalerite as shown by the table on p. 138.[9]

In the following discussions we shall for the sake of simplicity assume that the crystal lattice has an inversion center. ψ'_H as well as ψ''_H are then real quantities, i.e., $(\psi'_H)_i = (\psi''_H)_i = 0$. Let us furthermore set

$$\kappa \equiv \frac{\psi''_H}{\psi'_H} \quad [3\cdot179]$$

[8] G. Friedel, *Compt. rend.*, **157**, 1533 (1913).

[9] Observations are due in Column I to I. M. Geib and K. Lark-Horovitz, *Phys. Rev.*, **42**, 908 (1932), and in Column II to D. Coster, K. S. Knol, and J. A. Prins, *Z. f. Phys.*, **63**, 345 (1930).

TABLE 3·1

INTENSITY RATIOS $\frac{R_H}{R_{\bar{H}}}$ FOR SPHALERITE, ZnS

λ in A	$\frac{R_{111}}{R_{\bar{1}\bar{1}\bar{1}}}$ Observed I	$\frac{R_{111}}{R_{\bar{1}\bar{1}\bar{1}}}$ Observed II	$\frac{R_{111}}{R_{\bar{1}\bar{1}\bar{1}}}$ Calculated	$\frac{R_{333}}{R_{\bar{3}\bar{3}\bar{3}}}$ Observed I	$\frac{R_{333}}{R_{\bar{3}\bar{3}\bar{3}}}$ Observed II	$\frac{R_{333}}{R_{\bar{3}\bar{3}\bar{3}}}$ Calculated
1.2420	1.12		1.31	1.36	1.40	1.70
1.2599	1.22		1.35		1.58	1.87
1.2738	1.38		1.39	1.68		2.07
1.2792	1.42		1.46	2.13	2.0	2.56

and assume $|\kappa| \ll 1$ so that κ^2 is negligibly small compared with unity. Under these conditions we have

$$\begin{aligned} |\psi_H|^2 &\approx |\psi'_H|^2 \\ \psi_H\psi_{\bar{H}} &\approx |\psi'_H|^2[1 + i2\kappa] \end{aligned} \qquad [3\cdot180]$$

It is convenient to introduce symbols y, g, and A defined as follows

$$\begin{aligned} y &\equiv \frac{z_r}{K|\psi'_H|\sqrt{|b|}} = \frac{\frac{1-b}{2}\psi'_0 + \frac{b}{2}\alpha}{K|\psi'_H|\sqrt{|b|}} \\ g &\equiv \frac{z_i}{K|\psi'_H|\sqrt{|b|}} = \frac{\frac{1-b}{2}\psi''_0}{K|\psi'_H|\sqrt{|b|}} \\ A &\equiv aK|\psi'_H|\sqrt{|b|} = \pi k_0 K|\psi'_H|\frac{t_0}{\sqrt{|\gamma_0\gamma_H|}} \end{aligned} \qquad [3\cdot181]$$

In the limiting case of zero absorption $g = 0$ while A and y become identical with the same symbols as used in the preceding section. In terms of y, g, and A the quantity $\sqrt{q + z^2} \equiv v + iw$ becomes

$$\sqrt{q + z^2} = v + iw = K|\psi'_H|\sqrt{|b|}\sqrt{\pm(1 + i2\kappa) + (y + ig)^2} \qquad [3\cdot182]$$

where the positive sign is to be used in the Laue case, the negative sign in the Bragg case.

***A.* Symmetrical Laue Case.** In the symmetrical Laue case $b = +1$ so that $g = 0$. Remembering that $|\kappa|$ is supposed to be small compared with unity, Equation 3·182 gives

$$
\begin{aligned}
av &\approx A\sqrt{1+y^2} \\
aw &\approx \frac{\kappa A}{\sqrt{1+y^2}} \qquad [3\cdot183] \\
|q+z^2| &\approx K^2|\psi_H'|^2(1+y^2)
\end{aligned}
$$

With these approximations Equation 3·133 takes the following form

$$\frac{I_H}{I_0^e} \approx e^{-\mu_0\frac{t_0}{\gamma_0}}\left[\frac{\sin^2[A\sqrt{1+y^2}]}{1+y^2} + \frac{\sinh^2\left[\frac{\kappa A}{\sqrt{1+y^2}}\right]}{1+y^2}\right] \qquad [3\cdot184]$$

According to the assumptions we have made, ψ_H'' and ψ_0'' are small quantities compared with ψ_H'. (It follows from Equation 3·99 that $|\psi_H''| < |\psi_0''|$). Hence (unless $K \equiv |\cos 2\theta_B|$ is very small) we may set $\mu_0 \frac{t_0}{\gamma_0} \ll A$. A must therefore become large compared with unity in order to make true absorption effects noticeable. When A becomes very large it is reasonable to suppose that the thickness of the crystal plate is no longer sharply defined. Under this assumption the sine square term of Equation 3·184 may be replaced by the mean value of ½ and we have thus

$$\frac{I_H}{I_0^e} \approx \frac{e^{-\mu_0\frac{t_0}{\gamma_0}}}{2(1+y^2)}\left[1 + 2\sinh^2\frac{\kappa A}{\sqrt{1+y^2}}\right] \qquad [3\cdot185]$$

For $|\kappa|A < 0.4$ we may use the approximation

$$\frac{I_H}{I_0^e} \approx \frac{e^{-\mu_0\frac{t_0}{\gamma_0}}}{2(1+y^2)}\left[1 + 2\frac{(\kappa A)^2}{1+y^2}\right] \qquad [3\cdot186]$$

which leads to the following result for the integrated reflecting power

$$R_H^y \approx e^{-\mu_0\frac{t_0}{\gamma_0}} \frac{\pi}{2}[1 + (\kappa A)^2] \qquad [3\cdot187]$$

On the other hand for $|\kappa|A > 3$ one may set

$$\frac{I_H}{I_0^e} \approx \frac{e^{-\mu_0\frac{t_0}{\gamma_0}\left(1-\frac{\varepsilon}{\sqrt{1+y^2}}\right)}}{4(1+y^2)} \qquad [3\cdot188]$$

where

$$\varepsilon \equiv K\left|\frac{\psi_H''}{\psi_0''}\right| = \left|\frac{\psi_H''\cos 2\theta_B}{\psi_0''}\right| < 1$$

For very large values of $|\kappa|A$, the half width on the y-scale, w_y, is $\sqrt{\dfrac{\log 2}{|\kappa|A + 1}}$, and as $|\kappa|A$ decreases to zero w_y increases to 1.

It is seen from the equations given above that the integrated reflecting power increases monotonically with decreasing thickness of the crystal plate in the range $A \gg 1$. As t_0 (and hence also A) decreases still farther $|\kappa|A$ goes to zero and $e^{-\mu_0 \frac{t_0}{\gamma_0}}$ goes to 1 so that R_H^y assumes the expression given by Equation 3·165.

The diffraction pattern for a few intermediate values of $|\kappa|A$ is shown in Fig. 3·15.

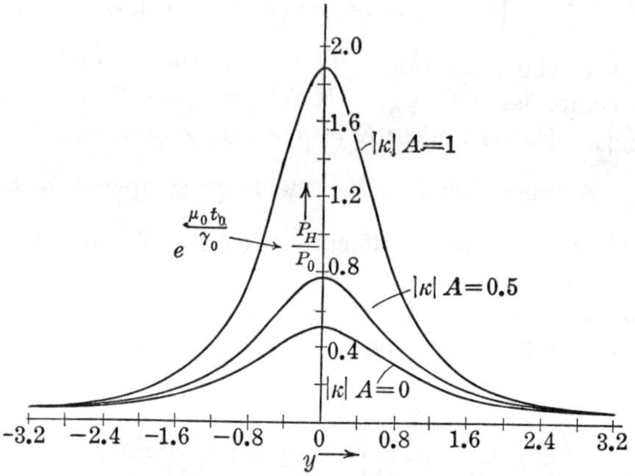

FIG. 3·15. Diffraction patterns in the Laue case for absorbing crystals. Note that the ordinate represents P_H/P_0 multiplied with the factor $e^{\frac{\mu_0 t_0}{\gamma_0}}$.

***B.* Bragg Case. Thick Crystal.** The general expression for the intensity ratio I_H/I_0^e is considerably more complicated in the Bragg case than it is in the Laue case. In order to attain some simplification of Equation 3·139, we shall therefore assume the crystal plate to be so thick that $\sinh^2 aw$ and $\sinh |2aw|$ become very large. The limiting form for Equation 3·139 as t_0 increases to large values (so that $aw \gg 1$) is seen to be

$$\frac{I_H}{I_0^e} = \frac{b^2K^2|\psi_H|^2}{|q + z^2| + |z|^2 + \sqrt{(|q + z^2| + |z|^2)^2 - |q|^2}} \qquad [3·189]$$

Using Equations 3·179–3·182 this expression can be written in a more convenient form as follows.

$$\frac{P_H}{P_0} = L - \sqrt{L^2 - (1 + 4\kappa^2)} \qquad [3·190]$$

where

$$L \equiv \left|\sqrt{(-1+y^2-g^2)^2+4(gy-\kappa)^2}\right| + y^2 + g^2 \qquad [3\cdot190a]$$

The Darwin Solution. We shall first consider the case of a negligibly small true absorption coefficient. We assume in other words that $|g|$ and $|\kappa|$ become negligibly small. However, we shall imagine that t_0 is correspondingly increased such that the terms $\sinh^2 aw$ and $\sinh |2aw|$ remain very large. The formula for the power ratio P_H/P_0 is consequently obtained from Equation 3·190 by setting $\kappa = g = 0$, i.e.,

$$\begin{aligned} \frac{P_H}{P_0} &= M - \sqrt{M^2 - 1} \\ M &\equiv |y^2 - 1| + y^2 \end{aligned} \qquad [3\cdot191]$$

In the range $|y| \leq 1$ we have thus

$$\frac{P_H}{P_0} = 1 \qquad [3\cdot192a]$$

and in the range $|y| \geq 1$

$$\frac{P_H}{P_0} = [|y| - \sqrt{y^2 - 1}\,]^2 \qquad [3\cdot192b]$$

The integrated reflecting power becomes

$$R_H^y = \int_{-\infty}^{\infty} [M - \sqrt{M^2 - 1}]\, dy = \frac{8}{3} \qquad [3\cdot193]$$

We shall refer to the expression of Equation 3·191 as the Darwin solution since it was first deduced by C. G. Darwin. It is of interest to compare the Darwin solution with the Ewald solution given in Equations 3·154 and 3·155 which holds for a thick crystal and zero absorption. Both solutions give total reflection in the range $|y| \leq 1$, but the Darwin solution shows the more rapid intensity decrease for $|y| > 1$. The diffraction patterns corresponding to the Darwin and the Ewald solutions are shown in Fig. 3·16, whereas the expressions for the diffracted power, the integrated reflecting power, and for the half widths are compiled in Table 3·2.

If we return now to a discussion of Equation 3·190 we see that the diffraction pattern is unsymmetrical with respect to its center ($y = 0$) unless $\kappa = 0$. The intensity attains its maximum value at $y = \kappa/g$, i.e., the intensity maximum on the glancing angle scale occurs at

$$\theta_B + \frac{\dfrac{1+|b|}{2}|\psi_0'| - \dfrac{\kappa}{|g|}K|\psi_H'|\sqrt{|b|}}{|b| \sin 2\theta_B} \qquad [3\cdot194]$$

TABLE 3·2

COMPARISON OF DARWIN AND EWALD SOLUTIONS

		Ewald	Darwin
		$\mu_0 = 0,\ \mu_0 t_0 = 0$	$\mu_0 \approx 0,\ \mu_0 t_0 \gg 0$
$\frac{P_H}{P_0}$	$\lvert y\rvert \leq 1$	1	1
	$\lvert y\rvert \geq 1$	$1 - \frac{\sqrt{y^2 - 1}}{\lvert y\rvert}$	$(\lvert y\rvert - \sqrt{y^2 - 1})^2$
R_H^y		π	$\frac{8}{3}$
w_y		$\frac{2}{3}\sqrt{3} = 1.155$	$\frac{3}{4}\sqrt{2} = 1.061$

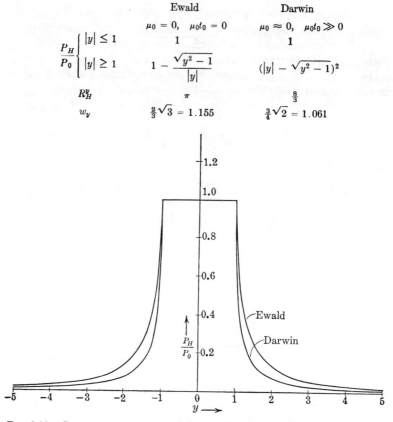

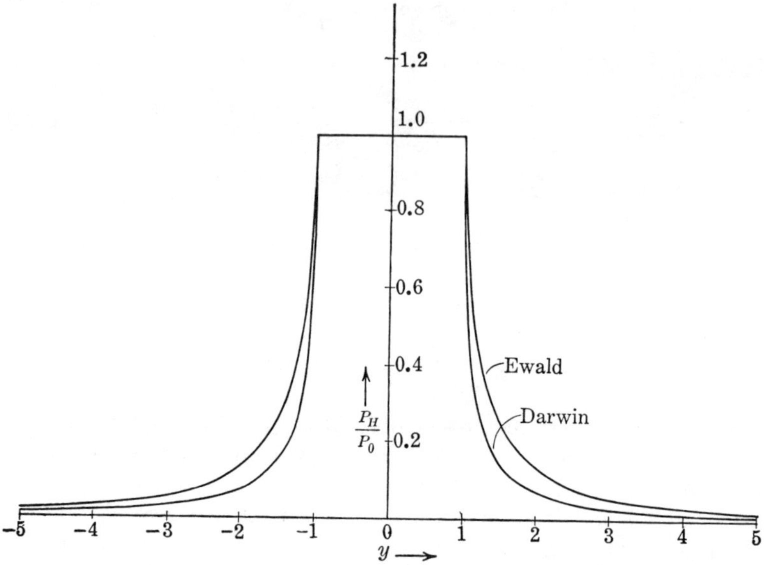

FIG. 3·16. Comparison of the diffraction patterns corresponding to the Ewald solution (zero absorption) and the Darwin solution (negligible absorption).

The intensity maximum is accordingly shifted from the center of the diffraction pattern towards or away from the ideal Bragg angle θ_B, depending upon whether κ is positive or negative. For strong reflections one would normally expect κ to be positive (meaning that ψ_H'' and ψ_H' have the same sign), but negative values of κ are theoretically possible. In Fig. 3·17 the diffraction pattern is plotted for different values of g and κ. Unless $\kappa = 0$ it is clearly necessary to distinguish between the center of the diffraction pattern ($y = 0$), the intensity maximum ($y = \kappa/g$), and the center of gravity of the diffraction peak. The maximum value of P_H/P_0 is $1 + 2g^2 - 2\sqrt{g^2(1 + g^2) - \kappa^2}$. For $|\kappa| = |g|$ this value is 1, i.e., we have then total reflection at $y = +1$ or at $y = -1$. Actually the value $\left|\frac{\kappa}{g}\right| = 1$ is unattainable since $|\kappa| < |g|$. The drawings of Fig. 3·17 show several interesting features. The area under the diffraction pattern, i.e., the integrated reflecting power R_H^y, depends primarily upon the value of $|g|$ which is directly proportional to the linear absorption coefficient μ_0. As a crude approximation for $|g| \ll 1$ one may set $R_H^y \approx \frac{8}{3}(1 - 2|g|)$. For a given value of g the integrated

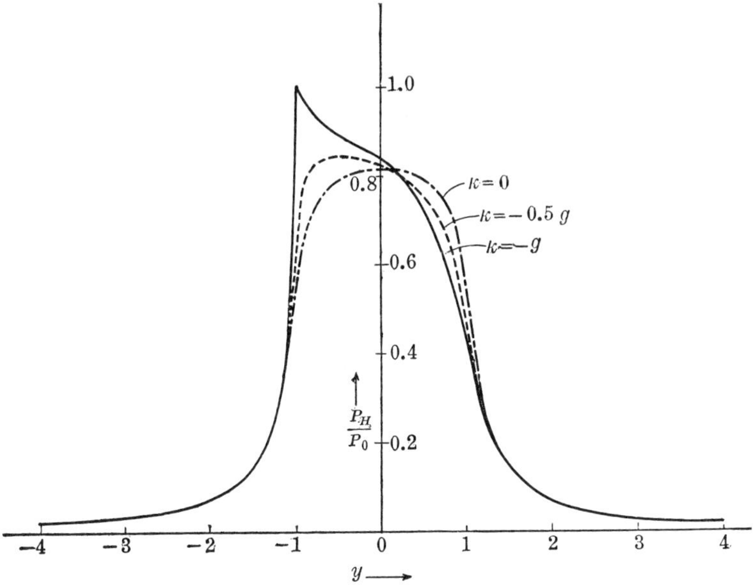

FIG. 3·17. Diffraction patterns of a thick, absorbing crystal in the Bragg case. The curves are calculated for $g = 0.10$ and for $\kappa = 0$, 0.05, and 0.10.

reflecting power increases with increasing $|\kappa|$, but this variation is quite small. As long as $|g|$ remains small compared with unity, the half-width value w_y is very nearly the same as for the Darwin solution, i.e., $w_y \approx \frac{3}{4}\sqrt{2}$.

It follows from the definition of g (see Equation 3·181) that the absorption is relatively greater for parallel polarization ($K = |\cos 2\theta_B|$) than for normal polarization ($K = 1$). It is similarly seen that a weaker reflection will be absorbed more heavily than a strong reflection. This relative enhancement of strong reflections is readily explained. Since extinction is smaller for a weak reflection, the mean depth of penetration will be considerably greater than for strong reflections. The mean length of path through the crystal medium is thus longest for the weakest reflections and hence the relative intensity decrease due to true absorption will be greatest. For a given reflection the absorption is minimized when $b = -1$, i.e., when the reflecting lattice plane is parallel to the boundary of the crystal plate, while the absorption is greatest for grazing incidence or exit.

Calculation of Diffraction Pattern for Calcite. As an example we shall calculate the diffraction pattern for the first-order reflection from the cleavage plane of calcite. We shall assume the crystal plate to be a cleavage slab, i.e., $b = -1$, and so thick that Equation 3·190 is valid. For the wavelength we shall assume $\lambda = 1.537$ A (Cu $K\alpha_1$). The x-ray wavelength is thus shorter than all critical absorption wavelengths, but is closest to the K-absorption wavelength of calcium which is $\lambda_K^{\text{Ca}} = 3.064$ A. The next closest critical absorption wavelength is $\lambda_K^{\text{O}} = 23.5$ A. With good approximation it may be assumed that true absorption is due to the anomalous dispersion of the K-electrons of calcium and oxygen atoms. According to Equation 3·31 we have thus

$$\begin{aligned} f_{\text{Ca}} &= f_{\text{Ca}}^0 + 2\xi_K^{\text{Ca}} + i2\eta_K^{\text{Ca}} \\ f_{\text{C}} &\approx f_{\text{C}}^0 \\ f_{\text{O}} &= f_{\text{O}}^0 + 2\xi_K^{\text{O}} + i2\eta_K^{\text{O}} \end{aligned} \qquad [3\cdot195]$$

The functions φ_j of Equation 3·31 have been set equal to unity since the volume containing the K-electrons has linear dimensions small compared to the x-ray wavelength. The anomalous contribution to the scattering power due to K-electrons can be calculated from the formulas developed by Hönl.[10] The contributions $2\xi_K^{\text{Ca}}$ and $2\xi_K^{\text{O}}$ are very small (for $\lambda =$ 1.537 A) compared with f_{Ca}^0 and f_{O}^0 and may be neglected. The formula for $2\eta_K$ is

$$2\eta_K = \pi \frac{2^7 e^{-4}}{9} \left\{ \frac{4x^2}{(1-\Delta)^2} - \frac{x^3}{(1-\Delta)^3} \right\} \qquad [3\cdot196]$$

where $x = \dfrac{\lambda}{\lambda_K} < 1$ and where $\Delta = 0.240$ for calcium and 0.30 for oxygen. Evaluation of Equation 3·196 gives $2\eta_K^{\text{Ca}} = 1.209$ and $2\eta_K^{\text{O}} = 0.028$.

The unit cell of calcite is a rhombohedron with the following dimensions: $a_1 = a_2 = a_3 = 6.361$ A and $\alpha_1 = \alpha_2 = \alpha_3 = 46°\ 7'$. There are two molecules of $CaCO_3$ in this unit cell. Choosing the origin in an

[10] H. Hönl, *Zeitschr. f. Phys.*, **84**, 1 (1933); *Ann. der Phys.*, **18**, 625 (1933).

inversion center the atomic positions become

$$2\text{Ca in } (000)(\tfrac{1}{2}\tfrac{1}{2}\tfrac{1}{2}),\ 2\text{C in } (\tfrac{1}{4}\tfrac{1}{4}\tfrac{1}{4})(\tfrac{3}{4}\tfrac{3}{4}\tfrac{3}{4}),\ 6\text{O in } \pm(u, \tfrac{1}{2} - u, \tfrac{3}{4})\curvearrowleft \quad [3\cdot197]$$

The parameter value u is found by experiment to be $u \approx 0$.

Inserting the appropriate numerical values in Equations 3·97–3·101 we find

$$\psi_0' = -17.44 \times 10^{-6}$$
$$\psi_0'' = -0.448 \times 10^{-6}, \quad \mu_0 = 183 \quad [3\cdot198]$$

The experimental value for ψ_0' is according to Larsson[11] 17.6×10^{-6} and the linear absorption coefficient obtained from the empirical mass absorption coefficients is 193.

The cleavage plane of calcite has Miller indices (211). The scattering powers of calcium, carbon, and oxygen for the 211-reflection ($\sin\theta/\lambda = 0.165$) are respectively

$$f_{\text{Ca}} = 15.3 + i1.209$$
$$f_{\text{C}} = 3.4 \quad [3\cdot199]$$
$$f_{\text{O}} = 6.0 + i0.028$$

Hence $F_{211} = 49.4 + i2.47$ which is obtained from Equation 3·44 setting $\bar{s} = 2\pi(2\bar{b}_1 + \bar{b}_2 + \bar{b}_3)$ and using the values for $\bar{r}_k$ given in Equation 3·197. By means of Equation 3·95 we find

$$\psi_{211}' = -8.57 \times 10^{-6}$$
$$\psi_{211}'' = -0.429 \times 10^{-6} \quad [3\cdot200]$$

The quantities κ and g may now be evaluated according to Equations 3·179 and 3·181 and become

$$\kappa = 0.050$$
$$g = \begin{cases} -0.052 & \text{for normal polarization,} \quad K = 1 \\ -0.060 & \text{for parallel polarization,} \quad K = 0.871 \end{cases} \quad [3\cdot201]$$

In order to find the conversion formula which must be used in passing from the y-scale to the glancing angle scale we solve Equation 3·148 for the glancing angle θ and obtain

$$\theta = \theta_B + 7.33'' + \begin{cases} 3.60''y & \text{for} \quad K = 1 \\ 3.14''y & \text{for} \quad K = 0.871 \end{cases} \quad [3\cdot202]$$

Since $|b| = 1$ we have $P_H/P_0 = I_H/I_0^e$ and Equation 3·190 gives

[11] A. Larsson, *Dissertation*, Upsala, 1929.

directly the diffraction pattern. The results obtained from Equation 3·190, using the numerical values of Equation 3·201 and the conversion formulas of Equations 3·202, are shown in Fig. 3·18.

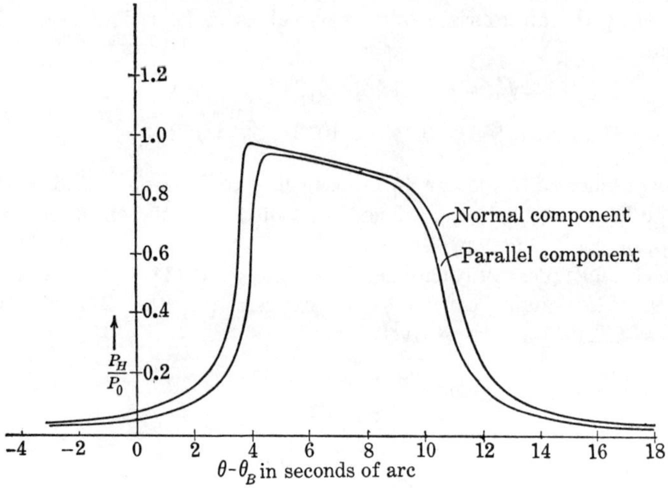

Fig. 3·18. Diffraction pattern for the (211)-reflection of a thick calcite crystal in the Bragg case. The wavelength is assumed to be $\lambda = 1.537$ A.

For comparison we shall also calculate the diffraction pattern for the (211) reflection in the Laue case. We shall assume $b = +1$, meaning that the crystal plate is cut normal to the cleavage plane. Let the mean

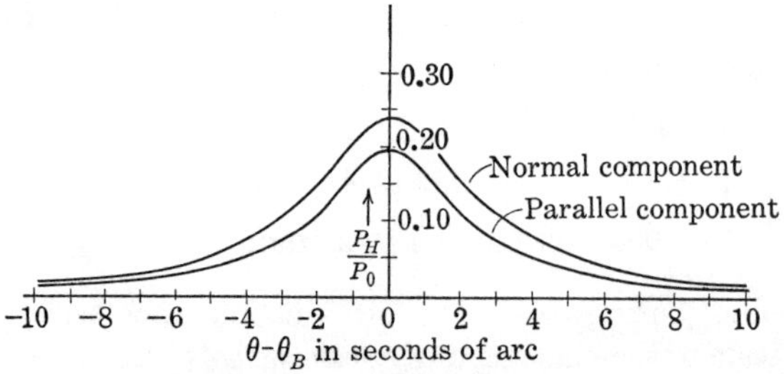

Fig. 3·19. Diffraction pattern for the (211)-reflection of calcite in the symmetrical Laue case. The wavelength is assumed to be $\lambda = 1.537$ A and the thickness $0.01 \times \gamma_0$ cm.

thickness of the crystal plate be $t_0 = 0.01\gamma_0$ cm. The variation in the thickness will be assumed to be sufficiently great, i.e., of the order of 0.001 cm., so that Equation 3·185 rather than Equation 3·184 may be used. Using the numerical values obtained above we find

$$e^{-\mu_0\frac{t_0}{\gamma_0}} = 0.160$$

$$\kappa A = \begin{cases} 0.876 & \text{for} \quad K = 1 \\ 0.763 & \text{for} \quad K = 0.871 \end{cases} \qquad [3\cdot203]$$

The relationship between the variable y and the glancing angle becomes

$$\theta_B - \theta = \begin{cases} 3.60''y & \text{for} \quad K = 1 \\ 3.14''y & \text{for} \quad K = 0.871 \end{cases} \qquad [3\cdot204]$$

The diffraction patterns for normal and parallel polarization obtained from Equation 3·185 are shown in Fig. 3·19.

13. DOUBLE CRYSTAL DIFFRACTION PATTERNS

The theoretical diffraction patterns discussed in the preceding sections were obtained on the assumption that the incident beam is monochromatic and parallel. The incident beam which is obtained when the radiation from an x-ray tube is passed through a set of slits contains wavelengths covering a very large range. This x-ray beam is furthermore divergent. The width of the slits cannot be decreased and the separation of the slits cannot be increased without a corresponding loss of power of the beam. The smallest angular divergence with which it is practical to work is therefore large compared with the half width of the diffraction pattern. Clearly, using an incident beam of this type we cannot obtain experimental data which may be directly compared with the theoretical diffraction patterns of the preceding sections.

By reflecting this beam from a crystal it is, however, possible to obtain a reasonably good approximation to a monochromatic beam. Let the angular divergence of the incident beam be Δ and let the crystal be so oriented that the central ray of the beam satisfies the Bragg equation for a lattice plane $\bar{B}_H$ and for a wavelength λ_0 which corresponds to the center of an intense x-ray spectrum line. The glancing angle for the central ray of wavelength λ_0 will be denoted by θ_B. The glancing angle for other rays will thus lie in the range $\theta_B - \Delta$ to $\theta_B + \Delta$. From the Bragg equation we find readily $d\lambda = \lambda \cot \theta \, d\theta$. The part of the spectrum which will be reflected by the crystal is thus the range from $\lambda_0 - \lambda_0\Delta \cot \theta_B$ to $\lambda_0 + \lambda_0\Delta \cot \theta_B$. (For the sake of convenience it is assumed that $\lambda_0 < 2\lambda_{\text{min.}}$ where $\lambda_{\text{min.}}$ is the shortest wavelength present in the incident beam.) The intensity distribution in this range of the spectrum will be denoted by $I_0(\lambda - \lambda_0)$. We shall assume that the crystal is in the form of a plane parallel plate and we shall neglect the divergence of the beam normal to the plane of incidence. The intensity ratio $\frac{I_H}{I_0}(\theta - \theta_B)$ for diffraction in a plane parallel crystal plate is known (see Equations 3·133 and 3·139). The intensity of the reflected central ray of wavelength λ_0 is thus given by $I_0(0)\frac{I_H}{I_0}(0)$. Consider now a neighboring ray of the incident beam with neighboring wavelength λ. Since $d\lambda = \lambda \cot \theta \, d\theta$ the Bragg angle for this wavelength is $\theta_B + \frac{\lambda - \lambda_0}{\lambda_0} \tan \theta_B$. After reflection the intensity of this neighboring ray is thus

$$I_0(\lambda - \lambda_0)\frac{I_H}{I_0}\left(\theta - \theta_B - \frac{\lambda - \lambda_0}{\lambda_0} \tan \theta_B\right) \qquad [3\text{·}205]$$

The glancing angle of incidence θ is related to the glancing angle of scattering θ_s by the equation

$$\theta_s = \theta_B - b(\theta - \theta_B) \qquad [3\text{·}206]$$

(We are accordingly not strictly correct when we speak of the *reflection* of x rays from a lattice plane. Only if $b = -1$ or if $\theta = \theta_B$ is the angle of incidence equal to the angle of reflection.) According to Equation 3·206 the angle between the reflected neighboring ray of wavelength λ and the reflected central ray of wavelength λ_0 becomes

$$\frac{\lambda - \lambda_0}{\lambda_0} \tan \theta_B - b\left(\theta - \theta_B - \frac{\lambda - \lambda_0}{\lambda_0} \tan \theta_B\right) \qquad [3\text{·}207]$$

The reflected beam from the first crystal will next be used as an incident beam for diffraction in a second plane parallel crystal plate. In order to distinguish the two crystals from each other we shall prime all quantities referring to the second crystal. In the second crystal we shall reflect from the lattice plane $\bar{B}'_{H'}$. We shall orient the second crystal so that the planes of incidence for the two crystals coincide. Let the reflected central ray of wavelength λ_0 make a glancing angle θ' with the lattice plane of the second crystal where $\theta' - \theta'_B$ is a small quantity. As shown in Fig. 3·20 two orientations of the lattice plane $\bar{B}'_{H'}$ come into consideration. We shall refer to these orientations as the (+) position and the (−) position respectively. The glancing angle of incidence on the second crystal corresponding to the neighboring ray of wavelength λ is

$$\theta' \mp \frac{\lambda - \lambda_0}{\lambda_0} \tan \theta_B \pm b\left(\theta - \theta_B - \frac{\lambda - \lambda_0}{\lambda_0} \tan \theta_B\right) \qquad [3\text{·}208]$$

where the upper signs are to be used for the (+) position, the lower signs for the (−) position. The intensity of the neighboring ray after reflection from the second crystal is thus

$$I_0(\lambda - \lambda_0)\,\frac{I_H}{I_0}\left(\theta - \theta_B - \frac{\lambda - \lambda_0}{\lambda_0}\tan\theta_B\right) \times$$
$$\frac{I'_H}{I_0}\left[\theta' - \theta'_B - \frac{\lambda - \lambda_0}{\lambda_0}(\tan\theta'_B \pm \tan\theta_B) \pm b\left(\theta - \theta_B - \frac{\lambda - \lambda_0}{\lambda_0}\tan\theta_B\right)\right] \qquad [3{\cdot}209]$$

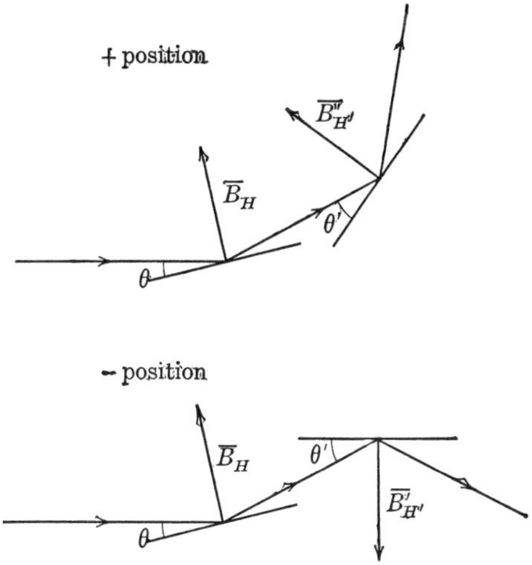

FIG. 3·20.

The mean ratio of the power reflected from the second crystal to that incident upon the second crystal is accordingly

$$P(\theta' - \theta'_B) \equiv \overline{\frac{P'_H}{P_0}(\theta' - \theta'_B)} =$$
$$\frac{S'_{H'}}{S_H}\,\frac{\displaystyle\int_{-\varepsilon}^{+\varepsilon}\int_{-\infty}^{\infty} I_0\left(\frac{I_H}{I_0}\right)\left(\frac{I_H}{I_0}\right)' d(\lambda - \lambda_0)\,d(\theta - \theta_B)}{\displaystyle\int_{-\varepsilon}^{+\varepsilon}\int_{-\infty}^{\infty} I_0\left(\frac{I_H}{I_0}\right) d(\lambda - \lambda_0)\,d(\theta - \theta_B)} \qquad [3{\cdot}210]$$

This equation gives in other words the diffraction pattern as obtained from the second crystal. The quantities S_H and $S'_{H'}$ represent the cross section of incident and diffracted beam respectively so that $S'_{H'}/S_H$ may be replaced by $1/|b'|$. The integration with respect to $\lambda - \lambda_0$

is to be made over that part of the spectrum which takes part in the reflection, i.e., from $-\varepsilon \equiv -\lambda_0\Delta \cot \theta_B$ to $+\varepsilon \equiv \lambda_0\Delta \cot \theta_B$. The bars over numerator and denominator on the right side of Equation 3·210 indicate the average value for normal and parallel polarization.

The area under the diffraction pattern of Equation 3·210 is called the double crystal integrated reflecting power (or the coefficient of reflection) and will be denoted by R, i.e.,

$$R \equiv \int_{-\infty}^{\infty} P(\theta' - \theta'_B)d(\theta' - \theta'_B) \qquad [3\text{·}211]$$

Since $\int_{-\infty}^{\infty} f(x)\,dx = \int_{-\infty}^{\infty} f(x-a)\,dx$ for any function $f(x)$ and for any constant a independent of x, the expression for the integrated reflecting power becomes

$$R = \frac{\overline{R_H^\theta(R_H^\theta)'}}{\overline{R_H^\theta}} \qquad [3\text{·}212]$$

where $R_H^\theta = \frac{1}{|b|}\int_{-\infty}^{\infty} \frac{I_H}{I_0}(\theta - \theta_B)d(\theta - \theta_B)$. The integrated reflecting power is thus independent of the intensity distribution $I_0(\lambda - \lambda_0)$ of the incident beam. In the formula for R it is convenient to make use of the y-scale (as defined by Equation 3·181). The integral $R_H^y = \frac{1}{|b|}\int_{-\infty}^{\infty} \frac{I_H}{I_0}(y)\,dy$ is in general a function of the parameters A and g (compare the definitions of Equation 3·181) which are different for normal and parallel polarization. Let A_0 and g_0 be the particular values of A and g for normal polarization. The corresponding values of A and g for parallel polarization are then $A_0|\cos 2\theta_B|$ and $g_0/|\cos 2\theta_B|$. We shall use the notation

$$\begin{aligned} {}^{\mathrm{n}}[R_H^y] &\equiv R_H^y(A_0, g_0) \\ {}^{\mathrm{p}}[R_H^y] &\equiv R_H^y\left(A_0|\cos 2\theta_B|,\ \frac{g_0}{|\cos 2\theta_B|}\right) \end{aligned} \qquad [3\text{·}213]$$

From the definition of y we have, furthermore,

$$\begin{aligned} {}^{\mathrm{n}}[R_H^\theta] &= \frac{|\psi'_H|}{|b|^{1/2}\sin 2\theta_B}\,{}^{\mathrm{n}}[R_H^y] \\ {}^{\mathrm{p}}[R_H^\theta] &= \frac{|\psi'_H||\cos 2\theta_B|}{|b|^{1/2}\sin 2\theta_B}\,{}^{\mathrm{p}}[R_H^y] \end{aligned} \qquad [3\text{·}214]$$

Accordingly Equation 3·212 may be written in the form

$$R = \frac{|\psi_H'|'}{|b'|^{1/2} \sin 2\theta_B'} \frac{{}^{\mathrm{n}}[R_H^y]{}^{\mathrm{n}}[R_H^y]' + |\cos 2\theta_B|\,|\cos 2\theta_B'|{}^{\mathrm{p}}[R_H^y]{}^{\mathrm{p}}[R_H^y]'}{{}^{\mathrm{n}}[R_H^y] + |\cos 2\theta_B|{}^{\mathrm{p}}[R_H^y]} \qquad [3\cdot215]$$

***A.* Case of Zero Dispersion.** It is seen from Equations 3·209 and 3·210 that the double crystal diffraction pattern depends upon the spectral intensity distribution $I_0(\lambda - \lambda_0)$ of the incident beam unless the second crystal is in the $(-)$ position and simultaneously $\theta_B = \theta_B'$. In this exceptional case, which evidently corresponds to negligibly small dispersion, the equation for the diffraction pattern becomes

$$P(y') = \frac{\displaystyle\int_{-\infty}^{\infty} {}^{\mathrm{n}}\left[\frac{I_H}{I_0}(y)\right]{}^{\mathrm{n}}\left[\frac{I_H}{I_0}(y' - by)\right]' dy + |\cos 2\theta_B| \int_{-\infty}^{\infty} {}^{\mathrm{p}}\left[\frac{I_H}{I_0}(y)\right]{}^{\mathrm{p}}\left[\frac{I_H}{I_0}\left(\frac{y'}{|\cos 2\theta_B'|} - by\right)\right]' dy}{|bb'|\{{}^{\mathrm{n}}[R_H^y] + |\cos 2\theta_B|{}^{\mathrm{p}}[R_H^y]\}} \qquad [3\cdot216]$$

where the symbols ${}^{\mathrm{n}}\left[\dfrac{I_H}{I_0}\right]$ and ${}^{\mathrm{p}}\left[\dfrac{I_H}{I_0}\right]$ are defined analogously to ${}^{\mathrm{n}}[R_H]$ and ${}^{\mathrm{p}}[R_H]$ (see Equation 3·214). $P(y')$ is in general not symmetrical $[P(y') \neq P(-y')]$. In special cases P may, however, become an even function of y', and P will then have a maximum at $y' = 0$.

Let us now assume that the two crystal plates are identical, i.e., we set $\dfrac{I_H}{I_0}(y) = \dfrac{I_H'}{I_0}(y)$ and $b = b'$. We shall further restrict our considerations to $b = b' = \pm 1$. When $b = -1$, the diffraction pattern is symmetrical for we have $\int_{-\infty}^{\infty} I_H(y) I_H(y' + y)\, dy = \int_{-\infty}^{\infty} I_H(y - \frac{1}{2}y') I_H(y + \frac{1}{2}y')\, dy$. When $b = +1$, $\dfrac{I_H}{I_0}(y)$ is an even function of y and it is then readily seen that P must be an even function of y'. In both cases $P(0)$ is thus the maximum value of $P(y')$. The quantity $100P(0)$ is usually called the *per cent reflection.* Clearly we have

$$P(0) = \frac{\displaystyle\int_{-\infty}^{\infty} {}^{\mathrm{n}}\left[\frac{I_H}{I_0}(y)\right]^2 dy + |\cos 2\theta_B| \int_{-\infty}^{\infty} {}^{\mathrm{p}}\left[\frac{I_H}{I_0}(y)\right]^2 dy}{{}^{\mathrm{n}}[R_H^y] + |\cos 2\theta_B|{}^{\mathrm{p}}[R_H^y]} \qquad [3\cdot217]$$

In the following we shall derive the detailed expressions for integrated reflecting power and for per cent reflection using the particular solutions for plane parallel crystal plates obtained in preceding sections of this chapter.

Thin Crystals. We shall assume that the two crystals are so thin that the thin crystal solution of Equation 3·157 can be used. According to Equation 3·160 we have $R_H^y = \pi A$ and hence

$$^{\mathrm{n}}[R_H^y] = \pi A_0, \quad ^{\mathrm{p}}[R_H^y] = \pi A_0 \left|\cos 2\theta_B\right|$$

$$\int_{-\infty}^{\infty} {}^{\mathrm{n}}\left[\frac{I_H}{I_0}(y)\right]^2 dy = \frac{\pi A_0^3}{\sqrt{2}}, \quad \int_{-\infty}^{\infty} {}^{\mathrm{p}}\left[\frac{I_H}{I_0}(y)\right]^2 dy = \frac{\pi A_0^3 \left|\cos^3 2\theta_B\right|}{\sqrt{2}} \qquad [3\cdot218]$$

where $A_0 = \dfrac{\pi}{\lambda}\left|\psi_H\right|\dfrac{t_0}{\gamma_0}$. Inserting in Equations 3·215 and 3·217 the following results are obtained

$$R = \frac{\pi\left|\psi_H\right|A_0}{\sin 2\theta_B}\,\frac{1+\cos^4 2\theta_B}{1+\cos^2 2\theta_B} = 2\,\frac{1+\cos^4 2\theta_B}{(1+\cos^2 2\theta_B)^2}\,\overline{R_H^\theta}$$

$$P(0) = \frac{1+\cos^4 2\theta_B}{\sqrt{2}(1+\cos^2 2\theta_B)}\,A_0^2 \qquad [3\cdot219]$$

Thick Crystals, $\kappa \approx 0$. When $A \gg 1$ and $\kappa A \approx 0$ we may use the Ewald solutions given in Equations 3·150 and 3·154–3·155. If, however, $A \gg 1$ and simultaneously $\kappa A > 1$, the Darwin solution of Equations 3·191 rather than the Ewald solution must be used. Since $^{\mathrm{n}}\left[\dfrac{I_H}{I_0}(y)\right] = {}^{\mathrm{p}}\left[\dfrac{I_H}{I_0}(y)\right]$ (in both Ewald and Darwin solutions) the expressions for integrated reflecting power and per cent reflection simplify to

$$R = \frac{\left|\psi_H\right|}{\sin 2\theta_B}\,\frac{1+\cos^2 2\theta_B}{1+\left|\cos 2\theta_B\right|}\,R_H^y = 2\,\frac{1+\cos^2 2\theta_B}{(1+\left|\cos 2\theta_B\right|)^2}\,\overline{R_H^\theta}$$

$$P(0) = \frac{\displaystyle\int_{-\infty}^{\infty}\left[\frac{I_H}{I_0}(y)\right]^2 dy}{R_H^y} \qquad [3\cdot220]$$

In the Ewald and Darwin solutions R_H^y is known and the integral $\mathfrak{J} \equiv \displaystyle\int_{-\infty}^{\infty}\left(\frac{I_H}{I_0}\right)^2 dy$ is of standard form so that the per cent reflection can be exactly evaluated. The results are

	R_H^y	$\mathfrak{J}$	$100P(0)$
Ewald solution Laue case	$\frac{\pi}{2}$	$\frac{\pi}{8}$	25
Ewald solution Bragg case	π	$2\pi - 4$	72.7
Darwin solution	$\frac{8}{3}$	$\frac{32}{15}$	80

14. COMPARISON WITH EXPERIMENTAL DATA

In comparing experimental and theoretical double crystal diffraction patterns it is convenient to fix the attention on three characteristic quantities. These quantities are the per cent reflection, $P(0)$, which in the simplest cases is synonymous with the maximum ordinate of the diffraction pattern, the half width at half maximum, w, and the integrated reflecting power, R, which is the area under the diffraction pattern on the glancing angle scale. It is not necessary to know the detailed diffraction pattern in order to measure the integrated reflecting power. Suppose, namely, that the second crystal is rotated with constant angular speed ω about an axis normal to the plane of incidence. Let the initial position of the second crystal correspond to $\theta - \theta_B = -\Delta$ and the final position to $\theta - \theta_B = +\Delta$. The ionization chamber (or any other recording device) is first set so as to receive the reflected beam from the second crystal. The total energy recorded by the ionization chamber as the second crystal is rotated from its initial to its final position will be denoted by E. Next the second crystal is removed and the position of the ionization chamber is altered so that the power, P_0, of the beam incident upon the second crystal can be measured. The ratio of the two measured quantities is evidently given by

$$\frac{E}{P_0} = \int_0^{2\Delta/\omega} P(\theta' - \theta'_B)\,dt = \frac{1}{\omega}\int_{-\Delta} P(\theta' - \theta'_B)d(\theta' - \theta'_B) \qquad [3\cdot221]$$

We shall now assume that Δ is large compared with the angular extension of the diffraction pattern. Hence we have

$$\frac{E\omega}{P_0} = R \qquad [3\cdot222]$$

Because of the comparative ease with which the integrated reflecting power can be measured, experimental values of R are known for a great many reflections of numerous crystal species. Accurate experimental determinations of the detailed double crystal diffraction patterns have, on the other hand, been made only in a small number of cases.

The exact theoretical treatment showed that the directions of the diffraction maxima are not accurately given by the Laue vector equation which was derived from elementary considerations in section 1. Thus the center of the diffraction pattern (which is either at or very near the maximum) does not correspond to a glancing angle $\theta_B = \sin^{-1}\left(\frac{\lambda}{2d_H}\right)$ but to θ_c as given by Equation 3·145*a*. The corrected Bragg equation is therefore

$$\lambda = \left[1 - \frac{1-b}{4b \sin^2 \theta_c} \psi_0\right] 2d_H \sin \theta_c \qquad [3\cdot223]$$

This deviation from Bragg's law has indeed been verified experimentally. The correction term in Equation 3·223 is greatest for small $|b|$, i.e., for grazing direction of incidence.

For most crystals the experimental values for R, $P(0)$, and w do not agree with theory. The observed values for integrated reflecting power and for half width are as a rule many times greater than the theoretical values, whereas the directly measured per cent reflection is much smaller than predicted by theory. The experiments show, furthermore, that the diffraction pattern for a given reflection of a given crystal species varies considerably from one individual to the next. The extent of this variation is well demonstrated by the following table based upon measurements by Renninger.[12]

TABLE 3·3

OBSERVATIONS FOR THE (200) REFLECTION OF ROCK SALT

Crystal	$R \times 10^5$	w in Seconds of arc
Theory	4.10	4.9
I + I	4.78	7.1
I + II	10.25	40–50
I + III	27.0	900

I Artificial crystal with fresh cleavage face.
II Natural crystal with fresh cleavage face.
III Natural crystal with polished cleavage face.

It is apparent from the experimental data of Table 3·3 that different rock salt crystals represent different degrees of approximation to the ideal crystal model for which the theory of x-ray diffraction has been developed. Measurements performed with other crystal species give similar results. Only after careful search among many specimens is it in general possible to find individual crystals which give satisfactory agreement with the theory of x-ray diffraction for ideal crystals. Good approximations to ideal crystals are not found with the same ease for different crystal species. Thus crystals of calcite and diamond approach the ideal much more closely than is true of rock salt crystals. A set of nearly perfect calcite crystals was used in the extensive studies by

[12] M. Renninger, *Zeitschr. f. Krist.*, **89**, 344 (1934).

Allison[13] and Parratt[14] who obtained satisfactory agreement with theory over a considerable range of wavelengths as shown by Table 3·4.

TABLE 3·4

OBSERVATIONS ON THE (211) REFLECTION OF CALCITE

λ	$R \times 10^5$		$100P(0)$		w	
	Obs.	Calc.	Obs.	Calc.	Obs.	Calc.
0.2086 A	2.34	0.58	33	80	4.2″	0.64″
0.7078	2.31	2.03	52	80	3.9	2.3
1.537	3.80	3.82	61	69	5.0	4.9
2.285	4.79	4.84	52	58	7.7	7.5
2.299	4.81	4.86	51	58	7.5	7.5
2.941	4.35	4.49	39	44	9.1	8.6
3.114	6.70	6.80	57	69	9.2	8.7
3.902	10.40	11.20	58	67	15.3	15.1
4.937	14.00	16.40	51	60	23.7	23.5

LITERATURE

A. General References

COMPTON, A. H., and S. K. ALLISON, *X-Rays in Theory and Experiment*, New York, D. Van Nostrand Co., 1935.

EWALD, P. P., *Handbuch der Physik*, XXIII/2, pp. 207–476, Second Edition, Berlin, Julius Springer, 1933.

LAUE, M. v., *Röntgenstrahl-Interferenzen*, Leipzig, Akademische Verlagsgesellschaft, 1941.

OTT, H., *Handbuch der Experimentalphysik*, VII/2, pp. 1–322, Leipzig, Akademische Verlagsgesellschaft, 1928.

B. Dynamical Theory

DARWIN, C. G., *Phil. Mag.*, **27**, 325, 675 (1914); **43**, 800 (1922).

EWALD, P. P., *Ann. der Phys.*, **54**, 519, 577 (1917); *Zeitschr. f. Phys.*, **2**, 232 (1920); **30**, 1 (1924); *Physik. Zeitschr.*, **26**, 29 (1925).

KOHLER, M., *Ann. der Phys.*, **18**, 265 (1933).

LAUE, M. v., *Ergeb. d. Exakt. Naturwiss.*, **10**, 133 (1931).

PRINS, J. A., *Zeitschr. f. Phys.*, **63**, 477 (1930).

WALLER, I., *Dissertation*, Upsala, 1925. *Ann. der Phys.*, **79**, 261 (1926).

[13] S. K. Allison, *Phys. Rev.*, **41**, 1 (1932).

[14] L. G. Parratt, *Phys. Rev.*, **41**, 561 (1932).

CHAPTER IV

X-RAY INTERFERENCE IN REAL CRYSTALS

1. REAL AND IDEAL CRYSTALS

The geometry of the x-ray diffraction effects observed with real crystals is in complete agreement with the theory of x-ray interference in ideal crystals as developed in the preceding chapter. In isolated instances there is also quantitative agreement between observed and calculated intensities, but for the great majority of real crystals the x-ray reflections are stronger than the theory allows. The experimental values for the integrated reflecting power often exceed the theoretical value by a factor of ten or more while at the same time the directly measured half width of the diffraction maximum amounts to minutes of arc instead of the few seconds of arc which theory predicts. Experiments show, furthermore, that the diffraction pattern for a given reflection of a given crystal species varies within wide limits from one crystal specimen to another. Variations of corresponding order of magnitude can be artificially produced with a given crystal specimen. Thus the polishing of a freshly cleaved surface may result in a tenfold increase in integrated reflecting power and half width. For scattering directions which are not in the immediate neighborhood of Laue-Bragg directions the theory predicts no other scattering than that due to the Compton effect. The experimentally measured background scattering is, however, too strong to be accounted for by the Compton effect alone.

Because of these discrepancies between theory and experiment one is forced to conclude that ideal crystals are not entirely satisfactory models of real crystals. As shown by the discussions in the three preceding chapters the lattice hypothesis has made it possible to predict many of the characteristic properties of real crystals. One is thus led to believe that the main features of this hypothesis must be retained. We shall therefore proceed on the assumption that real crystals have periodicity which is, however, imperfect in character.

All conceivable imperfections can be classified into two main types which will be called displacement disorders and substitution disorders. In an ideal lattice identical atoms occupy equivalent sites. The same scattering power f_k is thus associated with each site in the set $\bar{r}_k + \bar{A}_L$.

If the lattice disorder is of pure substitution type the atomic sites are $\bar{r}_k + \bar{A}_L$ as for an ideal lattice, but these sites are no longer occupied by atoms with the same scattering power. The scattering power associated with the site $\bar{r}_k + \bar{A}_L$ will therefore be denoted by a symbol f_k^L. If N is the total number of unit cells in the crystal, the mean scattering power for the set k is

$$g_k = \frac{1}{N} \sum_L f_k^L \qquad [4\cdot 1]$$

We shall set

$$f_k^L = g_k + \varphi_k^L \qquad [4\cdot 2]$$

so that the quantities φ_k^L measure the fluctuations from the mean.

As a simple illustration of substitution disorder imagine that a fraction r of the atoms have been removed from an ideal lattice which initially contained one atom of scattering power f_1 per unit cell. Suppose next that the removed atoms are replaced by atoms with a different scattering power f_2 (where $f_2 = 0$ if the sites are left vacant). The mean scattering power is then $g = f_1 + r(f_2 - f_1)$ with $\varphi_k^L = -r(f_2 - f_1)$ for sites occupied by atoms of scattering power f_1 and $\varphi_k^L = (1 - r)(f_2 - f_1)$ for the remaining sites.

In a lattice in which sites $\bar{r}_k + \bar{A}_L$ are occupied by atoms of the same species there is a small amount of substitution disorder which can be ascribed to the lack of synchronization of the electronic motions in the various atoms, or to the fact that the atoms at any given instant are not all in the same excited state. There is in other words substitution disorder due to small differences in the electronic configurations of atoms of the same species. Disorders of this type will be neglected in the following, for they are really to be regarded as intra-atomic disorders and are independent of the crystal lattice. It should, however, be remembered that the intra-atomic disorders give rise to a weak component of scattering, the Compton scattering, for which proper allowance must be made in comparing theory and experiment.

If there is displacement disorder, the atomic sites are no longer those of an ideal lattice. Rather, the sites of a set k are now $\bar{r}_k + \bar{A}_L + \bar{\Delta}_k^L$ so that the quantities $\bar{\Delta}_k^L$ represent displacements from the ideal sites. The same scattering power f_k is, however, associated with each site in a given set. It may be assumed that the periods $\bar{a}_1$, $\bar{a}_2$, $\bar{a}_3$ and the vectors $\bar{r}_k$ have been chosen so that $\sum_L \bar{\Delta}_k^L = 0$ for any k.

The atomic scattering power is by definition the ratio of the amplitude of scattering for the atom to that for a single electron placed at the nucleus. The effective scattering power of the atom at $\bar{r}_k + \bar{A}_L + \bar{\Delta}_k^L$

is similarly defined except for the difference that the amplitude of scattering for the atom is measured relative to that of an electron placed at the ideal lattice site $\bar{r}_k + \bar{A}_L$. Denoting the effective scattering power associated with the site (k, L) by g_k^L we have

$$g_k^L = f_k \, e^{i\bar{s}\cdot\bar{\Delta}_k^L} \quad [4\cdot3]$$

The mean effective scattering power for the set k is

$$g_k = \frac{1}{N}\sum_L g_k^L = f_k \frac{1}{N}\sum_L e^{i\bar{s}\cdot\bar{\Delta}_k^L} \quad [4\cdot4]$$

It is convenient to set

$$g_k^L = g_k + \varphi_k^L \quad [4\cdot5]$$

where

$$\varphi_k^L = f_k \, e^{i\bar{s}\cdot\bar{\Delta}_k^L} - g_k \quad [4\cdot6]$$

is the fluctuation from the mean. It is important to note that displacement disorder by the use of effective scattering powers in a formal way can be treated as substitution disorder.

It is to be expected that most lattice imperfections represent combinations of substitution disorder and displacement disorder. In the general case it must therefore be supposed that scattering powers f_k^L are associated with sites $\bar{r}_k + \bar{A}_L + \bar{\Delta}_k^L$. We shall assume

$$\sum_L Z_k^L \bar{\Delta}_k^L = 0 \quad [4\cdot7]$$

where Z_k^L is the number of electrons in the atom (k, L). The effective scattering power of the atom (k, L) becomes

$$g_k^L = f_k^L \, e^{i\bar{s}\cdot\bar{\Delta}_k^L} \quad [4\cdot8]$$

and the mean effective scattering power is

$$g_k = \frac{1}{N}\sum_L g_k^L = \frac{1}{N}\sum_L f_k^L \, e^{i\bar{s}\cdot\bar{\Delta}_k^L} \quad [4\cdot9]$$

The fluctuations φ_k^L from the mean effective scattering power are defined by

$$g_k^L = g_k + \varphi_k^L \quad [4\cdot10a]$$

$$\varphi_k^L = f_k^L \, e^{i\bar{s}\cdot\bar{\Delta}_k^L} - \overline{f_k^L \, e^{i\bar{s}\cdot\bar{\Delta}_k^L}} \quad [4\cdot10b]$$

The fluctuations φ_k^L may be functions of time as well as of position. If they are dependent upon time, it might seem necessary to consider time and space averages separately. We shall, however, assume that we are dealing with crystals which can be regarded as quasi-ergodic canonical ensembles in thermodynamical equilibrium with the surroundings. According to the fundamental postulate of statistical mechanics it is then justifiable to replace time averages with spatial averages over the instantaneous configuration.

The structure factor F is by definition the scattering power of the unit cell, i.e., it is the amplitude of scattering from the unit cell relative to that of a single electron placed at the origin of the cell. Because of the imperfections the various unit cells of the disordered lattice are no longer identical, and the structure factor may change from one unit cell to another. Let F_L denote the structure factor of the unit cell which has its origin at $\bar{A}_L$. We have then

$$F_L = \sum_k f_k^L \, e^{i\bar{s}\cdot(\bar{r}_k+\bar{\Delta}_k^L)} = \sum_k g_k^L \, e^{i\bar{s}\cdot\bar{r}_k} \quad [4\cdot11]$$

If $\bar{F}$ is the mean structure factor defined by

$$\bar{F} = \frac{1}{N}\sum_L F_L = \sum_k g_k \, e^{i\bar{s}\cdot\bar{r}_k} \quad [4\cdot12]$$

then Equation 4·11 can be written in the form

$$F_L = \bar{F} + \sum_k \varphi_k^L \, e^{i\bar{s}\cdot\bar{r}_k} \quad [4\cdot13]$$

The mean square structure factor $\overline{|F|^2}$ becomes

$$\overline{|F|^2} = \frac{1}{N}\sum_L F_L^2 = |\bar{F}|^2 + \sum_{k,k'} \varphi_{kk'}^0 \, e^{i\bar{s}\cdot(\bar{r}_k-\bar{r}_{k'})} \quad [4\cdot14a]$$

where

$$\varphi_{kk'}^0 = \frac{1}{N}\sum_L \varphi_k^L (\varphi_{k'}^L)^* \quad [4\cdot14b]$$

The quantity φ_k^L may conveniently be called the disorder at the site (k, L), and the ideal lattice in which effective scattering powers g_k are associated with sites $\bar{r}_k + \bar{A}_L$ may be called the mean lattice. Clearly, $\bar{F}$ as given by Equation 4·12 is the structure factor of the mean lattice.

2. THE MOSAIC CRYSTAL

We have referred to the lack of agreement between theory and experiment for the Laue-Bragg reflections as well as for the background scattering. These discrepancies are very large for most crystals although there may be fair agreement over a limited wavelength range for the Laue-Bragg reflections of exceptional crystal specimens.

The ideal crystal model which has been used in the preceding chapters is static and makes no provision for the thermal agitation of the atoms in the lattice. In all real crystals there must accordingly be disorder due to heat motion, but this seems to be the only imperfection the existence of which can be predicted from general theoretical considerations. It would be reasonable to suspect that this unavoidable disorder is the main cause of the lack of agreement between theory and experiment. In anticipation of results to be obtained later in this chapter it can be stated that the suspicion cannot be substantiated. Although the thermal disorder (together with the Compton effect) in most cases gives a quantitative explanation of the observed background scattering, the gap between theory and experiment is made even wider as far as the Laue-Bragg reflections are concerned. In order to account for the observations it is thus necessary to assume that all real crystals are afflicted with disorder in addition to that due to heat motion. This additional disorder is associated with the so-called mosaic structure.

The mosaic structure model of a real crystal was first proposed by C. G. Darwin.[1] He suggested that the imperfection of crystals could take either of two forms, warping or cracking: either the atoms are arranged in layers which are not quite plane, or they are arranged in blocks, each block being in itself an ideal crystal, but adjacent blocks not accurately fitted together. Darwin was inclined to believe the former alternative to be more probable, but he adopted the latter because it was simpler to treat mathematically. It is, of course, the second alternative which aptly is referred to as mosaic structure.[2] Darwin's adoption of the mosaic crystal model has proved to be fortunate, for the experimental evidence which is available today shows that mosaic structure rather than warping is the normal imperfection of real crystals.

Mosaic structure can be described as a displacement disorder in which the displacement $\bar{\Delta}_k^L$ remains constant throughout a given block, but changes discontinuously from one block to another. The displacements are of the form

$$\bar{\Delta}_k^L = \bar{R}_j + \bar{\varphi}_j \times (\bar{r}_k + \bar{A}_L) \qquad [4\cdot15]$$

where the first term represents a translation, the second a small rotation of the jth block as a whole. Since the relative displacements of the blocks are large compared to x-ray wavelengths, there can be no definite phase relationships between the scattering from the various blocks, i.e., the mosaic crystal is an aggregate of independently scattering ideal crystals.

[1] C. G. Darwin, *Phil. Mag.*, **27**, 315, 657 (1914); **43**, 800 (1922).

[2] The name mosaic crystal was proposed by P. P. Ewald.

The exact nature of the mosaic structure imperfection can be varied ad infinitum by changing the size and shape of the individual blocks as well as the distribution function $W(\bar{\varphi})$ which describes the orientation of the blocks. In exceptional cases the size of the blocks may be so large that it becomes possible, namely, by using small slits, to study the x-ray diffraction in one block at a time. This was indeed true for the artificial rock salt crystal examined by Renninger and referred to in Table 3·3. Normally the blocks are, however, of microscopic or submicroscopic size, and there is no macroscopic evidence of a mosaic structure. In the following we shall therefore assume that a great many blocks take part in the scattering, so many in fact that the fluctuations $\bar{\varphi}_j$ may be represented by means of a continuous rather than discrete distribution function $W(\bar{\varphi})$. For the sake of convenience it will be assumed that the distribution function W has cylindrical symmetry, i.e., is a function of one rather than two parameters. Accordingly we set

$$W(\bar{\varphi}) = W(\Delta) \qquad [4\cdot16]$$

where Δ is the magnitude of the angular deviation from the mean. If W is assumed to be an error function we have

$$W(\Delta) = \frac{1}{\sqrt{2\pi}\eta} e^{-\Delta^2/2\eta^2} \qquad [4\cdot17]$$

where η is the standard deviation.

3. THEORY OF X-RAY DIFFRACTION IN MOSAIC CRYSTALS

We shall discuss the diffraction of x rays for a mosaic crystal in the shape of a plane parallel plate of thickness T_0. Let the ideal crystal blocks also be plane parallel plates, nearly parallel to one another and to the large crystal plate. It will be assumed that the thickness of the individual crystal blocks fluctuates about a mean value t_0 which is so small that true x-ray absorption in any one block may be neglected. Because of the assumed discrete nature of the distortion there are no definite phase relationships between the x-ray scattering from different blocks, i.e., the various blocks scatter independently of one another.

Consider a beam of parallel and monochromatic x rays incident upon the mosaic crystal so that γ_0 is the direction cosine relative to the normal $\bar{n}$ of the crystal plate. Let the incident beam make a glancing angle θ with the mean lattice plane $\bar{B}_H$, θ being near the Bragg angle θ_B. For the sake of convenience we shall assume that the reflecting plane is either parallel or normal to the crystal plate so that $\gamma_0 = |\gamma_H|$.

We shall first find the expression for the reflecting power $\sigma\, dT$ of a layer of thickness dT in the crystal. It will be assumed that this layer contains many ideal crystal blocks and that the varying orientation of these blocks may be described by the same distribution function $W(\Delta)$ as for the crystal as a whole. Since the mean thickness of an ideal crystal block is t_0 the layer dT contains dT/t_0 layers of single crystal blocks. The reflecting power of a single block is $\frac{P_H}{P_0}(\theta' - \theta_B)$ and the detailed form of this function is known from the investigations of the preceding chapter. We have assumed that t_0 is so small that true absorption phenomena in any one block may be neglected. For P_H/P_0 we should therefore use the solutions corresponding to zero absorption given in section 3·11. The glancing angle θ' for a single block differs from the mean glancing angle θ by an amount Δ, i.e., $\theta' = \theta + \Delta$. The reflecting power of a single layer of ideal crystal blocks is thus

$$\int W(\Delta) \frac{P_H}{P_0} (\theta - \theta_B + \Delta)\, d\Delta \qquad [4\cdot18]$$

We shall assume that the half width of the distribution function W is large compared with the half width of the function P_H/P_0. Since P_H/P_0 is different from zero only in a narrow range near $\theta - \theta_B + \Delta = 0$, it becomes justifiable to treat W as a constant and take it outside the integral sign. Hence we find

$$\int W(\Delta) \frac{P_H}{P_0} (\theta - \theta_B + \Delta)\, d\Delta \approx W(\theta_B - \theta) R_H^\theta \qquad [4\cdot19]$$

where R_H^θ is the integrated reflecting power of a single block. The reflecting power of the layer dT is consequently

$$\sigma\, dT = W \frac{R_H^\theta}{t_0}\, dT \qquad [4\cdot20]$$

We shall next consider the variation in the power of incident and diffracted beams with the depth of penetration in the crystal plate. Let $\mathcal{P}_0(T)$ and $\mathcal{P}_H(T)$ represent the power of the incident and diffracted beams respectively at a depth T. Passing through a layer dT both x-ray beams lose power because of true absorption and diffraction. The power lost by one beam due to diffraction will, however, be gained by the other beam. (It is clear that the incident beam and the twice-reflected incident beam have the same propagation direction.) Accordingly we arrive at the following two equations

$$\begin{aligned} d\mathcal{P}_0 &= -\mu_0 \mathcal{P}_0 \frac{dT}{\gamma_0} - \sigma \mathcal{P}_0\, dT + \sigma \mathcal{P}_H\, dT \\ d\mathcal{P}_H &= \mp \mu_0 \mathcal{P}_H \frac{dT}{|\gamma_H|} \mp \sigma \mathcal{P}_H\, dT \pm \sigma \mathcal{P}_0\, dT \end{aligned} \qquad [4\cdot21]$$

The upper signs in the second equation are to be used in the Laue case (the diffracted beam is directed towards increasing T), while the lower signs correspond to the Bragg case (diffracted beam directed towards decreasing T). The first two terms on the right side of each equation represent the power decrease due to absorption and diffraction. The third term is the power increase of the incident or of the diffracted beam due to reflection of the diffracted and incident beams respectively.

The system of Equations 4·21 is readily solved, but the solution contains two arbitrary constants which must be determined from the boundary conditions. One boundary condition is obtained by assuming the incident power at the boundary $T = 0$ to be known, i.e.,

$$\mathcal{P}_0(T) = \mathcal{P}_0(0) \quad \text{at} \quad T = 0 \tag{4·22}$$

The diffracted beam is produced within the crystal plate and must hence emerge through one surface of the plate and vanish at the other. Accordingly we have as the second boundary condition

Bragg case

$$\mathcal{P}_H(T) = 0 \quad \text{at} \quad T = T_0 \tag{4·23a}$$

Laue case

$$\mathcal{P}_H(T) = 0 \quad \text{at} \quad T = 0 \tag{4·23b}$$

Clearly we seek an expression for the ratio of diffracted to incident power, i.e., for the ratio $\mathcal{P}_H(0)/\mathcal{P}_0(0)$ in the Bragg case and for the ratio $\mathcal{P}_H(T_0)/\mathcal{P}_0(0)$ in the Laue case. Determining the constants of integration in the solutions of Equations 4·21 from the boundary conditions given above we find:

Symmetrical Bragg case

$$\frac{\mathcal{P}_H(0)}{\mathcal{P}_0(0)} = \frac{\sigma + \frac{\mu_0}{\gamma_0} - U}{\sigma} - \frac{U\left[\sigma + \frac{\mu_0}{\gamma_0} - U\right]e^{-UT_0}}{\sigma\left[\left(\sigma + \frac{\mu_0}{\gamma_0}\right)\sinh UT_0 + U\cosh UT_0\right]} \tag{4·24}$$

Symmetrical Laue case

$$\frac{\mathcal{P}_H(T_0)}{\mathcal{P}_0(0)} = \sinh \sigma T_0 \, e^{-\left(\frac{\mu_0}{\gamma_0}+\sigma\right)T_0} \tag{4·25}$$

The symbol U occurring in Equation 4·24 has the following meaning

$$U \equiv \sqrt{\left(\sigma + \frac{\mu_0}{\gamma_0}\right)^2 - \sigma^2} \tag{4·26}$$

In the Bragg case we shall limit our considerations to a very thick crystal plate so that the second term in Equation 4·24 becomes negligibly small. Accordingly we set

Symmetrical Bragg case — thick crystal

$$\frac{\mathcal{P}_H(0)}{\mathcal{P}_0(0)} = \frac{\sigma + \frac{\mu_0}{\gamma_0} - \sqrt{\left(\sigma + \frac{\mu_0}{\gamma_0}\right)^2 - \sigma^2}}{\sigma} \qquad [4·27]$$

The extent of the imperfection of a mosaic crystal can be varied in two distinct ways, namely, by altering the thickness t_0 of the ideal crystal blocks and by altering the distribution function W. It should be noted, however, that the formula for σ given in Equation 4·20 does not hold if the blocks are in nearly perfect alignment, i.e., if the standard deviation is comparable to the half width of the ideal crystal diffraction pattern. For crystals in which the alignment of the blocks is exceptionally good the expression for σ must be left in the implicit form

$$\sigma = \frac{1}{t_0} \int_{-\infty}^{\infty} W(\Delta) \frac{P_H}{P_0} (\theta - \theta_B + \Delta)\, d\Delta \qquad [4·28]$$

In the Laue case we shall assume that the crystal plate is reasonably thin so that $\sigma T_0 \ll 1$. Expanding Equations 4·27 and 4·25 in series we find

Bragg case

$$\frac{\mathcal{P}_H(0)}{\mathcal{P}_0(0)} = \frac{\gamma_0\sigma}{2(\mu_0 + \gamma_0\sigma)} + \left[\frac{\gamma_0\sigma}{2(\mu_0 + \gamma_0\sigma)}\right]^3 + \cdots \qquad [4·29]$$

Laue case

$$\frac{\mathcal{P}_H(T_0)}{\mathcal{P}_0(0)} = e^{-\mu_0 \frac{T_0}{\gamma_0}} \sigma T_0[1 - \sigma T_0 + \tfrac{2}{3}(\sigma T_0)^2 + \cdots] \qquad [4·30]$$

In Chapter III we used the name extinction for the power loss of an x-ray beam caused by the production of a diffracted beam. It is convenient to speak of two types of extinction when dealing with a mosaic crystal. The extinction within any one ideal crystal block (which is the type of extinction encountered in Chapter III) will be called primary extinction. The power loss due to diffraction in the blocks traversed by the incident beam before it reaches the particular block under consideration will be referred to as secondary extinction. Primary extinction is implicitly taken account of in the expression for the reflecting power P_H/P_0 of a single block. Reference to Equations 4·21 show that the power loss due to true absorption and to diffraction may be described in terms of an effective absorption coefficient μ defined by

$$\mu = \mu_0 + \gamma_0 \sigma \qquad [4\cdot31]$$

The quantity $\gamma_0\sigma$ is the fractional power loss due to diffraction per unit length of path through the mosaic crystal and may hence properly be called the secondary extinction coefficient. The secondary extinction depends thus both upon the primary extinction, i.e., upon the thickness t_0 of the blocks, and upon the distribution function W.

A. **Negligible Primary and Secondary Extinction.** *The Ideal Mosaic Crystal.* The mosaic crystal is said to be ideally imperfect if primary as well as secondary extinction is negligibly small for all reflections. According to the discussion given in section 3·11 the condition for negligible primary extinction is

$$A_0 \equiv \frac{\pi}{\lambda} |\psi_H| \frac{t_0}{\gamma_0} \ll 1 \quad \text{or} \quad \frac{t_0}{\gamma_0} \ll \frac{\lambda}{\pi |\psi_H|} \qquad [4\cdot32]$$

where $|\psi_H|$ refers to the strongest reflection. Since $|\psi_H|$ for a given reflection is proportional to λ^2 the critical thickness $\lambda/\pi|\psi_H|$ is inversely proportional to the wavelength. A given mosaic crystal may therefore be ideally imperfect for small, but not for long wavelengths. It is similarly seen from Equation 4·32 that a given mosaic crystal may appear ideally imperfect for weaker, but not for stronger reflections. Let us take rock salt as a numerical example. The lattice plane (200) gives rise to the strongest reflection of all while the reflection from the lattice plane (111) is among the weaker ones. Setting $|F_{200}| = 84$, $|F_{111}| = 16.8$, $V = 5.628^3$ A^3 and $\lambda =$ 1.54 A (Cu $K\alpha$) or 0.209 A (W $K\alpha$) we find the following numerical values for the critical thickness.

	(200)-Reflection	(111)-Reflection
1.54 A	5×10^{-4} cm.	2.5×10^{-3} cm.
0.209 A	3.7×10^{-3} cm.	1.8×10^{-2} cm.

When the condition of Equation 4·32 is satisfied the integrated reflecting power of a single block is given by Equation 3·161. The expression for the secondary extinction coefficient is thus

$$\gamma_0 \sigma = W(\theta_B - \theta) Q \qquad [4\cdot33a]$$

where

$$Q = \left| \frac{e^2 F_H}{mc^2 V} \right|^2 \lambda^3 \frac{1 + \cos^2 2\theta_B}{2 \sin 2\theta_B} \qquad [4\cdot33b]$$

Negligible secondary extinction implies that the power loss due to diffraction is negligible compared with the loss due to true absorption, i.e., that

$$\gamma_0\sigma \ll \mu_0 \tag{4·34}$$

for all directions of incidence. $\gamma_0\sigma$ attains its maximum value for $\theta = \theta_B$. The condition for negligible secondary extinction is accordingly

$$W(0) \ll \frac{\mu_0}{Q} \tag{4·35}$$

where Q refers to the strongest reflection which comes into consideration. This condition may be expressed directly in terms of the standard deviation η if W is the error function given in Equation 4·17. Then we have

$$\eta \gg \frac{Q}{\sqrt{2\pi}\,\mu_0} \tag{4·36}$$

Since we use the approximation in Equation 4·19 there is another restriction on η, namely, that it is large compared with the half width of the diffraction pattern P_H/P_0. When Equation 4·32 is satisfied this half width is given by Equation 3·159 and we have thus

$$\eta \gg \sqrt{\frac{\log 2}{\pi}}\,\frac{\lambda}{\sin 2\theta_B}\,\frac{\gamma_0}{t_0} \tag{4·37}$$

Again taking rock salt as a numerical example we find from Equation 4·36 for the (200)-reflection

$$\lambda = 1.54\text{ A},\quad \mu_0 = 160,\quad Q = 1130 \times 10^{-4}$$
$$\eta \gg 2.8 \times 10^{-4} \approx 1 \text{ minute of arc}$$

$$\lambda = 0.61\text{ A},\quad \mu_0 = 10.7,\quad Q = 185 \times 10^{-4}$$
$$\eta \gg 7 \times 10^{-4} \approx 2\tfrac{1}{2} \text{ minutes of arc}$$

Since $\gamma_0\sigma$ by assumption is negligible compared with μ_0, we obtain the formula for the diffraction patterns of ideal mosaic crystals by taking the first approximation to Equations 4·29 or 4·30. Hence we have

Bragg case

$$\frac{\mathcal{P}_H(0)}{\mathcal{P}_0(0)} = W(\theta_B - \theta)\,\frac{Q}{2\mu_0} \tag{4·38}$$

Laue case

$$\frac{\mathcal{P}_H(T_0)}{\mathcal{P}_0(0)} = W(\theta_B - \theta)\,\frac{QT_0}{\gamma_0}\,e^{-\mu_0\frac{T_0}{\gamma_0}} \tag{4·39}$$

The diffraction pattern of the ideal mosaic crystal has thus the same shape and half width as the distribution function W. Since $\int W\,d(\theta - \theta_B) = 1$ the integrated reflecting power $\mathcal{R}_H^\theta$ of the ideal mosaic crystal becomes

Bragg case

$$\mathcal{R}_H^\theta = \frac{Q}{2\mu_0} \tag{4·40}$$

Laue case

$$\mathcal{R}_H^\theta = \frac{QT_0}{\gamma_0} e^{-\mu_0 \frac{T_0}{\gamma_0}} \tag{4·41}$$

These expressions give generally much greater values for the integrated reflecting power than do the corresponding formulas for ideal crystals. Applying Equation 4·40 to the (200)-reflection of rock salt using $\lambda = 1.54$ A we obtain $\mathcal{R}_H^\theta = 35 \times 10^{-5}$. The corresponding value for the ideal rock salt crystal is 4.1×10^{-5}. Reference to Table 3·3 shows that the observed values lie between the two extremes. The result for the polished crystal is 27.8×10^{-5} which is only 20 per cent smaller than calculated for the ideal mosaic crystal. The observed half width for the polished crystal was $\sim 15'$, showing that secondary extinction is small although not quite negligible. In a range of normal dispersion $Q/2\mu_0$ increases while R_H^θ for the corresponding ideal crystal decreases with decreasing wavelength. The ratio $\frac{Q}{2\mu_0}/R_H^\theta$ increases consequently rapidly as the wavelength is decreased.

***B.* Negligible Primary and Small Secondary Extinction.** If $\gamma_0\sigma$ is not negligible but still small compared with μ_0 it becomes necessary to go to the second approximation to Equations 4·29 or 4·30. We find then

Bragg case

$$\frac{\mathcal{P}_H(0)}{\mathcal{P}_0(0)} \approx \frac{WQ}{2\mu_0}\left[1 - \frac{WQ}{\mu_0}\right] \tag{4·42a}$$

$$\mathcal{R}_H^\theta \approx \frac{Q}{2(\mu_0 + gQ)} \tag{4·42b}$$

Laue case

$$\frac{\mathcal{P}_H(T_0)}{\mathcal{P}_0(0)} \approx WQ\frac{T_0}{\gamma_0} e^{-\mu_0 \frac{T_0}{\gamma_0}}\left[1 - WQ\frac{T_0}{\gamma_0}\right] \tag{4·43a}$$

$$\mathcal{R}_H^\theta \approx Q\frac{T_0}{\gamma_0} e^{-(\mu_0 + gQ)\frac{T_0}{\gamma_0}} \tag{4·43b}$$

where

$$gQ \equiv \int W\gamma_0\sigma \, d(\theta - \theta_B) = Q \int W^2 \, d(\theta - \theta_B) \qquad [4\cdot44]$$

is the mean secondary extinction coefficient.

If W is the error function of Equation 4·17 the expression for g becomes

$$g = \frac{1}{2\pi\eta^2} \int_{-\infty}^{\infty} e^{-\Delta^2/\eta^2} \, d\Delta = \frac{1}{2\sqrt{\pi}\eta} \qquad [4\cdot45]$$

Setting $\eta = 1.1 \times 10^{-3}$ (4′ of arc) we find thus $g = 260$. With this value of g the integrated reflecting power for the (200)-reflection of rock salt (in the Bragg case and with $\lambda = 1.54$ A) is reduced from 35×10^{-5} for the ideal mosaic crystal to 30×10^{-5}. Since gQ is proportional to $|F_H|^2$ it is clear that the reduction of $\mathcal{R}_H^\theta$ due to secondary extinction is greatest for the strongest reflections. This fact is well illustrated by the data on an aluminium crystal shown in Table 4·1 and due to James, Brindley, and Wood.[3] The mean secondary extinction coefficient decreases rapidly with the wavelength, approximately with λ^3. Going to a smaller wavelength and to a weaker reflection one may thus be able to eliminate the effect of secondary extinction.

TABLE 4·1

$\mathcal{R}_H^\theta \times 10^6$ FOR REFLECTIONS FROM ALUMINIUM

Bragg Case. $\lambda = 0.71$ A $\mu_0 = 14.35$

$H_1H_2H_3$	Observed	Calculated		
		Ideal crystal	Ideal mosaic crystal	Mosaic crystal $g = 300$
111	580	19.6	818	547
200	436	16.2	619	450
222	144	6.30	158	144
400	86	4.47	91	86
333	26.2	2.19	28.3	27.8
600	12.2	1.31	12.0	11.9
444	4.95	0.76	5.14	5.13
800	2.10	0.40	2.09	2.09
555	1.43	0.37	1.39	1.39

C. Primary Extinction, Small Secondary Extinction. When the condition of Equation 4·32 is no longer satisfied, the thin crystal solution

[3] R. W. James, G. W. Brindley, and R. G. Wood, *Proc. Roy. Soc. London*, **A 125** 401 (1929).

$R_H^\theta = Q\dfrac{t_0}{\gamma_0}$ cannot be used. Instead we must use the general expression for R_H^θ deduced in part C of section 3·11. The general formula for R_H^θ may be written in the form

$$R_H^\theta = Q'\frac{t_0}{\gamma_0} \equiv Qf(A_0)\frac{t_0}{\gamma_0} \qquad [4\cdot 46]$$

where Bragg case

$$f(A_0) \equiv \frac{\tanh A_0 + |\cos 2\theta_B| \tanh |A_0 \cos 2\theta_B|}{A_0(1 + \cos^2 2\theta_B)} \qquad [4\cdot 46a]$$

Laue case

$$f(A_0) \equiv \frac{\sum J_{2n+1}(2A_0) + |\cos 2\theta_B| \sum J_{2n+1}(2A_0|\cos 2\theta_B|)}{A_0(1 + \cos^2 2\theta_B)} \qquad [4\cdot 46b]$$

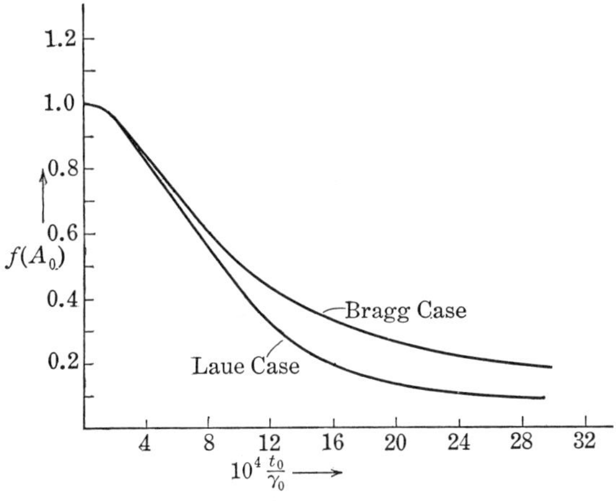

FIG. 4·1.

When $A_0 \ll 1$, i.e., when the condition of Equation 4·32 is satisfied, we have $f(A_0) = 1$ and $Q' = Q$. On the other hand, when $A_0|\cos 2\theta_B| \gg 1$ the expressions for $f(A_0)$ become

Bragg case

$$f(A_0) = \frac{1 + |\cos 2\theta_B|}{A_0(1 + \cos^2 2\theta_B)} \qquad [4\cdot 47a]$$

Laue case

$$f(A_0) = \frac{1 + |\cos 2\theta_B|}{2A_0[1 + \cos^2 2\theta_B]} \qquad [4\cdot 47b]$$

The variation of $f(A_0)$ with t_0/γ_0 for the (200)-reflection of rock salt and $\lambda = 1.54$ A is shown in Fig. 4·1.

Primary extinction can accordingly be included in the formulas deduced in the two preceding parts of this section by the simple procedure of replacing Q by the more general expression Q'. Since $A_0 = \frac{\pi|\psi_H|}{\lambda}\frac{t_0}{\gamma_0}$ it follows that primary extinction like secondary extinction decreases with decreasing wavelength and with decreasing $|F_H|$. Indeed, the extinction effects in some real crystals may be so extreme for strong reflections and long wavelengths that these crystals properly may be called ideal crystals. However, the mosaic character becomes apparent when we investigate very much weaker reflections or when we use very much shorter wavelengths. The particular calcite crystal for which the data given in Table 3·4 were obtained appears to be a perfect crystal for $\lambda > 1$ A, but its truly mosaic nature manifests itself in the lack of agreement between calculated and experimental values for $\lambda = 0.2086$ A.

***D.* Experimental Determination of the Mean Secondary Extinction Coefficient.** In mosaic crystals with small secondary extinction the distribution function W can be deduced from the experimental diffraction pattern (see Equations 4·42*a* and 4·43*a*), and having found W the mean extinction coefficient g is obtained from Equation 4·44. However, it is often difficult to measure the detailed diffraction pattern with sufficient accuracy and other methods for finding g, based upon experimental data for $\mathcal{R}_H^\theta$, have therefore been suggested.[4] When the structure of the crystal is known, the quantities Q can be calculated and it becomes possible to make an indirect determination of g. In that case g is treated as a parameter and adjusted until there is best possible agreement between calculated and observed values $\mathcal{R}_H^\theta$. (The value $g = 300$ given in the last column of Table 4·1 is found in this manner.) The second method which we will describe can be used when the crystal structure is unknown. It is based upon Equation 4·43*b*. The thickness of the crystal plate is decreased in steps by repeated polishing, cleaving, or etching. For each value of the thickness the integrated reflecting power (in the Laue case) is measured. Plotting $\log(\mathcal{R}_H^\theta\gamma_0/T_0)$ against T_0/γ_0 the experimental points should fall on a straight line. This line has a slope $-(\mu_0 + gQ')$, and its intercept on the ordinate axis is $\log Q'$. Having made an independent determination of μ_0, it is thus possible to find both Q' and g. It should be pointed out that difficulties may arise when the thickness of the plate is decreased by polishing, which is likely to affect both the size and the alignment of the ideal crystal blocks. Both g and Q' may then change from one value of T_0 to another

[4] W. L. Bragg, R. W. James, and C. H. Bosanquet, *Phil. Mag.*, **42**, 1 (1921).

so that the experimental points can no longer be fitted to a straight line.

E. **General Formula for the Symmetrical Bragg Case.** The differential equations 4·21 and their solutions Equations 4·24–4·27, are valid only for mosaic crystals in which the blocks are so thin that true absorption in any one block is negligible. When $\mu_0 \frac{t_0}{\gamma_0}$ becomes comparable to (or greater than) unity we are no longer able to use the approximation $e^{-\mu_0 \frac{t_0}{\gamma_0}} \approx 1 - \mu_0 \frac{t_0}{\gamma_0}$ and the differential equations 4·21 must be replaced by the corresponding difference equations. In this section we shall set up and solve these difference equations for the symmetrical Bragg case.

Let Ω denote the reflecting power of a single layer of blocks. The relationship between Ω and σ, which was defined as the reflecting power per unit thickness, is thus $\Omega = \sigma t_0$. We shall make no restrictive assumptions regarding the nature of the distribution function W. In accordance with Equation 4·28 we set therefore

$$\Omega(\theta - \theta_B) = \int_{-\infty}^{\infty} W(\Delta) \frac{P_H}{P_0} (\theta - \theta_B + \Delta)\, d\Delta \qquad [4\text{·}48a]$$

or, if the function W is discrete

$$\Omega(\theta - \theta_B) = \sum_j W_j \frac{P_H}{P_0} (\theta - \theta_B + \Delta_j) \qquad [4\text{·}48b]$$

As before P_H/P_0 represents the reflecting power of an ideal crystal plate of thickness t_0. Clearly, if $\mu_0 \frac{t_0}{\gamma_0}$ is comparable to or greater than unity, true absorption in any one block cannot be neglected, and for P_H/P_0 we must then use the expression given in Equation 3·139 rather than the zero absorption form which was used in the preceding parts of this section.

The various layers of crystal blocks will be numbered from the surface downwards as indicated in Fig. 4·2.

$\mathcal{P}_0^{(n)}$ is the power of the incident beam after passage through the nth layer, while $\mathcal{P}_H^{(n-1)}$ is the corresponding quantity for the diffracted beam (see Fig. 4·2). Passing through the nth layer both the incident beam and the diffracted beam will be absorbed as well as diffracted. The relationships between incident and diffracted power before and after passage through the nth layer are

$$\begin{aligned} \mathcal{P}_0^{(n)} &= (\alpha - \Omega)\,\mathcal{P}_0^{(n-1)} + \Omega\,\mathcal{P}_H^{(n)} \\ \mathcal{P}_H^{(n-1)} &= (\alpha - \Omega)\,\mathcal{P}_H^{(n)} + \Omega\,\mathcal{P}_0^{(n-1)} \end{aligned} \qquad [4\text{·}49]$$

The symbol α represents the quantity $e^{-\mu_0 \frac{t_0}{\gamma_0}}$, and it is clear that $1 \geq \alpha - \Omega \geq 0$. This system of difference equations takes the place of Equations 4·21 which we used earlier. From Equations 4·49 two different expressions for $\mathcal{P}_H^{(n)}/\mathcal{P}_0^{(n)}$ are readily obtained. They are:

$$\frac{\mathcal{P}_H^{(n)}}{\mathcal{P}_0^{(n)}} = \frac{1 - (\alpha - \Omega)\dfrac{\mathcal{P}_0^{(n-1)}}{\mathcal{P}_0^{(n)}}}{\Omega} \qquad [4·50a]$$

$$\frac{\mathcal{P}_H^{(n)}}{\mathcal{P}_0^{(n)}} = \frac{(\alpha - \Omega)\dfrac{\mathcal{P}_0^{(n+1)}}{\mathcal{P}_0^{(n)}} - (\alpha - \Omega)^2 + \Omega^2}{\Omega} \qquad [4·50b]$$

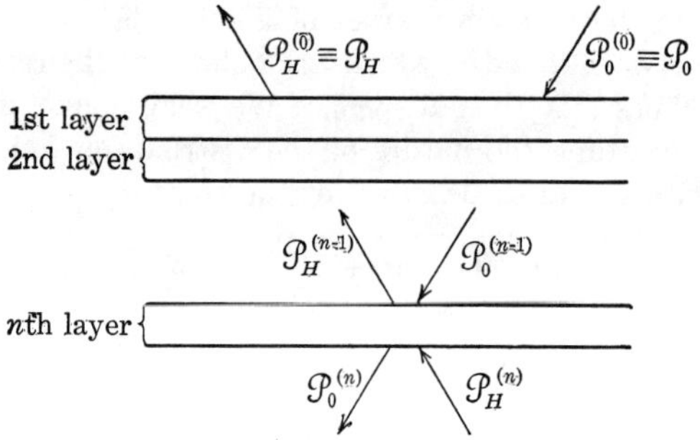

FIG. 4·2.

We shall now assume that the decrease in the power of the incident beam is exponential, i.e., $\mathcal{P}_0^{(n)} = \mathcal{P}_0^{(0)} e^{-nx}$, implying that $x = \mu \frac{t_0}{\gamma_0}$, where μ is an effective absorption coefficient. The unknown quantity x is determined by equating the two expressions for $\mathcal{P}_H^{(n)}/\mathcal{P}_0^{(n)}$ and this procedure gives

$$\cosh x = \frac{1 + \alpha^2 - 2\alpha\Omega}{2(\alpha - \Omega)} \qquad [4·51]$$

Clearly we seek a formula for the ratio $\mathcal{P}_H^{(0)}/\mathcal{P}_0^{(0)} \equiv \mathcal{P}_H/\mathcal{P}_0$. Using the result of Equation 4·51 in Equation 4·50b we find

$$\frac{\mathcal{P}_H}{\mathcal{P}_0} = \frac{2\Omega}{1 - \alpha^2 + 2\alpha\Omega + \sqrt{\{1 + \alpha^2 - 2\alpha\Omega\}^2 - 4(\alpha - \Omega)^2}} \qquad [4·52]$$

If the thickness of the blocks is so small that $\alpha \approx 1 - \mu_0 \frac{t_0}{\gamma_0}$, this equation becomes identical with Equation 4·27.

The nature of the diffraction pattern $\frac{\mathcal{P}_H}{\mathcal{P}_0}(\theta - \theta_B)$, and the value of the integrated reflecting power $\mathcal{R}_H^\theta = \int \frac{\mathcal{P}_H}{\mathcal{P}_0} d(\theta - \theta_B)$ vary greatly with the thickness of the blocks and with the distribution function W. When secondary extinction is negligible Equation 4·52 can be simplified. Negligible secondary extinction implies that the power loss due to diffraction is small compared with the power loss due to true absorption, i.e., $\Omega \ll 1 - \alpha$. When this condition is fulfilled Equation 4·52 reduces to

$$\frac{\mathcal{P}_H}{\mathcal{P}_0} = \frac{\Omega}{1 - \alpha^2} \qquad [4{\cdot}53a]$$

and hence

$$\mathcal{R}_H^\theta = \frac{R_H^\theta}{1 - \alpha^2} \qquad [4{\cdot}53b]$$

where R_H^θ is the integrated reflecting power of an ideal crystal plate of thickness t_0. When $\mu_0 \frac{t_0}{\gamma_0} \ll 1$ we may set $R_H^\theta = Q' t_0/\gamma_0$ (in accordance with Equation 4·46) and $1 - \alpha^2 \approx 2\mu_0 \frac{t_0}{\gamma_0}$ and we have the already known result $\mathcal{R}_H^\theta = Q'/2\mu_0$. On the other hand, for $\mu_0 \frac{t_0}{\gamma_0} \gg 1$ we have $\alpha^2 \approx 0$ and hence $\mathcal{R}_H^\theta = R_H^\theta$. In the latter case the blocks are so thick that the x rays do not penetrate beyond the first layer. This is readily seen from Equation 4·53a which may be given in the form

$$\frac{\mathcal{P}_H}{\mathcal{P}_0} = \sum_{n=1}^{n=\infty} \Omega\, e^{-2(n-1)\mu_0 \frac{t_0}{\gamma_0}} \qquad [4{\cdot}54]$$

where the first term in the series on the right side is the contribution from the first layer of blocks, the second term the contribution from the second layer and so forth. When $\mu_0 \frac{t_0}{\gamma_0} \gg 1$ the mosaic crystal and the perfect crystal give the same values for the integrated reflecting power, but the diffraction patterns will differ. According to Equations 4·48 the mosaic crystal diffraction pattern is composed of a number of ideal crystal diffraction peaks which are displaced relative to one another by amounts depending upon the degree of alignment of the blocks.

F. **Mosaic Crystals of Arbitrary Shape.** Our considerations have so far been limited to mosaic crystals in the form of plane parallel plates.

The general expression for the reflecting power of a mosaic crystal of arbitrary geometrical shape becomes very complicated. We shall therefore discuss only the case of negligible secondary extinction and in addition assume that $\mu_0 \dfrac{t_0}{\gamma_0} \ll 1$. In accordance with these assumptions the mean reflecting power per layer of blocks is given by

$$\Omega(\theta - \theta_B) = W(\theta_B - \theta)Q' \frac{t_0}{\gamma_0} \qquad [4\cdot55]$$

Consider now an elementary area dS of a particular layer. This area dS defines a volume element $dv = t_0\, dS$. The power incident upon the volume element is

$$I_0\, e^{-\mu_0 T_1}\, \gamma_0\, dS \qquad [4\cdot56]$$

where I_0 is the incident intensity measured outside the crystal and where T_1 is the distance which the incident beam has to travel through the mosaic crystal before it reaches the volume element under consideration. The power reflected by the volume element, as measured outside the crystal, is thus

$$I_0\, e^{-\mu_0(T_1+T_2)} W(\theta_B - \theta)Q'\, dv \qquad [4\cdot57]$$

where T_2 is the distance which the diffracted beam has to travel from the volume element to the surface of the crystal. The reflecting power of the entire crystal is thus

$$\frac{\mathcal{P}_H}{\mathcal{P}_0}(\theta - \theta_B) = \frac{W(\theta_B - \theta)Q'}{S_0} \int e^{-\mu_0(T_1+T_2)}\, dv \qquad [4\cdot58]$$

and the integrated reflecting power becomes

$$\mathcal{R}_H^\theta = \frac{Q'}{S_0} \int e^{-\mu_0(T_1+T_2)}\, dv \qquad [4\cdot59]$$

S_0 is the cross section of the incident beam, and the integration is to be extended over the irradiated part of the crystal.

The quantity

$$\frac{1}{S_0} \int e^{-\mu_0(T_1+T_2)}\, dv \qquad [4\cdot60]$$

may be termed the absorption factor. The integral can be explicitly evaluated if the crystal is a plane parallel plate. For the symmetrical Bragg case and a thick crystal plate the absorption factor becomes $1/2\mu_0$ and for the symmetrical Laue case we find $\dfrac{1}{\gamma_0} T_0 e^{-\mu_0 \frac{T_0}{\gamma_0}}$ in agreement with earlier results. For mosaic crystals of other geometrical shapes the integration in Equation 4·60 must be carried out by numerical methods.

G. **The Reflecting Power of Crystal Powders.** A sample of powdered crystals may be considered as an extreme case of a mosaic crystal. The theory presented in the preceding parts of this section may therefore be used to find the reflecting power of such a sample. It will be assumed that the crystal powder is very finely divided. True absorption in any one crystal particle may therefore be neglected. Let it be assumed further that the orientation of the ideal crystal blocks is entirely random. The latter assumption evidently implies that secondary extinction may be completely neglected. The density of the powder will be denoted by ρ' while ρ is the density of the corresponding single crystal. If μ_0 is the linear absorption coefficient of the single crystal, the absorption coefficient of the powder is thus $\mu_0 \dfrac{\rho'}{\rho}$. Similarly only a fraction ρ'/ρ of the volume of the powder sample corresponds to crystal particles.

Assuming the powder sample to be of arbitrary geometrical shape we may use the equations obtained in the preceding part of this section. The reflecting power per layer of blocks in the corresponding single crystal is given by Equation 4·55. For crystal powder we have thus

$$\Omega(\theta - \theta_B) = \frac{\rho'}{\rho} W(\theta_B - \theta)\, Q' \frac{t_0}{\gamma_0} \qquad [4\cdot61]$$

The function $W(\theta_B - \theta)$ measures the probability of finding a crystal block so oriented that the incident beam makes a glancing angle $\theta \equiv \theta_B + (\theta - \theta_B)$ with the lattice plane $\bar{B}_H$. With the assumed random orientation of the blocks this probability becomes (compare Equation 3·80) $W = \frac{1}{2} \cos \theta_B$. Accordingly the expression for the reflecting power of a powdered crystal sample becomes

$$\frac{\mathcal{P}_H}{\mathcal{P}_0} = \frac{Q'\rho' \cos \theta_B}{2S_0\rho} \int e^{-\mu_0 \frac{\rho'}{\rho}(T_1+T_2)}\, dv \qquad [4\cdot62]$$

In this equation $\mathcal{P}_H$ is the total power in the diffraction cone associated with the lattice plane $\bar{B}_H$. This cone intersects a plane normal to the incident beam in a circle Experimentally it is convenient to measure the power associated with a small section of this circle. If R is the distance from the crystal powder to the observation point, the radius of the diffraction circle becomes $R \sin 2\theta_B$ since $2\theta_B$ is the semi-apex angle of the diffraction cone. The power ratio per unit length of the diffraction circle, τ, is thus

$$\tau = \frac{Q'\rho'}{8\pi\ R\rho S_0 \sin\theta_B}\int e^{-\mu_0\frac{\rho'}{\rho}(T_1+T_2)}\ dv \tag{4·63}$$

In these equations we have used the symbol Q' rather than Q to indicate that primary extinction may not be negligible. When the particle size is less than the critical thickness given by Equation 4·32, primary extinction is truly negligible, i.e., we may use Q instead of Q'. It should be noted, however, that each crystal particle of which the powder is composed may itself be a mosaic crystal consisting of several or many ideal crystal blocks. Thus primary extinction may be negligible even though the particle size is considerably greater than the critical thickness.

4. THE HEAT MOTION

It has so far been assumed that the atoms are at rest in the crystal lattice although they actually must be vibrating about their equilibrium positions with amplitudes which are comparable to x-ray wavelengths. The thermal agitation decreases with decreasing temperature, but it does not vanish even at absolute zero because of the zero-point energy. In order to take account of the heat motion it becomes necessary to revise the ideal crystal model and give it dynamic character.

We shall assume that the atoms vibrate as entities about equilibrium positions $\bar{r}_k + \bar{A}_L$ which correspond to an ideal lattice. The instantaneous positions of the atoms are thus of the form $\bar{r}_k + \bar{A}_L + \bar{\Delta}_k^L$. It is to be expected that the vibrations will produce small changes in the electronic structure of the atoms. These perturbations will be neglected, and hence the same scattering power f_k is to be associated with each instantaneous site of a given set. Comparison with the discussion given in section 1 shows that heat motion represents disorder of the displacement type, the displacements $\bar{\Delta}_k^L$ being functions of time. We shall assume that the atomic displacements are sufficiently small so that only linear restoring forces need to be considered. The time average value of $\bar{\Delta}_k^L$ can then be set equal to zero for any L and k. As pointed out in section 1 it is justifiable to replace time averages by the corresponding spatial averages over the instantaneous structure. Accordingly we may set

$$\overline{\bar{\Delta}_k^L} = 0 \tag{4·64}$$

and the bar may be interpreted to mean either the average over time for given L, k or the average over L for given k and t.

The lattice vibrations are slow compared to x-ray frequencies, and consequently the scattering of x rays represents interaction with the instantaneous structure. The time required to make intensity measurements is, however, very long compared to the periods of the lattice vibrations. In order to obtain an intensity formula which can be directly compared with experimental observations one should accordingly proceed in the following manner: first the expression for the intensity of scattering from the instantaneous structure is to be found, and then the average value of the intensity (over t or over L) is to be formed.

For the sake of convenience we shall assume for the present that the crystal is sufficiently small to make extinction and absorption negligible. (The extension of the results to larger crystals will be discussed in section 9.) We shall imagine the little crystal to be a parallelopiped with edges $N_1\bar{a}_1$, $N_2\bar{a}_2$, $N_3\bar{a}_3$ and with n atoms per unit cell. There are thus $nN = nN_1N_2N_3$ atoms in the crystal and $0 \leq L_i \leq N_i - 1$, $k = 1, 2, \cdots n$.

The general definitions of effective scattering power g_k^L and mean effective scattering power g_k are given in Equations 4·8 and 4·9. As applied to thermal disorder these quantities become

$$g_k^L = f_k \, e^{i\bar{s}\cdot\bar{\Delta}_k^L} \qquad [4{\cdot}65a]$$

$$g_k = f_k \, \overline{e^{i\bar{s}\cdot\bar{\Delta}_k^L}} \qquad [4{\cdot}65b]$$

The expressions for amplitude and intensity of scattering from a small ideal crystal were deduced in Chapter III, sections 5 and 6. The corresponding expressions for our disordered crystal are readily found, using a similar procedure. The amplitude of scattering from the instantaneous structure becomes

$$E_{\text{xl.}} = E_e\bar{F}\sum_L e^{i\bar{s}\cdot\bar{A}_L} + E_e\sum_L e^{i\bar{s}\cdot\bar{A}_L}\sum_k \varphi_k^L \, e^{i\bar{s}\cdot\bar{r}_k} \qquad [4{\cdot}66]$$

where $\bar{F}$ and φ_k^L are given by Equations 4·12 and 4·10a. Since $\overline{\varphi_k^L} = 0$, the mean amplitude of scattering is

$$\bar{E}_{\text{xl.}} = E_e\bar{F}\sum_L e^{i\bar{s}\cdot\bar{A}_L} \qquad [4{\cdot}67]$$

The formula for the mean intensity of scattering is

$$\overline{I_{\text{xl.}}} = \frac{c}{8\pi}\overline{|E_{\text{xl.}}|^2} = J_1 + J_2 \qquad [4{\cdot}68]$$

$$J_1 = I_e|\bar{F}|^2\sum_{L,L'} e^{i\bar{s}\cdot\bar{A}_{L-L'}} = I_e|\bar{F}|^2\prod_i \frac{\sin^2\frac{1}{2}N_i\bar{s}\cdot\bar{a}_i}{\sin^2\frac{1}{2}\bar{s}\cdot\bar{a}_i} \qquad [4{\cdot}69]$$

$$J_2 = I_e\sum_{L,L'} e^{i\bar{s}\cdot\bar{A}_{L-L'}}\sum_{k,k'} f_k f_{k'}\left\{\overline{e^{i\bar{s}\cdot(\bar{\Delta}_k^L-\bar{\Delta}_{k'}^{L'})}} - \overline{e^{i\bar{s}\cdot\bar{\Delta}_k^L}}\;\overline{e^{-i\bar{s}\cdot\bar{\Delta}_{k'}^{L'}}}\right\} \qquad [4{\cdot}70]$$

It is seen that J_1 is proportional to the square of the mean amplitude. Consequently J_1 is the coherent, J_2 the incoherent part of the scattering. When the scattering is treated according to quantum mechanics the identical intensity formula is obtained, but the incoherently scattered radiation has a slightly modified frequency. This frequency shift is, however, of no importance since it is much too small to be observed.

It should be emphasized that $J_1 + J_2$ does not give the total scattering since we have neglected the scattering due to intra-atomic disorder. Hence the intensity of the Compton scattering must be added to $J_1 + J_2$ to give the correct expression for the total intensity.

The coherent part of the scattered radiation can be interpreted as the scattering from the mean lattice, and it is thus a measure of the long-range order in the dynamic lattice. Except for the difference between scattering power f_k and effective scattering power g_k, the scattering from the mean lattice is identical with that from the ideal lattice which is obtained when all atoms are frozen in their equilibrium positions. We shall therefore call J_1 the Laue-Bragg scattering. Any result which has been obtained for the scattering from a small ideal crystal will be valid for the Laue-Bragg scattering from the same crystal with heat motion considered, if everywhere in the equations f_k is replaced by g_k. It will be shown later in this chapter that the Laue-Bragg reflections are much more intense than the incoherent scattering. Accordingly the incoherent radiation can be neglected as far as primary and secondary extinction phenomena are concerned. This shows, however, that by replacing f_k by g_k also our formulas for the intensity of scattering from large ideal or mosaic crystals will be applicable to the Laue-Bragg scattering from the same crystals with heat motion taken into account.

The incoherent part of the scattering, J_2, is associated with the disorder due to the heat motion. As shown by Equation 4·70 this scattering is of much more complicated form than the Laue-Bragg scattering, and it will therefore have to be studied in considerable detail in the following sections.

5. FORMAL INTRODUCTION OF NORMAL COORDINATES

We shall assume that only central forces are acting between a pair of atoms in the dynamic lattice. Let the two atoms be of different types k and k' while r is the distance between the atoms. The forces may be derived from a potential energy function $V_{kk'}(r)$. In the dynamic lattice the atomic separations are $|\bar{r}_k - \bar{r}_{k'} + \bar{A}_{L-L'} + \bar{\Delta}_k^L - \bar{\Delta}_{k'}^{L'}|$. The total potential energy of the dynamic lattice is thus

$$V = \text{constant} + \tfrac{1}{2} \sum_{L,L'} \sum_{k,k'} V_{kk'}(|\bar{r}_k - \bar{r}_{k'} + \bar{A}_{L-L'} + \bar{\Delta}_k^L - \bar{\Delta}_{k'}^{L'}|) \qquad [4{\cdot}71]$$

while the kinetic energy is

$$T = \tfrac{1}{2}\sum_L \sum_k m_k \left(\frac{d\bar{\Delta}_k^L}{dt}\right)^2 \qquad [4·72]$$

The arbitrary constant in the expression for V may be chosen so that $V = 0$ when all the atoms are in their equilibrium positions. We shall now expand the potential energy function in terms of the displacement vectors $\bar{\Delta}_k^L$. Since we have assumed that the ideal static lattice represents a stable equilibrium state the linear terms in the expansion vanish and the quadratic terms correspond to positive quadratic forms. Assuming the displacements to be relatively small so that higher terms in the expansion may be neglected we have

$$V = \tfrac{1}{2}\sum_{L,L'}\sum_{k,k'} \bar{\Delta}_k^L \cdot \boldsymbol{\phi}_{kk'}^{L-L'} \cdot \bar{\Delta}_{k'}^{L'} \qquad [4·73]$$

The quantities $\boldsymbol{\phi}_{kk'}^{L-L'}$ are symmetrical tensors, the components being the negative second partial derivatives of $V_{kk'}$ evaluated at equilibrium. It is obviously true that $\boldsymbol{\phi}_{kk'}^{L-L'} = \boldsymbol{\phi}_{k'k}^{L'-L}$ and we shall set $\boldsymbol{\phi}_{kk'}^{0} = 0$, thus axiomatically assuming that an atom exerts no force on itself. When a constant vector $\bar{\varepsilon}$ is added to all displacements $\bar{\Delta}_k^L$, the interatomic distances do not change. Accordingly the potential energy must be invariant under the substitution $\bar{\Delta}_k^L \rightarrow \bar{\Delta}_k^L + \bar{\varepsilon}$ and this condition gives

$$\sum_{L'}\sum_{k'} \boldsymbol{\phi}_{kk'}^{L-L'} = 0 \qquad [4·74]$$

We shall assume that the thermal agitation corresponds to small vibrations of the lattice about its equilibrium state, i.e., that the potential energy is correctly given by Equation 4·73. It is then possible to describe the heat motion in terms of normal coordinates Z_i. These are formally defined by linear relations

$$\bar{\Delta}_k^L = \frac{1}{\sqrt{m_k}} \sum_{i=1}^{i=3nN} \bar{C}_{ki}^L Z_i \qquad [4·75]$$

where the coefficients $\bar{C}_{ki}^L$ satisfy the following conditions

$$\sum_i \bar{C}_{ki}^L \bar{C}_{k'i}^{L'} = \delta_{LL'}\delta_{kk'}\mathrm{I} \qquad [4·76]$$

$$\sum_i \omega_i^2 \bar{C}_{ki}^L \bar{C}_{k'i}^{L'} = \frac{1}{\sqrt{m_k m_{k'}}} \boldsymbol{\phi}_{kk'}^{L-L'} \qquad [4·77]$$

With the aid of Equations 4·76 it is possible to solve Equations 4·75 for the normal coordinates and the result is

$$Z_i = \sum_L \sum_k \sqrt{m_k}\,\bar{\Delta}_k^L \cdot \bar{C}_{ki}^L \qquad [4·78]$$

The expressions for kinetic and potential energy become

$$T = \tfrac{1}{2}\sum_i \left(\frac{dZ_i}{dt}\right)^2 \tag{4·79}$$

$$V = \tfrac{1}{2}\sum_i \omega_i^2 Z_i^2 \tag{4·80}$$

Accordingly the normal coordinates represent independent linear oscillators, $Z_i = \text{constant} \times e^{i\omega_i t}$.

The problem of finding the coefficients $\bar{C}_{ki}^L$ and the frequencies ω_i will be treated in the next section. At present we shall merely assume that this problem can be solved.

Using Equations 4·75 we have

$$\overline{e^{i\bar{s}\cdot\bar{\Delta}_k^L}} = \prod_j \overline{e^{iC_j^k Z_j}}, \quad C_j^k \equiv \frac{\bar{s}\cdot\bar{C}_{kj}^L}{\sqrt{m_k}}, \tag{4·81a}$$

$$\overline{e^{i\bar{s}\cdot(\bar{\Delta}_k^L - \bar{\Delta}_{k'}^{L'})}} = \prod_j \overline{e^{i\,[c_j^k - c_j^{k'}]Z_j}} \tag{4·81b}$$

Both of these expressions are products of factors $e^{ic_jZ_j}$ where c_j is a constant and where the average is to be extended over an assembly of linear oscillators in statistical equilibrium. It can be shown that

$$\overline{e^{ic_jZ_j}} = e^{-\frac{1}{2}c_j^2\overline{Z_j^2}} = e^{-\frac{1}{2}c_j^2\frac{Q_j}{\omega_j^2}} \tag{4·82}$$

where Q_j is the mean energy associated with the jth oscillator. Equation 4·82 is rigorously valid both in classical and in quantum statistics as shown by the investigations of I. Waller,[5] of H. Ott[6] and of M. Born and K. Sarginson.[7] We shall use the quantum expression for the mean energy Q_j and set

$$Q_j = \frac{\hbar\omega_j}{e^{\frac{\hbar\omega_j}{kT}} - 1} + \tfrac{1}{2}\hbar\omega_j \tag{4·83}$$

Making use of Equation 4·82 the averages of Equations 4·81 become

$$\overline{e^{i\bar{s}\cdot\bar{\Delta}_k^L}} = e^{-M_k} \tag{4·84a}$$

$$\overline{e^{i\bar{s}\cdot(\bar{\Delta}_k^L - \bar{\Delta}_{k'}^{L'})}} = e^{P_{kk'}^{L-L'} - M_k - M_k} \tag{4·84b}$$

[5] I. Waller, *Dissertation*, Upsala, 1925.

[6] H. Ott, *Ann. der Phys.*, **23**, 169 (1935).

[7] M. Born and K. Sarginson, *Proc. Roy. Soc.*, **A 179**, 69 (1941).

where the symbols M_k and $P_{kk'}^{L-L'}$ have the following meaning

$$M_k \equiv \frac{1}{2m_k}\,\bar{s}\cdot\left(\sum_i \bar{C}_{ki}^L \bar{C}_{ki}^L \frac{Q_i}{\omega_i^2}\right)\cdot \bar{s} \tag{4·85a}$$

$$P_{kk'}^{L-L'} \equiv \frac{1}{\sqrt{m_k m_{k'}}}\,\bar{s}\cdot\left(\sum_i \bar{C}_{ki}^L \bar{C}_{k'i}^{L'} \frac{Q_i}{\omega_i^2}\right)\cdot \bar{s} \tag{4·85b}$$

The justification for omitting a superscript L in the symbol M_k and for using the superscript $L - L'$ in the symbol $P_{kk'}^{L-L'}$ will be presented in the next section. $P_{kk'}^{L-L'}$ is usually a small quantity (this point will be discussed later) and we shall therefore make use of the approximation

$$e^{P_{kk'}^{L-L'}} \approx 1 + P_{kk'}^{L-L'} \tag{4·86}$$

The effective scattering power g_k and the intensity of the incoherent radiation J_2 can now be expressed in terms of the symbols M_k and $P_{kk'}^{L-L'}$ as follows.

$$g_k = f_k\, e^{-M_k} \tag{4·87}$$

$$J_2 = I_e \sum_{k,k'} g_k g_{k'}\, e^{i\bar{s}\cdot(\bar{r}_k - \bar{r}_{k'})} \sum_{L,L'} P_{kk'}^{L-L'}\, e^{i\bar{s}\cdot\bar{A}_{L-L'}} \tag{4·88}$$

6. STANDING WAVES AS THE NORMAL VIBRATIONS OF THE LATTICE

The results obtained in the preceding section are expressed in terms of the amplitudes $\bar{C}_{ki}^L$ and the frequencies ω_i of the normal vibrations of the lattice. In this section we shall show how these quantities can be calculated.

According to Equations 4·72 and 4·73 the equations of motion for the atoms in the lattice become

$$m_k \frac{d^2\bar{\Delta}_k^L}{dt^2} + \sum_{L'}\sum_{k'} \Phi_{kk'}^{L-L'}\cdot\bar{\Delta}_{k'}^{L'} = 0 \tag{4·89}$$

We shall try a plane wave solution

$$\bar{\Delta}_k^L = \frac{\bar{U}_{kj}}{\sqrt{m_k}}\, e^{i2\pi\bar{\tau}\cdot\bar{A}_L}\, e^{i\omega_j t} \tag{4·90}$$

$\bar{\tau}$ is the wave vector and both $\bar{U}_{kj}$ and ω_j are functions of $\bar{\tau}$, i.e., we should write $\bar{U}_{kj}(\bar{\tau})$ and $\omega_j(\bar{\tau})$. Equation 4·90 is periodic in $\bar{\tau}$ and wave vectors $\bar{\tau}$ and $\bar{\tau} + \bar{B}_H$ (where $\bar{B}_H \equiv H_1\bar{b}_1 + H_2\bar{b}_2 + H_3\bar{b}_3$) represent the same wave. In order to insure uniqueness we may therefore impose the condition

$$\tau \leq |\bar{\tau} + \bar{B}_H| \tag{4·91}$$

where $\bar{B}_H$ is any reciprocal lattice vector. Expressing in terms of the reciprocal vectors $\bar{b}_1$, $\bar{b}_2$, $\bar{b}_3$ we set

$$\bar{\tau} = \tau_1\bar{b}_1 + \tau_2\bar{b}_2 + \tau_3\bar{b}_3 \qquad [4{\cdot}92]$$

If the lattice is orthogonal the condition 4·91 implies $-\frac{1}{2} \leq \tau_i \leq +\frac{1}{2}$ and $\bar{\tau}$ lies entirely within a parallelopiped with edges $\bar{b}_1$, $\bar{b}_2$, $\bar{b}_3$ having its center at the origin of the reciprocal lattice. In the general case of a non-orthogonal lattice condition 4·91 restricts $\bar{\tau}$ to lie within a polyhedron about the origin of the reciprocal lattice. The region defined by this polyhedron is called the phase cell. Its volume is $V^{-1} = (\bar{b}_1\bar{b}_2\bar{b}_3)$ while its shape depends upon the lattice geometry.

By combining Equations 4·89 and 4·90 one finds

$$-\omega_j^2\bar{U}_{kj} + \sum_{k'} \psi_{kk'} \cdot \bar{U}_{k'j} = 0 \qquad [4{\cdot}93]$$

where the symbol $\psi_{kk'}$ is defined by

$$\psi_{kk'}(\bar{\tau}) \equiv \frac{1}{\sqrt{m_k m_{k'}}} \sum_{L'} \phi_{kk'}^{L-L'} e^{-i2\pi\bar{\tau}\cdot\bar{A}_{L-L'}} \qquad [4{\cdot}94]$$

Now $\phi_{kk'}^L$ is a symmetrical tensor and $\phi_{kk'}^L = \phi_{k'k}^{-L}$. Hence $\psi_{kk'}$ is also a symmetrical tensor and

$$\psi_{k'k}(\bar{\tau}) = \psi_{kk'}(-\bar{\tau}) = \psi_{kk'}^*(\bar{\tau}) \qquad [4{\cdot}95]$$

where ψ^* represents the complex conjugate of ψ.

To determine the frequencies ω_j the determinant of the linear and homogeneous system of Equation 4·93 is set equal to zero. As shown by Equations 4·95 the matrix of the system 4·93 is Hermitean and the secular equation has thus $3n$ real and positive roots $\omega_j^2(\bar{\tau})(j = 1, 2, \cdots 3n)$. The corresponding amplitude vectors $\bar{U}_{kj}(\bar{\tau})(k = 1, 2, \cdots n)$ can then be normalized according to

$$\sum_j \bar{U}_{kj}\bar{U}_{k'j}^* = \delta_{kk'}\,\mathrm{I} \qquad [4{\cdot}96]$$

By multiplying Equation 4·93 with $\bar{U}_{k'j}^*$, summing with respect to the index j, and using Equation 4·96, we find

$$\sum_j \omega_j^2\bar{U}_{kj}\bar{U}_{k'j}^* = \psi_{kk'} \qquad [4{\cdot}97]$$

Because of Equation 4·95 it follows that if

$$\Delta_k^L = \frac{\bar{U}_{kj}(\bar{\tau})}{\sqrt{m_k}} e^{i2\pi\bar{\tau}\cdot\bar{A}_L + i\omega_j(\bar{\tau})t}$$

is a solution of Equation 4·89 then another solution is

$$\Delta_k^L = \frac{\bar{U}_{kj}(-\bar{\tau})}{\sqrt{m_k}} e^{-i2\pi\bar{\tau}\cdot\bar{A}_L + i\omega_j(-\bar{\tau})t} = \frac{\bar{U}_{kj}^*(\bar{\tau})}{\sqrt{m_k}} e^{-i2\pi\bar{\tau}\cdot\bar{A}_L + i\omega_j(\bar{\tau})t} \qquad [4\cdot 98]$$

The sum of the two solutions and their difference multiplied by $i = \sqrt{-1}$ are also solutions. These two combinations are

$$\frac{1}{\sqrt{m_k}} [\bar{U}_{kj}(\bar{\tau}) e^{i2\pi\bar{\tau}\cdot\bar{A}_L} + \bar{U}_{kj}^*(\bar{\tau}) e^{-i2\pi\bar{\tau}\cdot\bar{A}_L}] e^{i\omega_j(\bar{\tau})t} \qquad [4\cdot 99a]$$

$$\frac{i}{\sqrt{m_k}} [\bar{U}_{kj}(\bar{\tau}) e^{i2\pi\bar{\tau}\cdot\bar{A}_L} - \bar{U}_{kj}^*(\bar{\tau}) e^{-i2\pi\bar{\tau}\cdot\bar{A}_L}] e^{i\omega_j(\bar{\tau})t} \qquad [4\cdot 99b]$$

It is readily seen that Equations 4·99 represent standing waves with real amplitudes.

Summarizing it may accordingly be stated that there are $3n$ progressive waves for any given wave vector $\bar{\tau}$. The $6n$ progressive waves corresponding to a pair of wave vectors $\pm\bar{\tau}$ can, however, be combined into $6n$ standing waves.

On the basis of the results obtained above it is possible to introduce normal coordinates Z_j by setting

$$\bar{\Delta}_k^L = \frac{1}{\sqrt{Nm_k}} \sum_p \sum_{j=1}^{j=3n} \bar{U}_{kj}(\bar{\tau}_p) e^{i2\pi\bar{\tau}_p\cdot\bar{A}_L} Z_j(\bar{\tau}_p) \qquad [4\cdot 100]$$

where $\bar{U}_{kj}(\bar{\tau}_p)$ is a solution of Equation 4·93 and where

$$\bar{\tau}_p = \tau_1\bar{b}_1 + \tau_2\bar{b}_2 + \tau_3\bar{b}_3 = \frac{2p_1 - 1}{2N_1}\bar{b}_1 + \frac{2p_2 - 1}{2N_2}\bar{b}_2 + \frac{2p_3 - 1}{2N_3}\bar{b}_3 \qquad [4\cdot 101]$$

p_1, p_2, p_3 are any three integers compatible with the condition given in Equation 4·91. The summation with respect to p in Equation 4·100 is thus to be carried out over the phase cell. Because of the periodicity of Equation 4·100 it is, however, permissible to carry out the summation over the parallelopiped of equal volume defined by

$$-N_i + 1 \leq 2p_i \leq N_i \qquad [4\cdot 102]$$

It is readily seen that for every vector $\bar{\tau}_p$ there is another vector $\bar{\tau}_{1-p} = -\bar{\tau}_p$. Since $\bar{\Delta}_k^L$ is real and since $\bar{U}_{kj}(-\bar{\tau}) = \bar{U}_{kj}^*(\bar{\tau})$, it must be demanded that

$$Z_j(-\bar{\tau}_p) = Z_j^*(\bar{\tau}_p) \qquad [4\cdot 103]$$

Hence Equation 4·100 may be written as a sum over pairs $\pm \bar{\tau}_p$

$$\bar{\Delta}_k^L = \frac{1}{\sqrt{N m_k}}$$

$$\sum_p{}' \sum_j [\bar{U}_{kj}(\bar{\tau}_p) \, e^{i2\pi\bar{\tau}_p \cdot \bar{A}_L} \, Z_j(\bar{\tau}_p) + \bar{U}_{kj}^*(\bar{\tau}_p) \, e^{-i2\pi\bar{\tau}_p \cdot \bar{A}_L} \, Z_j^*(\bar{\tau}_p)] \quad [4\cdot104]$$

where $\sum_p{}'$ indicates summation over half the phase cell. If Z_j is split into real and imaginary parts it is seen that the terms in this series correspond to standing waves of the type given in Equations 4·99. In the phase cell there are according to Equation 4·101 N vectors $\bar{\tau}_p$ or $N/2$ pairs $\pm\bar{\tau}_p$, and there are $6n$ independent standing waves for every pair $\pm\bar{\tau}_p$. Accordingly the expression 4·100 may be interpreted as a superposition of $3nN$ independent standing waves representing the normal modes of vibration of the crystal lattice. It remains to be shown, however, that the coefficients for Z_j in Equation 4·100 satisfy the conditions which transform the kinetic and potential energy expressions into

$$T = \tfrac{1}{2} \sum_p \sum_j \left| \frac{dZ_j(p)}{dt} \right|^2 \quad [4\cdot105a]$$

$$V = \tfrac{1}{2} \sum_p \sum_j \omega_j^2(p) |Z_j(p)|^2 \quad [4\cdot105b]$$

These conditions are given by Equations 4·76 and 4·77. By comparing Equations 4·75 and 4·100, we note that $\bar{C}_{ki}^L$ corresponds to $\dfrac{1}{\sqrt{N}} \bar{U}_{kj}(p) \, e^{i2\pi\bar{\tau}_p \cdot \bar{A}_L}$ while the summation with respect to the index i in Equations 4·75 and 4·77 corresponds to summation over j and p. Consequently we have to prove that

$$\sum_p \sum_j \bar{U}_{kj}(p) \bar{U}_{k'j}^*(p) \, e^{i2\pi\bar{\tau}_p \cdot \bar{A}_{L-L'}} = N \delta_{LL'} \delta_{kk'} \, \mathbf{I} \quad [4\cdot106a]$$

$$\sum_p \sum_j \omega_j^2(p) \bar{U}_{kj}(p) \bar{U}_{k'j}^*(p) \, e^{i2\pi\bar{\tau}_p \cdot \bar{A}_{L-L'}} = \frac{N}{\sqrt{m_k m_{k'}}} \, \boldsymbol{\phi}_{kk'}^{L-L'} \quad [4\cdot106b]$$

Using Equation 4·96 the left side of Equation 4·106a is transformed into

$$\delta_{kk'} \, \mathbf{I} \sum_p e^{i2\pi\bar{\tau}_p \cdot \bar{A}_{L-L'}} \quad [4\cdot107a]$$

Similarly using Equation 4·97 and the definition of $\boldsymbol{\psi}_{kk'}$ the left side of Equation 4·106b becomes

$$\frac{1}{\sqrt{m_k m_{k'}}} \, \boldsymbol{\phi}_{kk'}^{L''} \sum_p e^{i2\pi\bar{\tau}_p \cdot \bar{A}_{L-L'-L''}} \quad [4\cdot107b]$$

Consider the summation with respect to p. Assuming N_1, N_2, and N_3 to be even integers we have

$$\sum_p e^{i2\pi\bar{\tau}_p\cdot\bar{A}_{L-L'}} = \prod_i \sum_{p_i=-\frac{N_i}{2}+1}^{p_i=\frac{N_i}{2}} e^{i\pi\frac{2p_i-1}{N_i}(L_i-L_i')}$$

$$= \prod_i e^{i\pi\frac{1-N_i}{N_i}(L_i-L_i')}\frac{e^{i2\pi(L_i-L_i')}-1}{e^{\frac{i2\pi}{N_i}(L_i-L_i')}-1} = N\delta_{LL'} \qquad [4\cdot108]$$

With the aid of this result the expressions 4·107a and b reduce to the right side of Equations 4·106a and b respectively, and we have thus shown that Equation 4·100 actually represents the introduction of normal coordinates Z_j.

The formulas for M_k and $P_{kk'}^{L-L'}$ in Equations 4·85 contain the tensors $\sum_i \bar{C}_{ki}^L \bar{C}_{k'i}^{L'} \frac{Q_i}{\omega_i^2}$. Since $\bar{C}_{ki}^L$ is to be replaced by $\frac{\bar{U}_{kj}}{\sqrt{N}} e^{i2\pi\bar{\tau}_p\cdot\bar{A}_L}$ we find

$$\sum_i \bar{C}_{ki}^L \bar{C}_{k'i}^{L'} \frac{Q_i}{\omega_i^2} = \frac{kT}{N}\chi_{kk'}\, e^{i2\pi\bar{\tau}_p\cdot\bar{A}_{L-L'}} \qquad [4\cdot109]$$

where the symbol $\chi_{kk'}$ is defined by

$$\chi_{kk'}(\bar{\tau}_p) = \frac{1}{kT}\sum_j \bar{U}_{kj}(p)\bar{U}_{kj}^*(p)\frac{Q_j(p)}{\omega_j^2(p)} \qquad [4\cdot109a]$$

Hence the quantity M_k is independent of the index L, while the quantity $P_{kk'}^{L-L'}$ depends only upon the difference $\bar{A}_{L-L'}$. These facts were, indeed, anticipated when the symbols were introduced by the definitions 4·85.

The last factor in Equation 4·88 can now be evaluated. We have

$$\sum_{L,L'} P_{kk'}^{L-L'}\, e^{i\bar{s}\cdot\bar{A}_{L-L'}} = \frac{kT\bar{s}\cdot\chi_{kk'}\cdot\bar{s}}{N\sqrt{m_k m_{k'}}}\prod_i \frac{\sin^2[\frac{1}{2}N_i(\bar{s}+2\pi\bar{\tau}_p)\cdot\bar{a}_i]}{\sin^2[\frac{1}{2}(\bar{s}+2\pi\bar{\tau}_p)\cdot\bar{a}_i]}$$

$$= \begin{cases} \dfrac{NkT\bar{s}\cdot\chi_{kk'}\cdot\bar{s}}{\sqrt{m_k m_{k'}}} & \text{if } \bar{s}+2\pi\bar{\tau}_p = 2\pi\bar{B}_H \\ 0 \quad \text{if} \quad \bar{s}+2\pi\bar{\tau}_p \neq 2\pi\bar{B}_H \end{cases} \qquad [4\cdot110]$$

Accordingly the intensity formula for the incoherent radiation becomes

$$J_2(\bar{s}) = I_e NkT \sum_{k,k'} \frac{g_k g_{k'}}{\sqrt{m_k m_{k'}}}\, e^{i\bar{s}\cdot(\bar{r}_k-\bar{r}_{k'})}\bar{s}\cdot\chi_{kk'}(\bar{\tau})\cdot\bar{s} \qquad [4\cdot111]$$

where [since $\bar{s} \equiv 2\pi(\bar{k} - \bar{k}_0)]\bar{\tau}$ is given by

$$\bar{k} - \bar{k}_0 + \bar{\tau} = \bar{B}_H \qquad [4 \cdot 111a]$$

The latter equation associates a particular reciprocal lattice vector $\bar{B}_H$ and a particular vibrational wave vector $\bar{\tau}$ with each given vector $\bar{s}$. Because of the condition 4·91 Equation 4·111*a* uniquely determines both $\bar{\tau}$ and $\bar{B}_H$. Indeed, Equation 4·111*a* suggests a simple construction of $\bar{\tau}$ and $\bar{B}_H$. The given x-ray wave vectors of incidence and scattering,

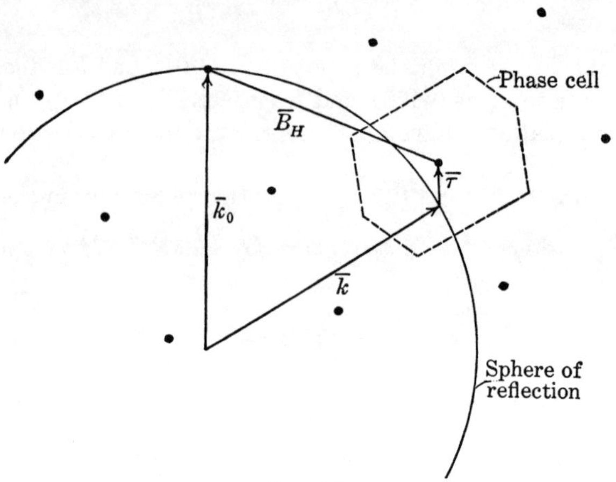

FIG. 4·3.

$-\bar{k}_0$ and $\bar{k}$, are plotted in the reciprocal lattice (compare the construction discussed in section 3·2). The reciprocal lattice point which lies closest to the terminus of the vector $\bar{k} - \bar{k}_0$ represents the sought vector $\bar{B}_H$, while the sought vector $\bar{\tau}$ is the vector separation between this vector $\bar{B}_H$ and the vector $\bar{k} - \bar{k}_0$ as shown in Fig. 4·3.

In the expression for M_k it is reasonable to replace the summation with respect to the index p by an integration over the phase cell. Since the points $\bar{\tau}_p$ are evenly distributed and since the phase cell has a volume V^{-1}, the density of the continuous distribution of vectors $\bar{\tau}$ becomes NV. Hence we have

$$M_k = \frac{VkT}{2m_k}\,\bar{s} \cdot \int_{\text{P.C.}} \chi_{kk}(\bar{\tau})\, dv \cdot \bar{s} \qquad [4 \cdot 112]$$

For many purposes sufficient accuracy is attained if the phase cell is replaced by a sphere of equal volume. The radius τ_m of this sphere is given by

$$\tau_m = \left(\frac{3}{4\pi V}\right)^{1/3} \qquad [4 \cdot 113]$$

With this approximation Equation 4·112 becomes

$$M_k = \frac{2\pi\ VkT}{m_k} \bar{s} \cdot \int_0^{\tau_m} \tau^2 \chi_{kk}(\bar{\tau})\, d\tau \cdot \bar{s} \qquad [4\cdot114]$$

The mean energy per degree of freedom $Q_j(\bar{\tau})$ can be written in the form

$$Q_j(\bar{\tau}) = kT\left(\frac{x_j}{e^{x_j} - 1} + \tfrac{1}{2}x_j\right), \quad x_j \equiv \frac{\hbar\omega_j(\bar{\tau})}{kT} \qquad [4\cdot115]$$

Hence, if x_j is small compared to unity we may set $Q_j = kT$. When this approximation is valid we have according to Equation 4·109*a*

$$\chi_{kk'} = \sum_j \frac{\bar{U}_{kj}\bar{U}^*_{k'j}}{\omega_j^2} \qquad [4\cdot116]$$

Multiplying Equation 4·93 with $\dfrac{1}{\omega_j^2}\bar{U}_{kj}$ and summing with respect to index j gives

$$\sum_{k'} \psi^*_{k''k'} \cdot \chi_{kk'} = \sum_{k'} \psi_{k'k''} \cdot \chi_{kk'} = \delta_{kk''}\,\mathbf{I} \qquad [4\cdot117]$$

Let us now introduce the symbol ψ for the $n \times n$ matrix formed by the tensors $\psi_{kk'}$ and the symbol χ for the matrix formed by the tensors $\chi_{kk'}$, i.e.,

$$\psi \equiv \begin{pmatrix} \psi_{11} & \psi_{12} & \cdots & \psi_{1n} \\ \psi_{21} & & & \\ \psi_{n1} & & & \end{pmatrix}, \quad \chi \equiv \begin{pmatrix} \chi_{11} & \chi_{12} & \cdots & \chi_{1n} \\ \chi_{21} & & & \\ \chi_{n1} & & & \end{pmatrix} \qquad [4\cdot118]$$

Equation 4·117 may then be written in the simple form $\psi \cdot \chi = \mathbf{1}$, or

$$\chi = \psi^{-1} \qquad [4\cdot119]$$

Because of Equation 4·95 both ψ and χ are Hermitean matrices. According to Equation 4·119 we have thus

$$\chi_{kk'} = (\psi^{-1})_{kk'} = \frac{\mathbf{\Delta}_{kk'}}{\Delta} \qquad [4\cdot120]$$

where Δ is the determinant of the matrix ψ and $\mathbf{\Delta}_{kk'}$ the cofactor for $\psi_{kk'}$ in this determinant.

Having deduced all basic formulas we shall next discuss these results and their significance as far as experimental observations are concerned. Our formulas can be greatly simplified if the crystal lattice contains only one atom per unit cell and the detailed discussion will therefore be restricted to this special case.

In the following, the coherent part of the scattering, J_1, from the dynamic lattice will be referred to as the Laue-Bragg scattering since it vanishes unless the Laue-Bragg equation is exactly or very nearly satisfied, i.e., unless $\bar{s} \approx 2\pi \bar{B}_H$. The incoherent part of the scattering, J_2, does not vanish for any value of the vector $\bar{s}$ (except for the trivial value $\bar{s} = 0$); it represents, in other words, diffusely scattered x rays. In order to avoid confusion with other types of incoherent scattering it is useful to adopt the name *temperature diffuse scattering* for J_2.

The Laue-Bragg scattering of the static lattice has been thoroughly discussed in Chapter III and in the first half of this chapter. This discussion remains valid also for the Laue-Bragg scattering of the dynamic lattice if everywhere the atomic scattering power f_k is replaced by the corresponding dynamic quantity $g_k = f_k e^{-M_k}$. Hence only the temperature diffuse scattering needs to be investigated further.

7. THE TEMPERATURE DIFFUSE SCATTERING OF SIMPLE LATTICES

In this section the discussion will be limited to lattices which can be represented by means of a primitive vector set $\bar{a}_1, \bar{a}_2, \bar{a}_3$ with only one atom per unit cell. Clearly, base-centered and body-centered lattices with two atoms per unit cell and face-centered lattices with four atoms per unit cell belong to this type.

Dealing with a simple lattice we set $n = 1$ and the index k can be omitted everywhere in the equations deduced in the preceding section. Accordingly the index j can assume only the values $j = 1, 2, 3$, i.e., there are only three frequency branches.

The fundamental Equation 4·93 becomes

$$-\omega_j^2 \bar{U}_j + \Psi \cdot \bar{U}_j = (\Psi - \omega_j^2 \mathbf{1}) \cdot \bar{U}_j = 0 \qquad [4{\cdot}121]$$

where Ψ is defined by

$$\Psi(\bar{\tau}) = \sum_L \Phi^L e^{-i2\pi\bar{\tau}\cdot\bar{A}_L} = \sum_L \Phi^L \cos\,(2\pi\bar{\tau}\cdot\bar{A}_L) \qquad [4{\cdot}122]$$

Thus the tensor Ψ and the three amplitudes $\bar{U}_j$ are real quantities, and $\bar{U}_1, \bar{U}_2, \bar{U}_3$ represent a set of three mutually orthogonal unit vectors. Indeed, Equation 4·121 shows that the sought directions $\bar{U}_j$ coincide with the principal axes of the tensor Ψ, while the quantities ω_j^2 are the components of Ψ referred to these principal axes.

The intensity formula for the temperature diffuse scattering of a simple lattice is

$$\frac{J_2(\bar{s})}{I_e} = \frac{NkTf^2e^{-2M}}{m}\, \bar{s} \cdot \mathrm{X} \cdot \bar{s} \qquad [4{\cdot}123]$$

where

$$M = \frac{kT}{2m}\,\bar{s}\cdot\overline{\chi}\cdot\bar{s} \qquad [4\cdot124]$$

$$\chi(\bar{\tau}) = \frac{1}{kT}\sum_j \frac{\bar{U}_j\bar{U}_j}{\omega_j^2}Q_j = \sum_j \frac{\bar{U}_j\bar{U}_j}{\omega_j^2}\frac{x_j}{2}\coth\left(\frac{x_j}{2}\right) \qquad [4\cdot125]$$

$\overline{\chi}$ is the mean value of the tensor χ over the phase cell, i.e.,

$$\overline{\chi} = V\int_{\text{P.C.}} \chi(\bar{\tau})\,dv \qquad [4\cdot126]$$

In order to solve Equations 4·121 it is necessary to know the tensor ψ. This quantity can be evaluated if the lattice geometry and the force constants are known. The interaction between a pair of atoms decreases rapidly with increasing distance between them. Hence, the series of Equation 4·122 converges rapidly. Indeed, one gets a good approximation to ψ if the interaction only with the nearest and next nearest neighbors is taken into account. As long as the amplitude of the displacement is small compared with the lattice periods one may with good approximation assume that the force between a pair of atoms is directed along the connection line between their equilibrium positions. With this approximation one may set

$$\phi^L \approx -K_L\frac{\bar{A}_L\bar{A}_L}{A_L^2} \qquad [4\cdot127]$$

where the force constant K_L decreases rapidly with increasing $\bar{A}_L$. According to Equation 4·74 $\sum_L \phi^L = 0$ and we have thus

$$\psi(\bar{\tau}) \approx 2\sum_L K_L\frac{\bar{A}_L\bar{A}_L}{A_L^2}\sin^2(\pi\bar{\tau}\cdot\bar{A}_L) \qquad [4\cdot128]$$

This equation together with symmetry considerations will in general permit a rapid evaluation of ψ in terms of the constants K_L.

It is seen from Equation 4·128 that ψ — and hence also ω_j — goes towards zero with decreasing τ. (Note that τ according to Equation 4·101 cannot be exactly zero, its smallest value being $b_i/2N_i$.) We may therefore define the velocity of propagation v_j by the relation

$$\omega_j(\bar{\tau}) = 2\pi\tau v_j(\bar{\tau}) \qquad [4\cdot129]$$

where v_j in general is a function both of the direction and of the magnitude of the wave vector $\bar{\tau}$. However, if the direction of $\bar{\tau}$ is held fixed while its magnitude is decreased towards zero, one sees from Equations 4·121 and 4·128 that v_j increases asymptotically towards a constant value. In other words, for small values of τ, i.e., for long wavelengths, the velocity v_j is independent of the magnitude of $\bar{\tau}$ although it still varies with the direction of $\bar{\tau}$.

When $x_j \ll 1$ so that the approximation $Q_j \approx kT$ may be used, we have $\chi = \psi^{-1}$. In this case we are thus able to calculate the intensity of the temperature diffuse scattering without first having to solve Equations 4·121.

According to Equations 4·123 and 4·129, J_2 is a maximum when $\bar{s} = 2\pi\bar{B}_H$, i.e., when the Laue-Bragg equation is satisfied. However, the value $\bar{\tau} = 0$ is excluded, as seen by Equation 4·101, and the smallest possible value of τ is $\dfrac{b_i}{2N_i} \approx \dfrac{1}{2(NV)^{1/3}}$. We may therefore set

$$\bar{s} \cdot \chi \cdot \bar{s} \approx 4 \frac{B_H^2}{v^2} (NV)^{2/3} \qquad [4\cdot130]$$

for

$$\bar{s} = 2\pi\bar{B}_H$$

where v is the mean value of v_j for small τ. Hence, as an admittedly crude approximation

$$\frac{J_2}{I_e} (2\pi\bar{B}_H) \approx \frac{4N^{5/3}\, V^{2/3}\, kT\, f^2\, e^{-2M}\, B_H^2}{mv^2} \qquad [4\cdot131]$$

When $\bar{s} = 2\pi\, \bar{B}_H$ theLaue-Bragg scattering does not vanish. Indeed, the maximum of J_1 coincides with that of J_2. The latter maximum is much weaker, and hence it cannot easily be detected. In the following discussion we shall therefore assume the incident x-ray wave vector to be so chosen that the Laue-Bragg equation cannot be exactly or very nearly satisfied. It is, in other words, assumed that the sphere of reflection does not pass through any reciprocal lattice point. Under these circumstances no Laue-Bragg scattering is produced and hence it cannot interfere with our observations of the temperature diffuse scattering.

A. **The Main Features of the Temperature Diffuse Scattering Pattern.** If we are interested only in the main features of the intensity distribution of the temperature diffuse scattering, an approximate evaluation of the quantity χ will suffice. We shall replace the three frequency branches ($j = 1, 2, 3$) by a single branch. It will furthermore be assumed that the frequency of this mean branch is a function only of the magnitude of the wave vector $\bar{\tau}$ and not of its direction, i.e., we set $\omega_j(\bar{\tau}) = 2\pi\tau v(\tau)$. According to Equation 4·96 $\sum_j \bar{U}_j\bar{U}_j = \mathbf{I}$ and the approximate form of Equation 4·125 becomes

$$\chi(\tau) \approx \frac{I\,Q}{4\pi^2\,kT\,v^2\tau^2} \tag{4·132}$$

The approximate intensity formula is therefore

$$\frac{J_2}{I_e}(\bar{s}) \approx \frac{4N\,f^2\,e^{-2M}\sin^2\theta}{m\lambda^2}\,\frac{Q}{v^2\tau^2} \tag{4·133}$$

The expression for the exponent M can be approximated in a similar manner. Using Equations 4·114 and 4·132 one finds readily

$$M \approx \frac{6h^2\sin^2\theta}{m\lambda^2\,k\,\Theta}\left[\frac{T}{\Theta}\,\Phi\left(\frac{\Theta}{T}\right) + \frac{1}{4}\right] \tag{4·134}$$

In this equation Θ is the characteristic temperature of the crystal. It is defined by the relation

$$\Theta \equiv \frac{h\,\bar{v}\tau_m}{k} \tag{4·135}$$

where $\bar{v}$ is the mean value of v over the phase cell. Φ is the Debye function defined by

$$\Phi(y) \equiv \frac{1}{y}\int_0^y \frac{x}{e^x - 1}\,dx \tag{4·136}$$

Of the two factors on the right side of Equation 4·133 the first is a slowly varying function of $\sin\theta/\lambda$. Accordingly the characteristic features of the intensity distribution will be chiefly determined by the second factor, $Q/v^2\tau^2$, which varies rapidly with the scattering direction. The mean energy Q can be replaced by kT when x, i.e., $\tau\Theta/\tau_m T$, is small compared with unity. The mean propagation velocity v decreases rather slowly as τ increases towards its maximum value τ_m, but it can be treated as a constant as long as τ is reasonably small. Quite generally it may be stated that the factor $Q/v^2\tau^2$ increases monotonically with decreasing τ. The temperature diffuse scattering accordingly exhibits intensity maxima in the scattering directions which correspond to minimum values of τ. The directions of the intensity maxima (and minima) are readily deduced from the reciprocal lattice construction referred to in connection with Equation 4·111*a*. Using Fig. 4·4 we find the following expression for the scattering angle $2\theta_m$ corresponding to an intensity maximum

$$\tan 2\theta_m \approx \frac{2\sin\theta_B\cos\theta_i}{1 - 2\sin\theta_B\sin\theta_i} \tag{4·137}$$

where θ_i is the actual glancing angle, θ_B the Bragg glancing angle relative to the lattice plane $\bar{B}_H$ associated with the maximum. For small differences $\theta_i - \theta_B \equiv \Delta$ Equation 4·137 becomes

$$2\theta_m \approx 2\theta_B + 2\Delta \sin^2 \theta_B \qquad [4\cdot137a]$$

These formulas for the position of the intensity maxima are not very accurate since they have been deduced from the approximate intensity expression given in Equation 4·133. In a subsequent section we shall learn that more detailed considerations lead to an appreciable modification of Equation 4·137*a*.

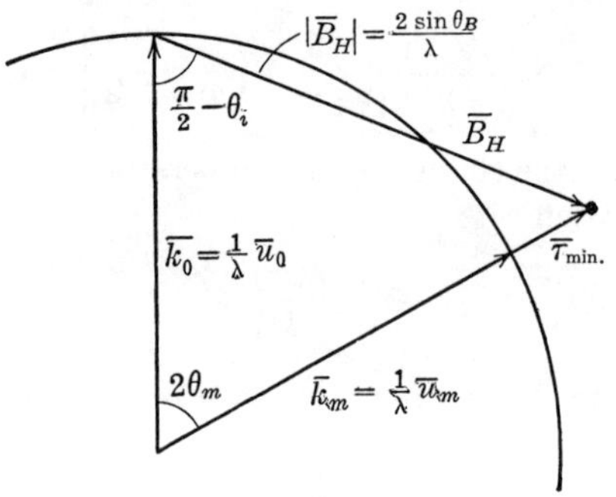

FIG. 4·4.

B. **Detailed Study of the Intensity Maxima.** In the preceding part of this section it was shown that the intensity of the temperature diffuse scattering is greatest in the directions for which the associated $\bar{\tau}$-values are smallest. The temperature diffuse scattering is very weak and accurate intensity measurements with well-defined x-ray beams are for this reason limited to scattering directions at or near the intensity maxima. It is therefore desirable to develop a more accurate intensity formula for small values of τ.

Because of the rapid convergence of the series given in Equations 4·128 we may use the following form for the tensor Ψ when τ is small compared with the reciprocal vectors b_i

$$\Psi(\bar{\tau}) = 2\pi^2 \sum_L (-\Phi^L)(\bar{\tau} \cdot \bar{A}_L)^2 \qquad [4\cdot138]$$

Equation 4·121 may then be written in the form

$$\left(\frac{\Psi}{4\pi^2\tau^2} - v_j^2\,\mathbf{1}\right) \cdot \bar{U}_j = 0 \qquad [4\cdot139]$$

where the components of the tensor $\Psi/4\pi^2\tau^2$ are quadratic functions of the direction cosines of $\bar{\tau}$. As stated earlier, the propagation velocities are accordingly functions only of the direction of the wave vector $\bar{\tau}$, but not of its magnitude.

When $\bar{\tau}$ is small compared with the vectors $\bar{b}_i$ the wavelength of the vibrational mode is long compared with the lattice periods a_i. Equation 4·139 is consequently to be identified with the well-known macroscopic equation for the elastic vibrations of a homogeneous medium.[8] This latter equation can be written in the form

$$\left(\frac{\mathbf{\Omega}}{\rho} - v_j^2\,\mathbf{1}\right) \cdot \bar{U}_j = 0 \qquad [4\cdot140]$$

For the sake of completeness we shall give the expression for the tensor $\mathbf{\Omega}$ for the most general case (triclinic crystal). It is

$$\mathbf{\Omega} = \bar{\tau}_u \cdot \begin{pmatrix} \begin{pmatrix} c_{11} & c_{16} & c_{15} \\ c_{61} & c_{66} & c_{65} \\ c_{51} & c_{56} & c_{55} \end{pmatrix} & \begin{pmatrix} c_{16} & c_{12} & c_{14} \\ c_{66} & c_{62} & c_{64} \\ c_{56} & c_{52} & c_{54} \end{pmatrix} & \begin{pmatrix} c_{15} & c_{14} & c_{13} \\ c_{65} & c_{64} & c_{63} \\ c_{55} & c_{54} & c_{53} \end{pmatrix} \\ \begin{pmatrix} c_{61} & c_{66} & c_{65} \\ c_{21} & c_{26} & c_{25} \\ c_{41} & c_{46} & c_{45} \end{pmatrix} & \begin{pmatrix} c_{66} & c_{62} & c_{64} \\ c_{26} & c_{22} & c_{24} \\ c_{46} & c_{42} & c_{44} \end{pmatrix} & \begin{pmatrix} c_{65} & c_{64} & c_{63} \\ c_{25} & c_{24} & c_{23} \\ c_{45} & c_{44} & c_{43} \end{pmatrix} \\ \begin{pmatrix} c_{51} & c_{56} & c_{55} \\ c_{41} & c_{46} & c_{45} \\ c_{31} & c_{36} & c_{35} \end{pmatrix} & \begin{pmatrix} c_{56} & c_{52} & c_{54} \\ c_{46} & c_{42} & c_{44} \\ c_{36} & c_{32} & c_{34} \end{pmatrix} & \begin{pmatrix} c_{55} & c_{54} & c_{53} \\ c_{45} & c_{44} & c_{43} \\ c_{35} & c_{34} & c_{33} \end{pmatrix} \end{pmatrix} \cdot \bar{\tau}_u \qquad [4\cdot141]$$

The coefficients $c_{ij} = c_{ji}$ are the elastic constants in Voigt's notation, ρ is the density of the crystal, and $\bar{\tau}_u \equiv \dfrac{\bar{\tau}}{\tau}$.

A comparison of Equations 4·139 and 4·130 shows that

$$\mathbf{\Psi} = \frac{4\pi^2\tau^2}{\rho}\mathbf{\Omega} \qquad [4\cdot142]$$

Since τ/τ_m is assumed to be small the approximation $Q_j = kT$ is valid at any temperature except in the immediate neighborhood of the absolute zero point. Accordingly we have $\mathbf{X} = \mathbf{\Psi}^{-1}$ or

$$\mathbf{X} = \frac{\rho}{4\pi^2\tau^2}\mathbf{\Omega}^{-1} \qquad [4\cdot143]$$

Setting $\bar{s} \approx 2\pi\bar{B}_H$ (since τ is supposed to be very small compared with B_H), the intensity formula becomes

$$\frac{J_2}{I_e} = \frac{kTf^2\,e^{-2M}}{V^2}\,\frac{\bar{B}_H \cdot \mathbf{\Omega}^{-1} \cdot \bar{B}_H}{\tau^2}\,\delta V \qquad [4\cdot144]$$

[8] W. Voigt, *Lehrbuch der Kristallphysik*, Leipzig and Berlin, 1910.

where $\delta V = NV$ is the volume of the crystal. The first factor in this expression is a slowly varying function of the scattering direction and may be treated as a constant if we restrict our considerations to a small solid angle about an intensity maximum. The intensity distribution within such a solid angle is thus determined by the second factor, $(\bar{B}_H \cdot \mathbf{\Omega}^{-1} \cdot \bar{B}_H)/\tau^2$.

The expression for the tensor $\mathbf{\Omega}$ as given in Equation 4·141 holds for an arbitrary triclinic crystal. In this section we are, however, restricting the considerations to lattices with only one atom per unit cell and it would seem that this restriction implies the existence of relationships between some of the elastic constants c_{ij}. Using Equations 4·138 and 4·142, we have

$$\Omega_{ij} = \frac{\rho}{2}\bar{\tau}_u \cdot [\sum_L (-\phi^L)_{ij}\bar{A}_L\bar{A}_L] \cdot \bar{\tau}_u \qquad [4\cdot145]$$

The tensor $\sum(-\phi^L)_{ij}\bar{A}_L\bar{A}_L$ is clearly symmetrical, and the elements of the matrix in Equation 4·141 should accordingly be symmetrical tensors too. The following conditions should thus be fulfilled

$$\begin{aligned} c_{44} &= c_{23}, & c_{36} &= c_{45} \\ c_{55} &= c_{13}, & c_{46} &= c_{25} \\ c_{66} &= c_{12}, & c_{56} &= c_{14} \end{aligned} \qquad [4\cdot146]$$

These are the celebrated Cauchy relations which would reduce the macroscopic elastic constants of simple triclinic lattices from 21 to 15. It should be remembered, however, that we have treated the interaction between atoms in the dynamic lattice as interaction between particles. This simplification is clearly not valid, and hence we cannot expect the Cauchy relations to hold. Indeed, measurements show that the Cauchy relations rarely are fulfilled.

The expressions for the tensors $\mathbf{\Omega}$ and $\mathbf{\Omega}^{-1}$ are quite complicated for crystals with low symmetry. We shall therefore give the explicit forms of these tensors only for cubic crystals. If the tensor $\mathbf{\Omega}$ is to be invariant under cubic symmetry operations one must require $c_{11} = c_{22} = c_{33}$, $c_{44} = c_{55} = c_{66}$, $c_{12} = c_{13} = c_{23}$, and the remaining elastic constants must vanish. Setting $\bar{\tau}_u = \alpha_1\bar{\imath} + \alpha_2\bar{\jmath} + \alpha_3\bar{k}$ where $\bar{\imath}$, $\bar{\jmath}$, $\bar{k}$ are unit vectors along the cube edges (so that $\alpha_1, \alpha_2, \alpha_3$ are the direction cosines of $\bar{\tau}$), one finds

$$\Omega_{11} = c_{44} + (c_{11} - c_{44})\alpha_1^2, \quad \Omega_{12} = (c_{12} + c_{44})\alpha_1\alpha_2$$

$$\Omega_{11}^{-1} = \frac{c_{44}[c_{11} - (c_{11} - c_{44})\alpha_1^2] + b(c_{11} + c_{12})\alpha_2^2\alpha_3^2}{\Delta} \qquad [4\cdot147]$$

$$\Omega_{12}^{-1} = -\frac{(c_{12} + c_{44})(c_{44} + b\alpha_3^2)\alpha_1\alpha_2}{\Delta}$$

The remaining components are obtained from those given by means of cyclic interchanges. The quantities b and Δ are defined as follows

$$b \equiv c_{11} - c_{12} - 2c_{44}$$

$$\Delta \equiv c_{11}c_{44}^2 + b^2(c_{11} + 2c_{12} + c_{44})\alpha_1^2\alpha_2^2\alpha_3^2 + bc_{44}(c_{11} + c_{12})(\alpha_2^2\alpha_3^2 + \alpha_3^2\alpha_1^2 + \alpha_1^2\alpha_2^2) \qquad [4·148]$$

The tensors $\mathbf{\Omega}$ and $\mathbf{\Omega}^{-1}$ assume particularly simple forms when the isotropy condition $b = 0$ is fulfilled. We have then

$$\mathbf{\Omega} = c_{44}\,\mathbf{1} + (c_{11} - c_{44})\bar{\tau}_u\bar{\tau}_u$$

$$\mathbf{\Omega}^{-1} = \frac{1}{c_{44}}\mathbf{1} + \left(\frac{1}{c_{11}} - \frac{1}{c_{44}}\right)\bar{\tau}_u\bar{\tau}_u \qquad [4·149]$$

and hence

$$\bar{B}_H \cdot \mathbf{\Omega}^{-1} \cdot \bar{B}_H = B_H^2\frac{c_{44} + (c_{11} - c_{44})\cos^2\varphi}{c_{11}c_{44}} \qquad [4·150]$$

where $\frac{\pi}{2} - \varphi$ is the angle between $\bar{B}_H$ and $\bar{\tau}$, i.e., φ is the angle between $\bar{\tau}$ and the lattice plane. The approximation given in Equation 4·132 is thus not valid even in isotropic crystals. The factor τ^{-2} in the intensity formula of Equation 4·144 is a maximum when $\bar{\tau} = \bar{\tau}_{\text{min.}}$ where

$$\bar{\tau}_{\text{min.}} = \left\{1 - \frac{k_0}{|\bar{B}_H + \bar{k}_0|}\right\}(\bar{B}_H + \bar{k}_0) \qquad [4·151]$$

$\bar{\tau}_{\text{min.}}$ is a vector in the plane of incidence making an angle approximately equal to θ_B with the lattice plane $(H_1H_2H_3)$. Its magnitude is approximately given by

$$\lambda\tau_{\text{min.}} \approx -\Delta\sin 2\theta_B \qquad [4·152]$$

where $\Delta = \theta_i - \theta_B$. Since the direction of the intensity maximum lies in the plane of incidence we shall consider the intensity distribution in this plane only. The intensity formula becomes

$$\frac{J_2}{I_e}(2\theta) = \frac{kTf^2e^{-2M}}{V^2c_{11}c_{44}\Delta^2\cos^2\theta_B}\,\delta V\{c_{44} + (c_{11} - c_{44})\cos^2\varphi\}\cos^2(\theta_B - \varphi) \qquad [4·153]$$

The scattering angle 2θ and the angle φ are related as follows.

$$2\theta \approx 2\theta_B + \frac{2\Delta}{1 + \cot \theta_B \cot \varphi} \qquad [4\cdot154]$$

The intensity is a maximum when $\varphi = \varphi_m$ where

$$\tan (\theta_B - \varphi_m) = \frac{(c_{11} - c_{44}) \tan \varphi_m}{c_{11} + c_{44} \tan^2 \varphi_m} \qquad [4\cdot155]$$

For small values of θ_B the following approximation may be used.

$$\varphi_m \approx \frac{c_{11}}{2c_{11} - c_{44}} \theta_B \qquad [4\cdot155a]$$

By comparing with Equation 4·137*a*, it is seen that the shift of the diffuse maximum from the Bragg position, i.e., $2\theta_m - 2\theta_B$, for an isotropic crystal is smaller than the value indicated by the approximate formula.

It may be stated quite generally that the approximate location of the diffuse intensity maxima is determined by the factor τ^{-2}, while the detailed structure of the maximum depends upon the factor $\bar{B}_H \cdot \Omega^{-1} \cdot \bar{B}_H$. In the isotropic case discussed above the expression $(\bar{B}_H \cdot \Omega^{-1} \cdot \bar{B}_H)/\tau^2$ is a maximum for only one value of $\boldsymbol{\tau}$, and the corresponding scattering direction lies in the plane of incidence.

8. THE TEMPERATURE DIFFUSE SCATTERING OF POLYATOMIC LATTICES

In this section we shall discuss the temperature diffuse scattering of lattices with more than one atom per unit cell. For the sake of convenience we shall consider only small values of the wave vector $\boldsymbol{\tau}$.

In a simple lattice all three frequencies ω_j go towards zero with decreasing $\boldsymbol{\tau}$. There are $3s$ rather than three frequency branches in a polyatomic lattice. We shall show that the frequencies of three of these branches approach zero with diminishing τ, while the remaining $3s - 3$ frequencies approach finite values $\omega_j^0 \neq 0$. For small values of $\boldsymbol{\tau}$ one may accordingly set

$$\begin{aligned} j &= 1, 2, 3, \quad \omega_j = 2\pi v \tau_j \\ j &= 4, \cdots 3s, \quad \omega_j = \omega_j^0 + 2\pi v_j \tau \end{aligned} \qquad [4\cdot156]$$

The frequency branches $j = 1, 2, 3$ are said to be of acoustical type, the branches $j = 4, \cdots 3s$ of optical type.

Let us consider the acoustical branches. If $\omega_j = 0$ for $\tau = 0$, Equation 4·93 demands

$$\sum_{k'} \frac{1}{\sqrt{m_{k'}}} \Phi_{kk'}^{L} \cdot \bar{U}_{k'j} = 0 \qquad [4\cdot157]$$

Because of Equation 4·74 this condition is satisfied if

$$\bar{U}_{kj} = \sqrt{m_k}\bar{V}_j \qquad [4\cdot158]$$

where $\bar{V}_j$ is an arbitrary vector. For small values of $\bar{\tau}$ Equation 4·93 becomes (again using Equation 4·74)

$$-4\pi^2 v_j^2 \tau^2 m_k \bar{V}_j - [i2\pi\bar{\tau} \cdot \sum_{k'}\sum_{L} \Phi_{kk'}^{L} \bar{A}_L$$
$$+ 2\pi^2 \bar{\tau} \cdot \sum_{k'}\sum_{L} \Phi_{kk'}^{L} \bar{A}_L \bar{A}_L \cdot \bar{\tau}] \cdot \bar{V}_j = 0 \qquad [4\cdot159]$$

Next we sum with respect to the index k. The sum $\sum_{k}\sum_{k'}\sum_{L}\Phi_{kk'}^{L}\bar{A}_L$ contains pairs $\Phi_{kk'}^{L}\bar{A}_L$ and $\Phi_{k'k}^{-L}\bar{A}_{\bar{L}} = -\Phi_{k'k}^{-L}\bar{A}_L$, and all pairs vanish since $\Phi_{kk'}^{L} = \Phi_{k'k}^{-L}$. Hence we find

$$\left[\frac{1}{\rho}\Omega - v_j^2 \mathbf{1}\right] \cdot \bar{V}_j = 0 \qquad [4\cdot160]$$

where

$$\Omega = -\frac{1}{2V}\bar{\tau}_u \cdot \sum_{k}\sum_{k'}\sum_{L} \Phi_{kk'}^{L} \bar{A}_L \bar{A}_L \cdot \bar{\tau}_u \qquad [4\cdot160a]$$

V being the volume of the unit cell. The components of the tensor Ω are thus quadratic functions of the direction cosines of the vector $\bar{\tau}$.

According to Equation 4·100 the vibrational modes corresponding to the solutions 4·158 represent nearly equal displacements for neighboring atoms. Equation 4·160 is therefore to be identified with the corresponding macroscopic equation for the vibrations of the homogeneous crystal medium. The tensor Ω can thus be expressed in terms of the macroscopic elastic constants. This macroscopic form of Ω (for a triclinic crystal) was given in Equation 4·141.

The characteristic equation of the system (4·160) has only three roots v_j^2. Consequently there are only three solutions of the type given in Equation 4·158, i.e., there exist three frequency branches of the acoustical type. The three vibration directions $\bar{V}_j$ are mutually orthogonal. According to Equation 4·96 the vectors $\bar{V}_j$ are to be normalized so that

$$\sum_{j=1}^{j=3} \bar{V}_j \bar{V}_j = \frac{1}{\sum_k m_k} \mathbf{I} \qquad [4\cdot161]$$

Since τ is assumed to be small, the quantity $\chi_{kk'}$ occurring in the intensity formula 4·111 is given by Equation 4·116. This equation can be written in the form

$$\chi_{kk'} = \sqrt{m_k m_{k'}} \sum_{j=1}^{j=3} \frac{\bar{V}_j \bar{V}_j}{\omega_j^2} + \sum_{j=4}^{j=3s} \frac{\bar{U}_{kj} \bar{U}^*_{k'j}}{\omega_j^2} \qquad [4\cdot162]$$

Because of Equation 4·156 we are justified in neglecting the second term of this expression when τ is small. The quantity $\sum_{j=1}^{j=3} \frac{\bar{V}_j \bar{V}_j}{\omega_j^2}$ can be expressed in terms of the tensor $\mathbf{\Omega}$. To show this we shall multiply Equation 4·160 with $\frac{\bar{V}_j}{\omega_j^2}$, sum with respect to the index j, and use the normalization condition 4·161. The result is

$$\mathbf{\Omega} \cdot \sum_{j=1}^{j=3} \frac{\bar{V}_j \bar{V}_j}{\omega_j^2} = \frac{\rho\, \mathrm{I}}{4\pi^2 \tau^2 \sum_k m_k} = \frac{\mathrm{I}}{4\pi^2 \tau^2 V} \qquad [4\cdot163]$$

Hence we have

$$\frac{\chi_{kk'}}{\sqrt{m_k m_{k'}}} = \frac{\mathbf{\Omega}^{-1}}{4\pi^2 \tau^2 V} \qquad [4\cdot164]$$

With this approximation the intensity formula of Equation 4·111 becomes

$$\frac{J_2}{I_e} = \frac{kT|\bar{F}|^2}{V^2} \frac{\bar{s} \cdot \mathbf{\Omega}^{-1} \cdot \bar{s}}{4\pi^2 \tau^2} \delta V \qquad [4\cdot165]$$

where

$$\bar{F} \equiv \sum_k g_k \, e^{i\bar{s} \cdot \bar{r}_k} = \sum_k f_k \, e^{-M_k} e^{i\bar{s} \cdot \bar{r}_k} \qquad [4\cdot166]$$

may be called the dynamic structure factor. Since $\bar{\tau}$ is small (by assumption) it is justifiable to replace $\bar{s}$ by the approximate value $2\pi \bar{B}_H$ and Equation 4·165 goes into

$$\frac{J_2}{I_e} = \frac{kT|\bar{F}_H|^2}{V^2} \frac{\bar{B}_H \cdot \mathbf{\Omega}^{-1} \cdot \bar{B}_H}{\tau^2} \delta V \qquad [4\cdot167]$$

It is readily seen that the corresponding formula for a simple lattice, Equation 4·144, represents a special case ($\bar{F}$ reduces to fe^{-M} for a simple lattice).

Once the elastic constants are known we are thus able to calculate the intensity distribution of the temperature diffuse scattering for any crystal in scattering directions corresponding to reasonably small values of τ.

9. COMPARISON WITH EXPERIMENTS

The formulas for the temperature diffuse scattering developed in the preceding section are valid for a small crystal in which true absorption and extinction can be neglected. The calculations assume furthermore that the incident and scattered x-ray wave vectors can be sharply defined relative to the crystal lattice. As shown by the general formula of Equation 4·111, when these conditions are fulfilled, the intensity of scattering is proportional to the volume of the little crystal. Quite generally we may therefore set

$$\frac{J_2}{I_0} = \frac{K}{R^2}\,\delta V \qquad [4\cdot168]$$

where I_0 is the incident intensity, R the distance from the crystal to the observation point, δV the volume of the crystal. The symbol K is an abbreviation for the expression

$$K \equiv \left(\frac{e^2}{mc^2}\right)^2 \frac{1+\cos^2 2\theta}{2}\,\frac{kT}{V}\sum_k\sum_{k'} g_k g_{k'}\, e^{i\bar{s}\cdot(\bar{r}_k-\bar{r}_{k'})}\,\bar{s}\cdot\frac{\chi_{kk'}}{\sqrt{m_k m_{k'}}}\cdot\bar{s} \qquad [4\cdot169]$$

It is of interest to compare Equation 4·168 with the results obtained for the Laue-Bragg scattering of a small crystal. We learned that the total scattering associated with a Laue-Bragg reflection, i.e., the total blackening of a Laue-Bragg spot on the photographic plate, must be measured in terms of the integrated reflecting power. It was shown (see Equation 3·78) that the integrated reflecting power of a small crystal is directly proportional to the scattering volume. The relative blackening of the temperature diffuse scattering and of the Laue-Bragg scattering is thus independent of the crystal size. (This statement is clearly true even when true absorption phenomena are taken into account, since true absorption affects both types of scattering in the same manner. The statement is, however, not valid for large crystals of the perfect kind in which extinction is great, since extinction occurs only when the Laue-Bragg equation is satisfied.) One of the opponents of the theory of temperature diffuse scattering has argued that the Laue-Bragg scattering is proportional to the square of the crystal volume.[9] The intensity of a Laue-Bragg reflection for a small crystal is truly proportional to N^2 at the center of the diffraction pattern as shown by Equation 3·54. In section 3·7 we show, however, that it is the area under the diffraction pattern which is observed experimentally and which thus measures the blackening of a Laue-Bragg spot. But the area under the

[9] C. V. Raman, *Proc. Ind. Acad. Sci.*, **13**, 330 (1941); *Proc. Roy. Soc.*, **179**, 289 (1942).

diffraction pattern is proportional to N, i.e., to the volume of the crystal. The argument put forth by this opponent of the theory is thus incorrect.

Let us assume at first that the crystal truly is small enough so that Equation 4·168 can be used. Assuming the cross section of the crystal to be greater than the cross section of the incident beam δV in Equation 4·168 obviously is to be interpreted as the volume of the scattering part of the crystal. We have then

$$\delta V = S_0 t_0 \qquad [4{\cdot}170]$$

where S_0 is the cross section of the incident beam and t_0 the mean thickness of the crystal parallel to the incident beam. Equation 4·168 may then be written in the form

$$\frac{J_2}{I_0} = K t_0 \sigma \qquad [4{\cdot}171]$$

where $\sigma \equiv S_0/R^2$ can be interpreted as the solid angle subtended by the incident beam (the incident beam is assumed to be strictly parallel). In order to be able to measure the variation of J_2 with scattering direction it is necessary to make σ so small that J_2 does not vary appreciably for scattering directions within this solid angle.

We shall next show that the expression 4·171 is a special case of a general formula which holds for absorbing crystals. Most experimental investigations of the temperature diffuse scattering have indeed been made with large crystals for which absorption phenomena cannot be neglected.

In agreement with an earlier understanding we suppose the incident x-ray wave vector to be so chosen that no Laue-Bragg scattering is produced. Extinction, which by definition is absorption caused by the production of Laue-Bragg scattering, is then zero and the intensity decrease of an x-ray beam passing through the crystal can be described in terms of the linear absorption coefficient μ. For purposes of discussion we shall write

$$\mu = \mu_0 + \mu_C + \mu_T \qquad [4{\cdot}172]$$

μ_0 is the true absorption coefficient, μ_C and μ_T are the contributions to the linear absorption coefficient due to Compton scattering and temperature diffuse scattering respectively. μ_T is a function of the temperature, and it may also show a slight variation with the direction of incidence. Ordinarily $\mu_C + \mu_T$ is small compared with μ_0, and the dependence of μ on temperature and propagation direction cannot easily be demonstrated experimentally.

Consider a volume element dV in the interior of a large crystal. The intensity of scattering due to this volume element is given by Equation 4·168 if I_0 is the incident intensity at the volume element and if the absorption of the scattered radiation is neglected. Taking account of the absorption of incident and of scattered radiation we have

$$\frac{J_2}{I_0} = \frac{K}{R^2} \int e^{-\mu(t_1+t_2)} \, dV \tag{4·173}$$

where the integration is to be extended over the irradiated part of the crystal. I_0 is the incident intensity outside the crystal, t_1 is the length of path along an incident ray from the crystal surface to the volume element, and t_2 is the length of path along a scattered ray from the volume element to the crystal surface. The integral can be expressed in the form

$$\int e^{-\mu(t_1+t_2)} \, dV = S_0 A \tag{4·174}$$

The quantity A may be called the absorption factor, and it is easily evaluated if the crystal has the shape of a plane-parallel plate (compare Equation 4·60). Hence we have

$$\frac{J_2}{I_0} = KA\sigma \tag{4·175}$$

For small crystals where $\mu(t_1 + t_2) \approx 0$, A becomes t_0 and Equation 4·175 reduces to Equation 4·171.

It is seen that the intensity ratio J_2/I_0 is proportional to the solid angle σ. As a consequence estimates of the intensity ratio given by different investigators show a wide divergence. In order to get comparable results it is clearly necessary to give intensity ratios per unit solid angle σ.

It is of value to have an idea of the order of magnitude of the intensity ratio, and we shall therefore carry out a numerical computation. Sodium chloride will be chosen as a suitable example. The elastic constants of this crystal are $c_{11} = 5.02 \times 10^{11}$, $c_{12} = 1.31 \times 10^{11}$, $c_{44} = 1.27 \times 10^{11}$. We shall get considerable simplification in our formulas without appreciable loss of accuracy if the values $c_{11} = 4.5 \times 10^{11}$, $c_{12} = c_{44} = 1.5 \times 10^{11}$ are used rather than the correct ones. Assuming τ to be small and using formulas given in the preceding sections, Equation 4·169 becomes

$$K = \left(\frac{\mathrm{e}^2}{mc^2}\right)^2 \frac{1 + \cos^2 2\theta_B}{6 \cos^2 \theta_B} \frac{kT|\overline{F}|^2}{V^2 c_{44} \Delta^2} (1 + \cos^2 \varphi) \cos^2 (\theta_B - \varphi) \tag{4·176}$$

The dynamic structure factor $\overline{F}$ defined by Equation 4·166 may change quite rapidly with $\bar{s}$ and the approximation $\bar{s} \approx 2\pi\bar{B}_H$ in the expression for $\bar{F}$ is therefore permissible only if τ is very small. This statement has interesting implications. Although a Laue-Bragg reflection is zero because $\bar{F}(2\pi\bar{B}_H) = 0$, a diffuse maximum may be associated with this lattice plane since the dynamic structure factor for the diffuse scattering is $\bar{F}(2\pi\bar{B}_H - 2\pi\bar{\tau})$ and generally different from zero. Inserting numerical values for the known quantities K becomes

$$K = 3.8 \times 10^{-10} \frac{1 + \cos^2 2\theta_B}{\cos^2 \theta_B} \frac{T|\bar{F}|^2}{\Delta^2} \times (1 + 2\cos^2 \varphi) \cos^2 (\theta_B - \varphi) \qquad [4\cdot177a]$$

We are interested in the intensity at the diffuse maximum associated with the lattice plane (200). Assuming Cu $K\alpha$ radiation $\lambda = 1.54$ A we have $\theta_B = 15° \, 50'$, $\varphi_m = 9° \, 30'$, $|\bar{F}| \approx 80$. Hence

$$K_{\text{max.}} = 1.3 \times 10^{-5} \frac{T}{\Delta^2} \qquad [4\cdot177b]$$

For $T = 290°$ and $|\Delta| = 1°$, we have thus $K_{\text{max.}} = 12$. If the crystal is very thick and if the directions of incidence and scattering correspond to the symmetrical Bragg case, $A = \dfrac{1}{2\mu}$ where $\mu = 160$ for the wavelength used. This gives then

$$\left.\begin{array}{l} T = 290 \\ |\Delta| = 1° \\ A = \dfrac{1}{320} \end{array}\right. \quad \left(\frac{J_2}{I_0}\right)_{\text{max.}} = 4 \times 10^{-2}\sigma \qquad [4\cdot177c]$$

In order to attain sufficient resolution in the measurements it must be demanded that J_2 varies but little within the solid angle σ. This requires σ to be small compared to $(\Delta \sin 2\theta_B)^2$, i.e., $\sigma < 10^{-4}$. As a suitable value for σ we shall use $\sigma = 4 \times 10^{-5}$ (corresponding, say, to $R = 5$ cm. and a circular aperture of diameter 0.36 mm.). The resulting value for J_2/I_0 is 1.6×10^{-6}. Thus a 170-hour exposure would be needed to produce the same blackening at the center of the diffuse maximum (for $|\Delta| = 1°$) as is obtained with a 1-second exposure of the incident beam.

The result of this numerical calculation is in general agreement with the estimate of the order of magnitude of J_2/I_0 given by various experimenters.

We shall next consider the variation of the intensity of the diffuse scattering with temperature. Since we are primarily interested in getting the main features of the temperature variation, somewhat crude approximations will suffice. For the sake of convenience we shall again restrict the discussion to scattering directions at or near the intensity maxima. We shall, in other words, assume τ to be relatively small so that the optical frequency branches do not contribute appreciably to the intensity of scattering.

Under these conditions the following expression is a reasonably good approximation to the correct intensity formula

$$J_2 \approx \frac{I_e|F|^2\, e^{-2M}Q}{V^2}\, \frac{\bar{s}\cdot\Omega^{-1}\cdot\bar{s}}{4\pi^2\tau^2}\,\delta V \qquad [4{\cdot}178]$$

In this equation M is the mean value of M_k for the different atoms and Q is the mean value of Q_j for the three acoustical branches. For M we may consequently use the expression given in Equation 4·134, interpreting m as the mean atomic mass. Similarly we have

$$Q = \frac{hv\tau}{2}\coth\left(\frac{hv\tau}{2kT}\right) \qquad [4{\cdot}179]$$

where v is the mean value of the propagation velocities. Disregarding the variation of v with τ we may introduce the mean characteristic temperature Θ defined by Equation 4·135, and hence we may set

$$Q = \frac{hv\tau}{2}\coth\left(\frac{\tau\Theta}{2\tau_m T}\right) \qquad [4{\cdot}179a]$$

As T decreases towards zero, Q will asymptotically approach the zero-point energy value of $hv\tau/2$. Accordingly the temperature diffuse scattering does not completely vanish at absolute zero. In order to follow the intensity variation with temperature let us express the intensity at a temperature T in terms of the intensity at $T = 0$, assuming $\bar{s}$ and $\bar{\tau}$ to remain constant. Using Equations 4·134 and 4·178, one readily finds

$$\frac{(J_2)_T}{(J_2)_0} \approx e^{-a\frac{\sin^2\theta}{\lambda^2}\frac{\phi(y)}{y}}\coth\left(\frac{y\tau}{2\tau_m}\right) \qquad [4{\cdot}180]$$

where $y = \Theta/T$ and $a = 12h^2/mk\Theta$. This formula is illustrated graphically in Fig. 4·5. The rock salt curves are obtained using $\sin\theta/\lambda = 1/2d_{200}$, $\Theta = 281°$ K., and $\tau/\tau_m = 0.25$ and 0.10. The values for the diamond curves are $\sin\theta/\lambda = 1/2d_{111}$, $\Theta = 1800°$ K., and $\tau/\tau_m = 0.25$ and 0.10. The two curves clearly demonstrate the differences in the behavior of soft and hard crystals. If the temperature is raised from absolute zero to room temperature the diffuse scattering from rock salt is increased by a factor of 8 for $\tau/\tau_m = 0.25$, while the corresponding factor for diamond is only 1.6.

Unfortunately there are few experimental data with which to test Equation 4·180 quantitatively. Baltzer[10] has measured the ratio of

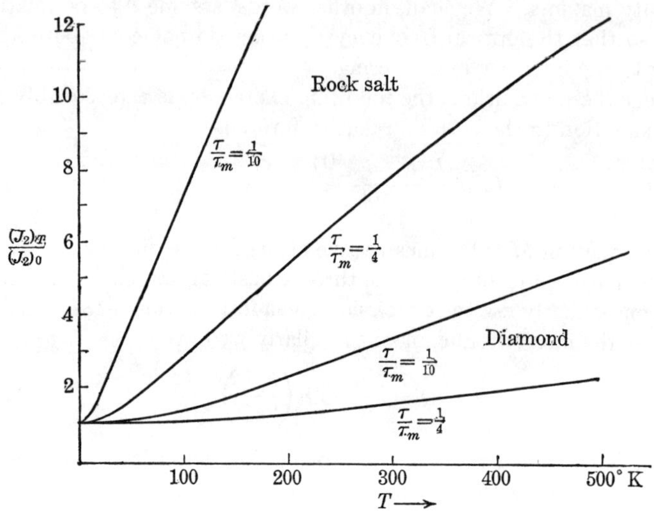

FIG. 4·5.

intensities observed at $T = 300°$ and $T = 100°$ for the diffuse maxima associated with the lattice planes (200), (400), and (600) of rock salt. His observed values and the values calculated from Equation 4·180 are given in Table 4·2.

TABLE 4·2

TEMPERATURE VARIATION OF THE INTENSITY OF DIFFUSE SCATTERING FOR ROCK SALT

Associated Lattice Plane	$\frac{\tau}{\tau_m}$	$\frac{(J_2)_{300}}{(J_2)_{100}}$ Obs.	$\frac{(J_2)_{300}}{(J_2)_{100}}$ Calc.
200	0.10	2.25	2.8
400	0.17	2.18	2.4
600	0.24	1.91	1.9

No quantitative data are available for crystals with high characteristic temperature. In qualitative agreement with Equation 4·180 it has,

[10] O. J. Baltzer, *Phys. Rev.*, **60**, 460 (1941).

however, been reported that the intensity of the diffuse scattering of hard crystals like diamond and silicon carbide is only slightly decreased when T is lowered from room temperature to liquid air temperature.

The intensity of the diffuse scattering near an intensity maximum is given by Equation 4·165. $\bar{F}$ and $\bar{s}$ change rather slowly with scattering direction and may be treated as constants over small solid angles. The relative intensity distribution about a maximum is thus given by the expression

$$J_2 \propto \frac{\bar{s} \cdot \Omega^{-1} \cdot \bar{s}}{\tau^2} \qquad [4{\cdot}181]$$

and can be calculated numerically if the elastic constants are known. The x-ray wave vector of scattering corresponding to the intensity maximum, $\bar{k}_m$, is

$$\bar{k}_m = \bar{k}_0 + \bar{B}_H - \bar{\tau}_0 \qquad [4{\cdot}182]$$

where $\bar{\tau}_0$ is the value of $\bar{\tau}$ for which $(\bar{s} \cdot \Omega^{-1} \cdot \bar{s})/\tau^2$ is a maximum. If $\theta_i = \theta_B + \Delta$ is the actual glancing angle of incidence on the lattice plane $\bar{B}_H$ and θ_B the Bragg glancing angle, the scattering angle $2\theta_m$ for the intensity maximum becomes

$$2\theta_m = 2\theta_B + \Delta + \frac{\bar{\tau}_0 \cdot \bar{k}_0}{\sin 2\theta_B} \qquad [4{\cdot}183]$$

It is quite difficult to obtain accurate intensity measurements with which Equation 4·181 can be directly compared. The experimental procedure must provide for a sharp definition of the vector $\bar{\tau}$. Since $\bar{\tau}$ is to be determined from Equation 4·111*a*, it follows that the experimental uncertainties in the vectors $\bar{k}_0$, $\bar{k}$, and $\bar{B}_H$ must be very small. These conditions require the use of monochromatic x rays, very narrow slits and a crystal specimen in which the distribution function for the orientation of the mosaic blocks has a very small half width. As a result of these precautions the intensity of the temperature diffuse scattering becomes very small, and very long exposure times are required. For this reason there is very little experimental material with which to test Equation 4·181. J. Hamilton Hall[11] has made very accurate measurements using KCl crystals and found intensity distributions in remarkably good agreement with Equation 4·181, as shown by Table 4·3. Similar measurements have been performed with NaCl crystals[12] again giving satisfactory agreement with theory.

[11] J. Hamilton Hall, *Phys. Rev.*, **61**, 158 (1942).
[12] S. Siegel and W. H. Zachariasen, *Phys. Rev.*, **57**, 795 (1940).

TABLE 4·3

SCATTERING ANGLES AND HALF WIDTHS FOR THE DIFFUSE MAXIMA OF KCl

$H_1H_2H_3$	Δ	$2\theta_m - 2\theta_B$		Half Width		
		Experiment	Theory	Experiment I	Experiment II	Theory
400	$-56'$	$-5.0'$	$-4.8'$	$34.5'$	$30'$	$27.0'$
	-37	-3.3	-3.0	24.5	20	19.0
	-28	-2.5	-2.3	19	15	15.0
	-17	-1.0	-1.5	14	10	10.0
	$+23$	8.0	8.0	16	12	12.5
	$+31$	6.7	7.0	21	17	15.8
440	-33	-25	-28.0	25.5	20	20.0

Note. Since the incident beam contained two wavelengths, Cu $K\alpha_1$ and Cu $K\alpha_2$, the theoretical values were obtained as follows. The intensity distribution was calculated from Equation 4·181 for each of the two wavelengths and the two curves combined giving the α_1-curve twice the weight of the α_2-curve. Δ and θ_B refer to Cu $K\alpha_1$. The two columns of experimental half widths have the following meaning: the numbers in column I are the directly measured half widths while the numbers in column II are the directly measured half widths corrected for the effect of the vertical height of the slits.

Most experimental studies of the temperature diffuse scattering have been made with slits which are too wide to give a sufficiently sharp definition of the vector $\bar{\tau}$. While experiments of this sort do not give intensity distributions which can be compared with Equation 4·181 they may lead to reliable determinations of the scattering angle for the intensity maximum. Accurate measurements of the angles $2\theta_m$ have been reported for NaCl crystals by Jauncey and Baltzer.[13] Their results agree with the theoretical values $2\theta_m$ calculated[14] from Equation 4·183, using the known elastic constants of NaCl as shown by Table 4·4.

Rather extensive experimental studies have been made with diamond crystals. It is found that all diamond crystals give rise to temperature diffuse scattering effects of the type demanded by theory. However, most diamond specimens show additional scattering effects which cannot be explained by the theory (compare, however, section 12).

10. HEAT MOTION AND THE LAUE–BRAGG SCATTERING

The heat motion of the atoms affects the x-ray scattering of a lattice in two ways: it gives rise to the temperature diffuse scattering and to a decrease in the intensity of the Laue-Bragg scattering as compared to

[13] G. E. M. Jauncey and O. J. Baltzer, *Phys. Rev.*, **59**, 699 (1941).

[14] W. H. Zachariasen, *Phys. Rev.*, **59**, 909 (1941).

TABLE 4·4

OBSERVED AND CALCULATED VALUES OF $2\theta_m - 2\theta_B$ FOR NaCl

$(H_1H_2H_3) = (400)$			$(H_1H_2H_3) = (620)$		
Δ	Experimental	Theoretical	Δ	Experimental	Theoretical
7.0°	2.4°	2.7°	3.87°	4.5°	4.4°
6.0	2.4	2.3	2.87	3.2	3.2
5.0	2.1	1.9	1.87	1.8	2.1
4.0	1.6	1.5	0.87	0.9	1.0
3.0	1.3	1.2	−0.13	0	−0.1
2.0	0.8	0.8	−1.13	−1.2	−1.3
1.0	0.6	0.4	−2.13	−2.3	−2.4
0	0	0	−3.13	−3.6	−3.5
−1.0	−0.4	−0.4	−4.13	−4.5	−4.7
−2.0	−0.6	−0.8	−5.13	−5.4	−5.8
−3.0	−1.2	−1.2			
−4.0	−1.8	−1.5			
−5.0	−1.8	−1.9			

that of a static lattice. We have shown that all formulas for the Laue-Bragg scattering of a static lattice will be valid for the dynamic lattice if everywhere the atomic scattering power f_k is replaced by the corresponding dynamical quantity $g_k \equiv f_k e^{-M_k}$. The general formula for the exponent M_k is given in Equation 4·112. As shown by Equations 4·81–4·85 M_k can also be expressed in terms of the mean square displacement of the atom from its equilibrium position

$$M_k = \tfrac{1}{2}\bar{s} \cdot \overline{\bar{\Delta}_k^L \bar{\Delta}_k^L} \cdot \bar{s} \qquad [4\cdot184]$$

According to Equations 4·109 we have

$$\overline{\bar{\Delta}_k^L \bar{\Delta}_k^L} = \frac{1}{m_k} \overline{\sum_j \bar{U}_{kj} \bar{U}_{kj}^* \frac{Q_j}{\omega_j^2}} \qquad [4\cdot185]$$

where the bar on the right side indicates averaging over the phase cell. Since the exponents M_k represent mean values over all vibrational modes, it becomes clear that experimental studies of the effect of temperature on the Laue-Bragg scattering cannot give information about the details of the frequency distribution. Such detailed information can be obtained, as we have seen, from experimental investigations of the temperature diffuse scattering where the intensity in a given scattering direction is associated with only one point of the phase cell.

In order to calculate the intensity of the Laue-Bragg scattering the exponents M_k must be known. Conversely, experimental data on the temperature variation of the Laue-Bragg scattering can be used to determine M_k. In this section we shall consider the theoretical and experimental evaluation of M_k. For the sake of convenience the discussion will be restricted to monatomic lattices. The index k may then be omitted, and there is only one exponent M and this is given by

$$M = \frac{kT}{2m}\,\bar{s}\cdot\bar{\chi}\cdot\bar{s} \qquad [4\cdot186]$$

where $\bar{\chi} \equiv V\int_{\text{P.C.}} \chi\, dv$ is the mean value of the tensor χ over the phase cell. We shall set

$$\bar{\chi} = \chi_1\bar{\imath}_1\bar{\imath}_1 + \chi_2\bar{\imath}_2\bar{\imath}_2 + \chi_3\bar{\imath}_3\bar{\imath}_3 \qquad [4\cdot187]$$

where $\bar{\imath}_1, \bar{\imath}_2, \bar{\imath}_3$ are unit vectors along the principal axes of $\bar{\chi}$. Hence

$$M = 8\pi^2\frac{kT}{m}\left(\frac{\sin\theta}{\lambda}\right)^2\{\gamma_1^2\chi_1 + \gamma_2^2\chi_2 + \gamma_3^2\chi_3\} \qquad [4\cdot188]$$

where $\gamma_1, \gamma_2, \gamma_3$ are the direction cosines of $\bar{s}$ in the reference frame $\bar{\imath}_1, \bar{\imath}_2, \bar{\imath}_3$. The tensor $\bar{\chi}$ must be invariant under the symmetry operations of the lattice and symmetry considerations may therefore give us some information about $\bar{\chi}$. In cubic lattices the tensor ellipsoid must degenerate into a sphere, i.e., $\bar{\chi} = \chi\mathbf{1}$ and we have

$$M = 8\pi^2\frac{kT}{m}\left(\frac{\sin\theta}{\lambda}\right)^2\chi \qquad [4\cdot188a]$$

The tensor ellipsoid must have rotational symmetry about the principal symmetry axis in hexagonal, tetragonal, and trigonal lattices, $\chi_1 = \chi_2$, and hence hexagonal, tetragonal, and trigonal lattices

$$M = 8\pi^2\frac{kT}{m}\left(\frac{\sin\theta}{\lambda}\right)^2\{\chi_1\sin^2\varphi + \chi_3\cos^2\varphi\} \qquad [4\cdot188b]$$

where φ is the angle between $\bar{s}$ and the principal symmetry axis. The vectors $\bar{\imath}_1, \bar{\imath}_2, \bar{\imath}_3$ are along the three twofold symmetry axes of orthorhombic lattices and in monoclinic crystals one of these vectors must coincide with the single symmetry axis of the lattice. Thus M (and hence the mean square displacement) has anisotropic character except for crystals of cubic symmetry.

In Equation 4·134 was given an expression for M in terms of the characteristic temperature Θ. This formula is based upon the approximation of Equation 4·132 which disregards the anisotropy and thus Equation 4·134 applies only to cubic crystals. Let us therefore try to find another convenient expression for M applicable to crystals of any symmetry.

As a reasonably good approximation to Equation 4·125 we shall use

$$\chi(\boldsymbol{\tau}) \approx \frac{Q(\boldsymbol{\tau})}{kT} \sum_j \frac{\bar{U}_j\bar{U}_j}{\omega_j^2} = \frac{Q(\boldsymbol{\tau})}{kT} \Psi^{-1}(\boldsymbol{\tau}) \qquad [4·189]$$

where we have used Equation 4·119, and where Q is the mean value of Q_j for the three frequency branches. For relatively small values of $\boldsymbol{\tau}$ the tensor Ψ is given by Equation 4·142, and this formula for Ψ will be used as a sufficiently good approximation throughout the entire phase cell. Accordingly we have

$$\bar{\chi} \approx \frac{m}{\pi} \int_{\text{P.C.}} \frac{Q\Omega^{-1}}{kT\, 4\pi\tau^2}\, dv \qquad [4·190]$$

The correct value of χ for large $\boldsymbol{\tau}$ will be somewhat greater than is indicated by Equation 4·142, since the propagation velocities actually decrease with increasing τ. The formula 4·190 may therefore be expected to yield too small a value for $\bar{\chi}$.

Let us replace Q and Ω^{-1} in the integral above by their mean values $\bar{Q}$ and $\overline{\Omega^{-1}}$ over all directions of $\boldsymbol{\tau}$, and let us for the phase cell substitute a sphere of equal volume. The resulting expression for $\bar{\chi}$ is

$$\bar{\chi} \approx \frac{m\overline{\Omega^{-1}}}{\pi} \int_0^{\tau_m} \frac{Q}{kT}\, d\tau = \frac{m\overline{\Omega^{-1}}}{\pi} \tau_m \left[\phi(x_m) + \frac{x_m}{4}\right] \qquad [4·191]$$

τ_m is the radius of the sphere having the same volume as the phase cell, i.e., $\tau_m = \left(\dfrac{3}{4\pi V}\right)^{1/3}$. ϕ is the function defined by Equation 4·136, and $x_m = hv\tau_m/kT$. In terms of the characteristic temperature $\Theta = hv\tau_m/k$ we have $x_m = \Theta/T$. The formula for M becomes

$$M \approx (\gamma_1^2 C_1 + \gamma_2^2 C_2 + \gamma_3^2 C_3) \left(\frac{\sin\theta}{\lambda}\right)^2 T \left[\phi(x_m) + \frac{x_m}{4}\right]$$

$$C_i = 4\left(\frac{6\pi^2}{V}\right)^{1/3} k\, \overline{\Omega_i^{-1}} \qquad [4·192]$$

The function $\phi(x_m) + \dfrac{x_m}{4}$ is very nearly unity over a considerable temperature range as shown by Table 4·5.

For $x < 2\pi$ the following expansion can be used

$$\phi(x) + \frac{x}{4} = 1 + \frac{x^2}{36} - \frac{x^4}{3600} + \cdots \qquad [4·193]$$

and hence for $T \gg \dfrac{\Theta}{2\pi}$

$$T\left[\phi(x_m) + \frac{x_m}{4}\right] \approx T + \frac{\Theta^2}{36}T^{-1} \qquad [4\cdot194]$$

The tensor $\overline{\mathbf{\Omega}^{-1}}$ can be expressed in terms of the elastic constants using

TABLE 4·5

THE FUNCTION $\psi(x) \equiv \phi(x) + \dfrac{x}{4}$

x	$\psi(x)$	x	$\psi(x)$	x	$\psi(x)$	x	$\psi(x)$
0	1	1.2	1.040	3	1.233	9	2.433
0.2	1.001	1.4	1.054	4	1.388	10	2.664
0.4	1.004	1.6	1.069	5	1.571	12	3.137
0.6	1.010	1.8	1.087	6	1.771	14	3.614
0.8	1.018	2.0	1.107	7	1.984	16	4.103
1.0	1.028	2.5	1.165	8	2.205	20	5.082

the formula for $\mathbf{\Omega}$ given in Equation 4·141. Thus we find for cubic crystals

$$\overline{\Omega^{-1}} = \frac{c_{44}\dfrac{2c_{11}+c_{44}}{3} + b\dfrac{c_{11}+c_{12}}{15}}{c_{11}c_{44}^2 + b^2\dfrac{c_{11}+2c_{12}+c_{44}}{105} + bc_{44}\dfrac{c_{11}+c_{12}}{5}} \qquad [4\cdot195]$$

The quantity $\overline{\mathbf{\Omega}^{-1}}$ occurring in Equations 4·191 and 4·192 should represent a mean value over the entire phase cell, but we propose to approximate by using instead the mean value of $\mathbf{\Omega}^{-1}$ for small values of τ. As stated earlier this procedure will yield a too small value for M.

If the characteristic temperature of the crystal is accurately known from the experimental specific heat curve it may be convenient to rewrite Equation 4·192 in another form. In order to find this alternative expression for M we proceed as follows. According to Equation 4·140 we have $\rho\overline{\Omega^{-1}} = \overline{v^{-2}}$ where $\overline{\Omega^{-1}} = \frac{1}{3}\sum_i \overline{\Omega_i^{-1}}$. However, $\overline{v^{-2}}$ can also be expressed in terms of the characteristic temperature. Equating the two expressions for $\overline{v^{-2}}$, we find

$$\overline{\Omega^{-1}} \approx \frac{h^2\tau_m^2}{\rho k^2\Theta^2} \qquad [4\cdot196]$$

Thus the coefficients C_i in Equation 4·192 can be written as

$$C_i \approx \frac{6h^2}{mk\Theta^2} \frac{\overline{\Omega_i^{-1}}}{\overline{\Omega^{-1}}} \tag{4·197}$$

By this procedure only the ratios $\overline{\Omega_i^{-1}}/\overline{\Omega^{-1}}$ are determined from the elastic constants while the absolute value of $\overline{\Omega^{-1}}$ is determined from the characteristic temperature by means of Equation 4·196. It is readily seen that Equation 4·192 for cubic symmetry becomes identical with Equation 4·134 if the coefficients C_i are given by Equation 4·197 rather than by Equation 4·192*a*.

The coefficients C_i can be determined experimentally, and hence the theory can be tested. For that purpose the integrated reflecting power of a given Laue-Bragg reflection is measured at different temperatures. (Since our theory of the heat motion assumes linear restoring forces the theoretical formulas cannot be expected to hold at very high temperatures, and in the following discussion it will therefore be assumed that the experimental measurements are made in a temperature range for which the theory is valid.) Let us for the sake of convenience suppose that the crystal under investigation is of the mosaic type and that all extinction effects are negligible. According to the results of section 3 the integrated reflecting power is then proportional to e^{-2M} (remembering that f is to be replaced by fe^{-M} to make the results valid for dynamic lattices). Hence the ratio of the integrated reflecting powers measured at two temperatures T_1 and T_2 is given by $e^{-2(M_1-M_2)}$ and

$$M_2 - M_1 = \frac{1}{2} \log \frac{R_1}{R_2} \tag{4·198}$$

Using Equation 4·192 we have, on the other hand,

$$M_2 - M_1 = (\gamma_1^2 C_1 + \gamma_2^2 C_2 + \gamma_3^2 C_3) \left(\frac{\sin \theta}{\lambda}\right)^2 [T_2\phi_2 - T_1\phi_1] \tag{4·199}$$

Thus

$$(\gamma_1^2 C_1 + \gamma_2^2 C_2 + \gamma_3^2 C_3) = \frac{\frac{1}{2} \log \frac{R_1}{R_2}}{\left(\frac{\sin \theta}{\lambda}\right)^2 [T_2\phi_2 - T_1\phi_1]} \tag{4·200}$$

Since the direction cosines γ_1, γ_2, γ_3 depend upon the Miller indices of the reflecting lattice plane, the coefficients C_1, C_2, C_3 can be found if the ratio R_1/R_2 is measured for different reflections.

Accurate measurements of $M_2 - M_1$ (for room temperature and liquid air temperature) have been obtained for NaCl,[15] KCl,[16] Al,[17] NaF,[18] and Zn.[19] Of these only Al corresponds to a monatomic lattice. However, NaCl, KCl, and NaF are fairly good approximations to monatomic lattices. Zn is the only non-cubic crystal in the list, but the elastic constants for Zn are known so that we are able to calculate the anisotropy. The following table shows the values of C_i obtained from the experimental data together with the theoretical values calculated from Equations 4·192*a* and 4·197. NaF is not included in this list since neither the elastic constants nor the characteristic temperature is known for this substance.

TABLE 4·6

OBSERVED AND CALCULATED VALUES OF C_i

Crystal	Experimental	Theoretical	
		Eq. 4·192*a*	Eq. 4·197
NaCl	4.6×10^{-19}	4.0×10^{-19}	5.0×10^{-19}
KCl	5.7	5.7	6.0
Al	2.54		2.8
Zn	C_1 2.3		2.1
	C_3 7.9		4.2

Once the constants C_i have been found the mean square displacement $\overline{\Delta^2}$ of an atom from its equilibrium position can be evaluated. By using Equation 4·185 one finds readily

$$\overline{\Delta^2} = \frac{\gamma_1^2 C_1 + \gamma_2^2 C_2 + \gamma_3^2 C_3}{8\pi^2} T \left\{ \phi(x_m) + \frac{x_m}{4} \right\} \quad [4·201]$$

With the experimental value $C = 2.54 \times 10^{-9}$ for Al this formula gives a root mean square displacement of 0.099 A at $T = 290°$, of 0.064 A at $T = 86°$.

[15] R. W. James and E. M. Firth, *Proc. Roy. Soc.*, **A117**, 62, (1927). I. Waller and R. W. James, *Proc. Roy. Soc.* **A117,** 214 (1927).

[16] R. W. James and G. W. Brindley, *Proc. Roy. Soc.*, **A121**, 155 (1928).

[17] R. W. James, G. W. Brindley, and R. G. Wood, *Proc. Roy. Soc.*, **A125**, 401 (1929).

[18] J. J. Shonka, *Phys. Rev.*, **43**, 947 (1933).

[19] G. E. M. Jauncey and W. A. Bruce, *Phys. Rev.*, **50**, 408 (1936).

11. A GENERAL THEORY OF X-RAY DIFFRACTION IN DISORDERED LATTICES

Mosaic structure and heat motion are the two most important causes of crystal imperfections. Heat motion will, of course, be present in all crystals, and there seem to be few, if any, crystal specimens which are entirely free of mosaic structure. We shall not attempt to prepare a complete list of all other disorders which so far have been found, although we shall mention some of them later on. A general discussion of the effect of disorder on the x-ray scattering is much more important. In this section we shall therefore present a theory of x-ray diffraction in disordered lattices. No assumption will be made regarding the nature of the imperfection, and the results which we shall obtain will accordingly be applicable to any one disorder or to any combination of disorders.

Whatever may be the nature of the crystal imperfections we may, as shown in section 1, associate effective scattering powers g_k^L with ideal lattice sites $\bar{r}_k + \bar{A}_L$. The extent of the disorder can be expressed in terms of the fluctuations φ_k^L of the effective scattering power from the mean value g_k. The general definitions of the quantities g_k^L, g_k, and φ_k^L are given in Equations 4·8, 4·9, and 4·10. According to these definitions g_k^L, g_k, and φ_k^L are to be regarded as slowly varying functions of the vector $\bar{s} = 2\pi(\bar{k} - \bar{k}_0)$, i.e., of the scattering direction for given incident wave vector $\bar{k}_0$.

The expression for the intensity of scattering from a small disordered crystal is readily obtained by comparison with the derivation given in Chapter III, section 6. We find

$$I = I_e \sum_{L,\,L'} F_L (F_{L'})^* \, e^{i\bar{s}\cdot\bar{A}_{L-L'}} \qquad [4{\cdot}202]$$

where F_L, defined by Equation 4·11, is the structure factor for the unit cell at $\bar{A}_L$. With the aid of Equation 4·13 the intensity formula can be written in the form

$$I = J_1 + J_2 \qquad [4{\cdot}203a]$$

$$J_1 = I_e |\overline{F}|^2 \sum_{L,\,L'} e^{i\bar{s}\cdot\bar{A}_{L-L'}} = I_e |\overline{F}|^2 \prod_i \frac{\sin^2 \frac{1}{2} N_i \bar{s}\cdot\bar{a}_i}{\sin^2 \frac{1}{2}\bar{s}\cdot\bar{a}_i} \qquad [4{\cdot}203b]$$

$$J_2 = I_e \sum_{L,\,L'} e^{i\bar{s}\cdot\bar{A}_{L-L'}} \sum_{k,\,k'} \varphi_k^L (\varphi_{k'}^{L'})^* \, e^{i\bar{s}\cdot(\bar{r}_k - \bar{r}_{k'})} \qquad [4{\cdot}203c]$$

Equation 3·48 shows that J_1 is the scattering from a small ideal crystal with structure factor $\overline{F}$, i.e., J_1 is the scattering from the mean lattice of the disordered crystal. Since J_1 is different from zero only in a narrow range about the Laue-Bragg directions, $\bar{s} = 2\pi\overline{B}_H$, we shall call it the

Laue-Bragg scattering. The characteristic features of this scattering have been dealt with in great detail in preceding sections of this volume, and no further discussion is needed beyond the general statement that all results which we have obtained for the scattering of ideal crystals become valid for the Laue-Bragg scattering of disordered crystals if everywhere f_k is replaced by g_k.

Whereas J_1 is a measure of the long-range order in the lattice, J_2 measures the disorder and will therefore be called the disorder scattering. We shall assume that the crystal under consideration gives a fair sample of the disorder. If this is true, the disorder scattering from our little crystal is indistinguishable from the mean value of the disorder scattering from a large number of crystals of identical shape and volume which we imagine are cut out of the infinite disordered lattice. Accordingly we replace Equation 4·203c by

$$J_2 = I_e \sum_{L, L'} e^{i\bar{s}\cdot\bar{A}_{L-L'}} \sum_{k, k'} \varphi_{kk'}^{L-L'} e^{i\bar{s}\cdot(\bar{r}_k - \bar{r}_{k'})} \tag{4·204}$$

where

$$\varphi_{kk'}^{M} = \frac{1}{N} \sum_{L} \varphi_k^L (\varphi_{k'}^{L-M})^* \tag{4·205}$$

The quantity $\varphi_{kk'}^M$ represents the mean value of the products of the disorders at sites having a vector separation $\bar{A}_M + \bar{r}_{k'} - \bar{r}_k$. It is obviously true that

$$\varphi_{k'k}^{-M} = (\varphi_{kk'}^{M})^* \tag{4·206}$$

$$\sum_{M} \varphi_{kk'}^{M} = 0 \tag{4·207}$$

When there is no correlation between disorders of different unit cells $\varphi_{kk'}^M$ has the same value for every M except $M = 0$, and we have

$$\varphi_{kk'}^{M} = \begin{cases} \varphi_{kk'}^{0} & \text{for} \quad M = 0 \\ -\dfrac{1}{N-1}\varphi_{kk'}^{0} & \text{for} \quad M \neq 0 \end{cases} \tag{4·208}$$

There is an even higher degree of randomness if the various disorders within the same unit cell also are independent of one another. Then

$$\varphi_{kk'}^{M} = \begin{cases} 0 & \text{for} \quad k \neq k' \\ \varphi_{kk}^{0} & \text{for} \quad k = k' \quad \text{and} \quad M = 0 \\ -\dfrac{1}{N-1}\varphi_{kk}^{0} & \text{for} \quad k = k' \quad \text{and} \quad M \neq 0 \end{cases} \tag{4·209}$$

The disorders φ_k^L associated with the kth set of sites can be expanded

ments will yield J_2 rather than J_2. However, because of the identity of Equations 4·216*b* and 4·217 the experiments may incorrectly be interpreted as confirming the former equation, i.e., as proving the random character of the disorder. This mistake has indeed been made. G. E. M. Jauncey[20] studied the temperature diffuse scattering under experimental conditions such as we have described, and his measurements seemingly confirmed the incorrect Debye theory[21, 22, 23] which assumed that the atoms were vibrating independently of one another.[24]

It may be assumed that the disorders φ_k^L are not periodic in three dimensions. Suppose, namely, that they were spatially periodic. The periods would necessarily be of the form $\bar{a}_i' = \sum_j c_{ij}\bar{a}_j$ ($i = 1, 2, 3$ and $j = 1, 2, 3$), where all coefficients c_{ij} are integers. But then the "disordered" lattice could be represented as an ideal lattice with periods $\bar{a}_1'$, $\bar{a}_2'$, $\bar{a}_3'$. It is, however, possible for the disorders φ_k^L to be periodic in one or two dimensions without having spatial periodicity. We shall indeed have to consider the following possibilities.

A. Three-dimensional disorder.
The disorders φ_k^L are not periodic in any direction.

B. Two-dimensional or planar disorder.
The disorders φ_k^L are periodic in one direction.

C. One-dimensional or linear disorder.
The disorders φ_k^L are periodic in two directions.

The character of the disorder scattering is quite different in the three cases as we shall learn presently.

A. **Three-Dimensional Disorder.** When the disorders φ_k^L have no periodicity, none of the Fourier coefficients $\psi_{kk'}^p$ (other than $\psi_{kk'}^0$) is identically zero. Hence $J_2 \neq 0$ for any value of $\bar{s}$ (except $\bar{s} = 2\pi\bar{B}_H$), and the disorder scattering is diffuse.

The vector $\bar{s}$, or better $\bar{s}/2\pi$, can be interpreted as representing a point in reciprocal space. Accordingly we may imagine all points $\bar{B}_H - \bar{\tau}_p$ plotted and the appropriate value of J_2 associated with each of these points. In this manner we obtain a scalar field representation of J_2 in reciprocal space. The points $\bar{B}_H - \bar{\tau}_p$ are discrete, but neighboring points are so close together that the distribution may be regarded as continuous for all practical purposes. In order better to visualize the variation of J_2 from point to point it is convenient to draw the level

[20] A great many articles in *The Physical Review* in the period 1930–40.

[21] P. Debye, *Ann. der Phys.*, **43**, 49 (1914).

[22] G. E. M. Jauncey and G. G. Harvey, *Phys. Rev.*, **37**, 1203 (1931).

[23] Y. H. Woo, *Phys. Rev.*, **38**, 1 (1931); **41**, 21 (1932).

[24] W. H. Zachariasen, *Phys. Rev.*, **57**, 597 (1940).

surfaces J_2 = constant. Let it be supposed that we are interested in finding the intensity distribution J_2 as function of scattering direction for given incident wave vector $\bar{k}_0$. We may then construct the sphere of reflection corresponding to the given vector $\bar{k}_0$ as described in Chapter III, section 2. The values $\bar{s}/2\pi$ which come into consideration are then given by vectors drawn from the origin of the reciprocal lattice (the point O in Fig. 3·2) and terminating upon the sphere of reflection while the scattering directions are radius vectors of the sphere. We shall assume that the sphere of reflection does not pass through any reciprocal lattice point, i.e., that no Laue-Bragg scattering is produced. The level surfaces J_2 = constant will intersect the sphere of reflection in closed curves which define a set of cones, the generatrices of which are directions of equal intensity of scattering.

If the various disorders within the same unit cell are independent of one another, we may set $\varphi_{kk'}^M = 0$ for $k \neq k'$ and Equation 4·215a reduces to

$$J_2 = NI_e\sum_k \psi_{kk}^p = NI_e\sum_k |\psi_p^k|^2 \qquad [4\cdot218]$$

Since I_e and φ_k^L are slowly varying functions of $\bar{s}$ the Fourier coefficient ψ_{kk}^p will not change very much when $\bar{s}$ is given an increment $\pm 2\pi\bar{b}_i$. Accordingly J_2 is quasi-periodic in reciprocal space with periods $\bar{b}_1, \bar{b}_2, \bar{b}_3$. If the disorders within the same unit cell are correlated, they will no longer scatter independently of one another, and the quasi-periodicity will be partly destroyed because of interference.

It is not possible to say very much about the level surfaces J_2 = constant unless specific assumptions are made concerning the nature of the correlation. It is justifiable to assume that there is negligibly small interaction between the disorders at sites which are far apart in the lattice. This implies that $\varphi_{kk'}^M$ approaches zero for large values of M. Since the mean value is zero, $\varphi_{kk'}^M$ plotted as function of M must oscillate between positive and negative values. The manner in which these oscillations take place is, however, entirely dependent upon the character of the disorder and its correlation.

The distance between an atom and its next neighbors cannot be changed a great deal without making the lattice unstable. In displacement disorders it is accordingly to be expected that the relative displacement of neighboring atoms is small. As M increases from zero, $\varphi_{kk'}^M$ will thus decrease from its maximum value $\varphi_{kk'}^0$, eventually become negative, pass through a minimum and then, as schematically indicated in Fig. 4·6, asymptotically approach zero (possibly after a few additional oscillations of steadily diminishing amplitude). The corresponding

Fourier coefficients $\psi^p_{kk'}$ will behave as indicated in Fig. 4·7. As p increases the Fourier coefficient will rapidly attain its maximum value and then show a monotonous decrease. The radius of the crater at

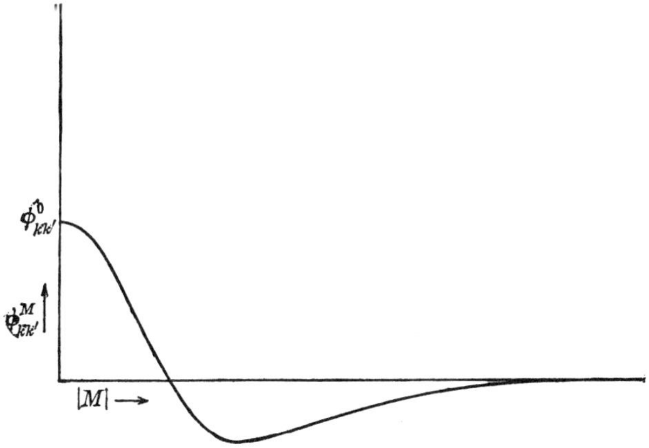

FIG. 4·6.

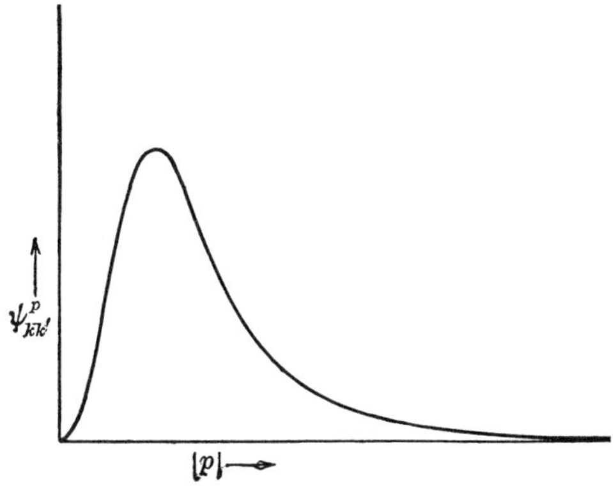

FIG. 4-7.

$p = 0$ is usually too small to be observed. It may thus be anticipated that the scattering function $J_2(\bar{s}/2\pi)$ for displacement disorders will exhibit maxima in the immediate vicinity of the reciprocal lattice points. As a consequence the level surfaces will usually be closed surfaces about the points $\bar{B}_H$, and the directions of maximum scattering will correspond to small values of $\bar{r}_p$. If the level surfaces are spherical, the scattering directions $\bar{u}_m$ for which there is maximum intensity are readily found.

It is seen from Fig. 4·8 that these directions are given by

$$\bar{u}_m = \frac{\bar{k}_0 + \bar{B}_H}{|\bar{k}_0 + \bar{B}_H|} \tag{4·219}$$

Hence the intensity maximum lies in the plane of incidence and occurs at a scattering angle $2\theta_m$ which is

$$\tan 2\theta_m = \frac{|\bar{u}_m \times \bar{k}_0|}{\bar{u}_m \cdot \bar{k}_0} = \frac{2 \sin \theta_B \cos \theta_i}{1 - 2 \sin \theta_B \sin \theta_i} \tag{4·220}$$

This result is identical with Equation 4·137 which gave the approximate location of the intensity maxima for the temperature diffuse scattering. Even if the interaction is approximately isotropic it is not in general justifiable to assume that the level surfaces are spheres, and Equations

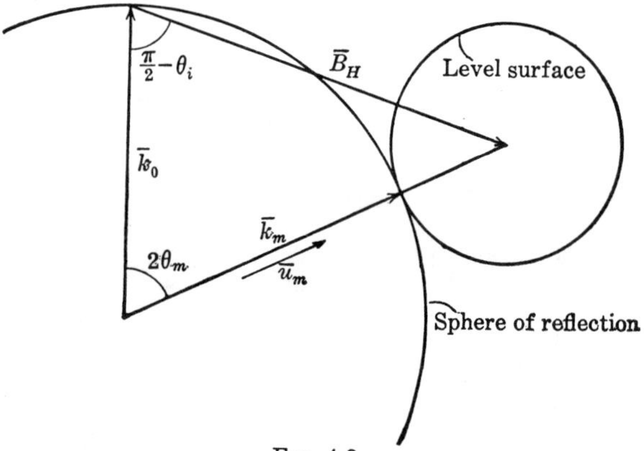

FIG. 4-8.

4·219 and 4·220 should therefore be used with reservations. It is seen from Fig. 4·9 that the exact direction of the intensity maximum depends upon the shape of the level surfaces. Indeed, the intensity maximum need not even lie in the plane of incidence.

It must be emphasized that the conclusions reached in the preceding paragraph refer to the specific type of correlation which seems probable for displacement disorders. Correlations of entirely different character may be expected for substitution disorders.

***B.* Planar Disorder.** Let us assume that the disorders φ_k^L are periodic in one direction with period $\bar{A}_K$. We shall then have

$$\varphi_k^L = \varphi_k^{L+K} \tag{4·221}$$

for any L and any k. As shown by Equations 4·210 and 4·213 this condition implies

$$\psi_{kk'}^p = 0 \quad \text{if} \quad \bar{\tau}_p \cdot \bar{A}_K \neq \text{integer} \tag{4·222}$$

Hence $J_2 \neq 0$ only in the sequence of reciprocal lattice planes normal to $\bar{A}_K$ which is defined by the equation $\bar{\tau}_p \cdot \bar{A}_K =$ integer. The variation of J_2 within these planes is, of course, determined by the correlation normal to $\bar{A}_K$, but we shall not investigate this point. The sequence of reciprocal lattice planes intersects the sphere of reflection in equidistant and parallel circles which define a discrete set of circular diffraction

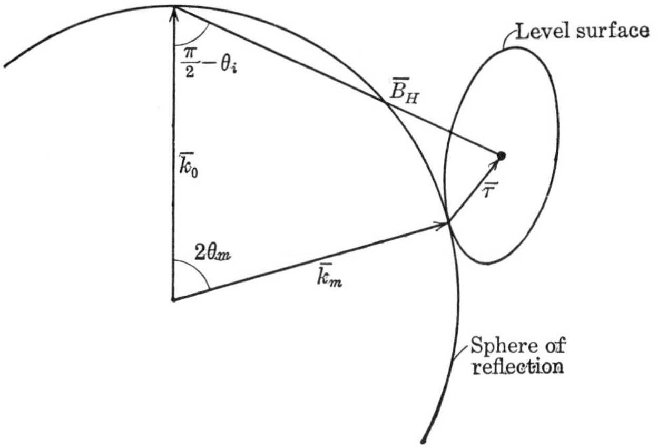

FIG. 4·9.

cones, and disorder scattering consequently takes place only in those directions which are generatrices of these cones. These directions $\bar{u}$ are given by

$$\bar{u} = \bar{u}_0 + \lambda \bar{B}_H - \lambda \bar{\tau}_p, \quad \bar{\tau}_p \cdot \bar{A}_K = \text{integer} \tag{4·223}$$

The disorder scattering will thus appear on a photographic plate as a set of sharply defined streaks which are ellipses, parabolas, or hyperbolas. The positions of these streaks are the same as for a linear grating with period $\bar{A}_K$.

C. Linear Disorder. We shall finally consider the nature of the disorder scattering when the disorders φ_k^L have two-dimensional periodicity. Let the disorders φ_k^L be periodic in any direction which is parallel to a given lattice plane characterized by a vector $\bar{B}_h$. The following condition is then fulfilled

$$\varphi_k^L = \varphi_k^{L+K} \quad \text{if} \quad \bar{A}_K \cdot \bar{B}_h = 0 \tag{4·224}$$

for any L and for any k. It follows from Equations 4·210 and 4·213 that

$$\psi_{kk'}^p = 0 \quad \text{if} \quad \bar{\tau}_p \times \bar{B}_h \neq 0 \tag{4·225}$$

Accordingly J_2 is different from zero only along the reciprocal lattice rows which are parallel to $\bar{B}_h$. These intersect the sphere of reflection in discrete points. The disorder scattering consequently occurs in sharply defined directions $\bar{u}$ given by

$$\bar{u} = \bar{u}_0 + \lambda \bar{B}_H - \lambda \bar{\tau}_p, \qquad \bar{\tau}_p \times \bar{B}_h = 0 \qquad [4\cdot226]$$

The positions of the interference spots on a photographic plate are clearly the same as for a two-dimensional grating.

The formula for the intensity of the disorder scattering given in Equation 4·215a holds for small crystals in which absorption and extinction are negligible. Experimental measurements are usually made on large crystals, and hence the observations cannot be directly compared with this equation.

We shall assume that the direction of incidence is such that no Laue-Bragg scattering is produced. All extinction effects in a large crystal are then negligibly small and only absorption phenomena need to be considered. The treatment of the temperature diffuse scattering from large crystals given in the first part of section 9 can readily be generalized to arbitrary disorders. For this purpose Equation 4·215a will be rewritten in the same form as Equation 4·168, and we have

$$\frac{J_2}{I_0} = \frac{K}{R^2}\,\delta V \qquad [4\cdot227a]$$

$$K = \left(\frac{e^2}{mc^2}\right)^2 \frac{1 + \cos^2 2\theta}{2}\, V^{-1} \sum_{kk'} \psi^p_{kk'}\, e^{i\bar{s}\cdot(\bar{r}_k - \bar{r}_{k'})} \qquad [4\cdot227b]$$

The intensity ratio J_2/I_0 for large crystals is then given by Equation 4·175.

12. SOME COMMON DISORDERS

The two most important disorders, mosaic structure and heat motion, were discussed in detail earlier in this chapter. Since the individual mosaic blocks scatter independently, and since it is necessary to take account of extinction as well as of absorption, the general theory presented in the preceding section is not very useful for the treatment of x-ray diffraction in mosaic crystals. A comparison will show, however, that the theory of the temperature diffuse scattering which we have given represents a special case of the general theory. The explicit expressions for g^L_k, g_k, $\varphi^M_{kk'}$, and $\psi^p_{kk'}$ as applied to heat motion are

$$g^L_k = f_k\, e^{i\bar{s}\cdot\bar{\Delta}^L_k} \qquad [4\cdot228a]$$

$$g_k = f_k\, e^{-M_k} \qquad [4\cdot228b]$$

$$\varphi_{kk'}^{M} = g_k g_{k'}(e^{P_{kk'}^{M}} - 1) \approx g_k g_{k'}\, P_{kk'}^{M} \qquad [4{\cdot}228c]$$

$$\psi_{kk'}^{p} = \frac{g_k g_{k'}}{\sqrt{m_k m_{k'}}}\, kT\, \bar{s} \cdot \chi_{kk'}(p) \cdot \bar{s} \qquad [4{\cdot}228d]$$

and substitution of Equation 4·228*d* in Equation 4·215*a* gives the correct intensity formula for the thermal disorder scattering.

Rotation of Radicals and Molecules. The lattice vibrations do not represent the only thermal disorder. It has been shown that in some crystals groups of atoms, radicals, or molecules have rotational motion at elevated temperatures. The onset of the rotation is accompanied by anomalies in the physical properties, in particular the transition point is readily observed in the specific heat curve. In some instances the rotation axes of the various groups have random orientation, whereas in other cases the rotation seems to take place about axes which are all parallel to a fixed direction in the crystal.

It cannot be expected that neighboring groups will rotate independently of one another, but there is no experimental or theoretical information about the correlation. Under the circumstances we shall derive only the expression for the mean disorder scattering $\overline{J_2}$ since it is independent of the correlation. It will be assumed for the sake of convenience that there is only one rotating group per unit cell, and it may then be supposed that the origin of the unit cell is at the center of mass of the group. The instantaneous position vector of the kth atom in the unit cell at $\bar{A}_L$ measured relative to the origin of this cell will be denoted by $\bar{R}_k^L$. The length of this vector is independent of the index L, and we set therefore

$$R_k = |\bar{R}_k^L| \quad R_{kk'} = |\bar{R}_k^L - \bar{R}_{k'}^L| \qquad [4{\cdot}229]$$

When the rotation axes of the various groups are oriented at random the mean value of $\bar{R}_k^L$ over all unit cells is zero. The mean sites for all rotating atoms are therefore $\bar{A}_L + \bar{r}_k$ with $\bar{r}_k = 0$, and $\bar{R}_k^L$ becomes identical with the displacement $\bar{\Delta}_k^L$. Accordingly we have

$$F_L = \sum_k g_k^L = \sum_k f_k\, e^{i\bar{s}\cdot\bar{R}_k^L} \qquad [4{\cdot}230]$$

The mean structure factor becomes

$$\bar{F} = \sum_k f_k \tfrac{1}{2} \int_0^{\pi} e^{isR_k \cos\varphi} \sin\varphi\, d\varphi = \sum_k f_k \frac{\sin sR_k}{sR_k} \qquad [4{\cdot}231]$$

The mean square structure factor is

$$\overline{|F|^2} = \sum_{k,\,k'} f_k f_{k'} \frac{\sin sR_{kk'}}{sR_{kk'}} \qquad [4{\cdot}232]$$

Substitution of Equations 4·231 and 4·232 in Equation 4·217 gives

$$\overline{J_2} = NI_e \sum_{k,\,k'} f_k f_{k'} \left(\frac{\sin sR_{kk'}}{sR_{kk'}} - \frac{\sin sR_k}{sR_k} \frac{\sin sR_{k'}}{sR_{k'}} \right) \qquad [4\cdot233]$$

Next we shall find the expression for the mean disorder scattering when the rotation axes are parallel to a fixed direction $\bar{u}$. The mean position vector is then $\bar{r}_k = R_k \cos \varphi_k \, \bar{u}$ where φ_k is the angle between $\bar{u}$ and $\bar{R}_k^L$. The quantity $\bar{s} \cdot \bar{\Delta}_k^L$ becomes

$$\bar{s} \cdot \bar{\Delta}_k^L = sR_k \sin \psi \sin \varphi_k \cos \chi_L \qquad [4\cdot234]$$

where ψ is the angle between $\bar{s}$ and $\bar{u}$ and χ_L the instantaneous angle of rotation for the group in the cell at $\bar{A}_L$. Hence we find

$$g_k = \overline{f_k e^{i\bar{s}\cdot\bar{\Delta}_k^L}} = f_k J_0(sR_k \sin \psi \sin \varphi_k) \qquad [4\cdot235]$$

and

$$\bar{F} = \sum_k f_k J_0(sR_k \sin \psi \sin \varphi_k)\, e^{isR_k \cos \varphi_k \cos \psi} \qquad [4\cdot236]$$

where J_0 is the Bessel function of order zero. This gives for the mean disorder scattering

$$\begin{aligned} \overline{J_2} = NI_e \sum_{k,\,k'} f_k f_{k'} \cos (sR_{kk'} \cos \varphi_{kk'} \cos \psi) \{ J_0(sR_{kk'} \sin \varphi_{kk'} \sin \psi) \\ - J_0(sR_k \sin \varphi_k \sin \psi) J_0(sR_{k'} \sin \varphi_{k'} \sin \psi) \} \end{aligned} \qquad [4\cdot237]$$

where $\varphi_{kk'}$ is the angle between $\bar{u}$ and $\bar{R}_k^L - \bar{R}_{k'}^L$.

Substitution Disorders. Next to heat motion and mosaic structure in frequency of occurrence are the disorders associated with isomorphous substitution and related phenomena. So many different kinds of substitution disorders have been observed that we shall have to be satisfied with a brief general discussion. Common to all disorders of the substitution type is the fact that the scattering power is not the same for all sites of a given set. All the various sites of the same set may either be occupied by atoms (or groups of atoms) of different kinds or a certain fraction of the sites may be vacant. Substitution disorders are no doubt always accompanied by displacement disorders due to local disturbances in the lattice geometry. In the following we shall, however, disregard these displacement disorders. In lattices with substitution disorder there may be very strong interaction between the disorders at neighboring sites. The nature of this correlation varies, however, so greatly from one kind of substitution disorder to another that no general statements can be made regarding the functions $\varphi_{kk'}^M$ and $\psi_{kk'}^p$. Accordingly we shall have to be content with the evaluation of the mean disorder scattering $\overline{J_2}$.

Let the scattering power of the atoms which occupy sites $\bar{r}_k + \bar{A}_L$ be denoted by f_{kj}, $j = 1, 2, \cdots p$ so that f_k^L has to assume one of the p values f_{kj} (where one of the values f_{kj} is zero if some of the sites are vacant). The probability that any one site of type k is occupied by an atom of scattering power f_{kj} shall be w_{kj} where $\sum_j w_{kj} = 1$. These probabilities may sometimes be deduced directly from the result of a chemical analysis, but this is not in general possible. The mean scattering power for the set k is

$$g_k = \sum_j w_{kj} f_{kj} \tag{4·238}$$

and the mean structure factor is

$$\bar{F} = \sum_k \sum_j w_{kj} f_{kj}\, e^{i\bar{s}\cdot\bar{r}_k} \tag{4·239}$$

The mean square structure factor becomes

$$\overline{|F|^2} = \sum_{kk'} \overline{f_k f_{k'}}\, e^{i\bar{s}\cdot(\bar{r}_k - \bar{r}_{k'})} \tag{4·240a}$$

where

$$\overline{f_k f_{k'}} = \frac{1}{N} \sum_L f_k^L f_{k'}^L \tag{4·240b}$$

This latter quantity cannot be evaluated unless specific assumptions are made concerning the correlation within the same unit cell. If the disorders within the same unit cell are entirely independent of one another we have

$$\overline{f_k f_{k'}} = \begin{cases} \sum_{j,j'} w_{kj} w_{k'j'} f_{kj} f_{k'j'} & \text{for } k \neq k' \\ \sum_j w_{kj} f_{kj}^2 & \text{for } k = k' \end{cases} \tag{4·241}$$

and hence

$$\overline{J_2} = N I_e \sum_k \{ \sum_j w_{kj} f_{kj}^2 - \sum_{jj'} w_{kj} w_{kj'} f_{kj} f_{kj'} \} \tag{4·242a}$$

which can be rewritten in the form

$$\overline{J_2} = \tfrac{1}{2} N I_e \sum_k \sum_{jj'} w_{kj} w_{kj'} (f_{kj} - f_{kj'})^2 \tag{4·242b}$$

Substitution disorders of planar and linear type are readily imagined. It is customary to study the x-ray diffraction effects using a rotating rather than a stationary crystal. As shown by Equations 4·223 and 4·226 the disorder scattering due to planar disorders will then take place in all directions and hence produce a general blackening on the photographic film or plate whereas the scattering due to linear disorders will be registered as streaks. The streaks are readily observed, and linear substitution disorders have indeed been reported for several crystals. General blackening of the photographic film is, on the other hand, easily overlooked, and the fact that no planar disorders have been reported may be due to this circumstance rather than to their non-existence. If there is no correlation between the individual lattice rows A_K in planar disorder or between the individual lattice planes B_h in linear disorder, the expression for the intensity of the disorder scattering becomes

Planar disorder

$$\overline{J_2} = N^{4/3} I_e \{ \overline{|F|^2} - |\overline{F}|^2 \} \quad \text{if} \quad \bar{\tau}_p \cdot \bar{A}_K = \text{integer} \qquad [4{\cdot}243a]$$

$$\overline{J_2} = 0 \quad \text{if} \quad \bar{\tau}_p \cdot \bar{A}_K \neq \text{integer} \qquad [4{\cdot}243b]$$

Linear disorder

$$\overline{J_2} = N^{5/3} I_e \{ \overline{|F|^2} - |\overline{F}|^2 \} \quad \text{if} \quad \bar{\tau}_p \times \bar{B}_h = 0 \qquad [4{\cdot}244a]$$

$$\overline{J_2} = 0 \quad \text{if} \quad \bar{\tau}_p \times \bar{B}_h \neq 0 \qquad [4{\cdot}244b]$$

where we have assumed $N_1 = N_2 = N_3 = N^{1/3}$.

We shall illustrate linear substitution disorders by means of a typical example. Consider a structure built up of identical and parallel layers of atoms. Let the vectors $\bar{a}_1$ and $\bar{a}_2$ be chosen parallel to the layers. The atomic positions within a layer are then of the form $\bar{R}_k + L_1\bar{a}_1 + L_2\bar{a}_2$ where $\bar{R}_k = x_1^k\bar{a}_1 + x_2^k\bar{a}_2$, and there is perfect periodicity in this plane. We shall suppose that the displacements of all other layers relative to a given one are of the following form. There are in the first place layers displaced by amounts $L_3\bar{a}_3$, $L_3 = \pm 1, \pm 2, \cdots$. Secondly, between any two consecutive layers of this kind is one other layer either with a displacement $\bar{\sigma}_1 + L_3\bar{a}_3$ or with a displacement $\bar{\sigma}_2 + L_3\bar{a}_3$. We shall assume that the two values $\bar{\sigma}_1$ and $\bar{\sigma}_2$ are equally probable, and that there is no correlation between different layers. The atomic sites are thus $\bar{R}_k + \bar{A}_L$, $\bar{R}_k + \bar{\sigma}_1 + \bar{A}_L$ and $\bar{R}_k + \bar{\sigma}_2 + \bar{A}_L$. The first kind of sites are all occupied, but only half of the sites in the second and third kind are filled. The mean structure factor becomes

$$\overline{F} = K\{1 + \tfrac{1}{2}(e^{i\bar{s}\cdot\bar{\sigma}_1} + e^{i\bar{s}\cdot\bar{\sigma}_2})\} \qquad [4{\cdot}245a]$$

where

$$K \equiv \sum_k f_k \, e^{i\bar{s}\cdot\bar{R}_k} \qquad [4{\cdot}245b]$$

The mean square structure factor is

$$\overline{|F|^2} = |K|^2(2 + \cos \bar{s} \cdot \bar{\sigma}_1 + \cos \bar{s} \cdot \bar{\sigma}_2) \qquad [4\cdot246]$$

According to Equations 4·244 we have as result

$$J_2 = N^{5/3} I_e |K|^2 \sin^2 \tfrac{1}{2}\bar{s} \cdot (\bar{\sigma}_2 - \bar{\sigma}_1) \quad \text{if} \quad \bar{\tau}_p = \tau_3 \bar{b}_3 \qquad [4\cdot247a]$$

$$J_2 = 0 \quad \text{if} \quad \bar{\tau}_p \neq \tau_3 \bar{b}_3 \qquad [4\cdot247b]$$

The x-ray scattering due to various linear substitution disorders has been discussed in detail by Hendricks and Teller.[25]

Disorder in Diamond Crystals. In normal crystals there is mosaic structure and thermal disorder. In some crystals there are additional disorders, and these are as a rule accompanied by corresponding anomalies in macroscopic chemical or physical properties. Macroscopic evidence of additional disorder may easily be overlooked, and the presence of anomalous imperfection is then first revealed by scattering effects which cannot be accounted for by mosaic structure, heat motion, and Compton effect.

Raman and collaborators[26] observed scattering effects from diamond crystals which could not be explained in terms of normal disorders. These investigators overlooked the possibility that their crystals were afflicted with additional disorder and claimed instead that their experiments proved the theory of temperature diffuse scattering to be incorrect. Prior to the work carried out by Raman and his group Robertson, Fox, and Martin[27] had observed significant variations in some physical properties of diamond (notably in the absorption of infrared and ultraviolet light) and had accordingly classified diamond crystals into two types. The ordinary type (type I) is characterized by greater apparent homogeneity, while the rarer type II diamonds have a more pronounced mosaic structure. Type II diamonds show greater optical isotropy in polarized light than is true of the first type.

The disorder scattering of both types of diamond has recently been studied by Lonsdale and Smith.[28] According to their investigations the disorder scattering of type II diamonds agrees with that predicted by the theory of temperature diffuse scattering. Type I diamonds, on the other hand, give not only the temperature diffuse scattering, but also

[25] S. B. Hendricks and E. Teller, *J. Chem. Phys.*, **10**, 147 (1942).

[26] C. V. Raman and P. Nilakantan, *Proc. Ind. Acad. Sci.*, **11**, 389 (1940).
C. V. Raman, *Proc. Roy. Soc.*, **A179**, 315 (1942).

[27] R. Robertson, J. J. Fox, and A. E. Martin, *Phil. Trans.*, **A232**, 463 (1934); *Proc. Roy. Soc.*, **A157**, 579 (1936).

[28] K. Lonsdale and H. Smith, *Nature*, **148**, 112, 257 (1941); *Proc. Phys. Soc.*, **53**, 529 (1941); K. Lonsdale, *Proc. Roy. Soc.*, **A179**, 315 (1942).

additional disorder scattering which consequently must be attributed to some other disorder. These additional scattering effects are relatively intense for some specimens, with intensity maxima much stronger than those of the temperature diffuse scattering. The maxima of the additional scattering appear on a photographic plate partly as spots, partly as streaks. The spots, which are quite sharp, usually occur in groups of three, forming a small triangle about the diffuse spot due to the heat motion, and they lie at the intersection points of the streaks. Lonsdale further showed that there is a very small increase in the intensity of the additional scattering effects when the temperature is raised, in sharp contrast to the marked temperature sensitiveness of the temperature diffuse scattering. The accumulated experimental evidence permits only one conclusion: type II diamonds have mosaic structure, but the only disorder within the mosaic blocks is due to heat motion; type I diamonds are relatively free of mosaic structure, but they are afflicted with additional disorder.

The diamond crystals used in the experiments of Raman and collaborators belong to the common variety, type I. The intensity maxima reported and studied by the Indian group of physicists are those of the additional disorder scattering while they overlooked the diffuse maxima of the thermal disorder scattering. Their objection to the theory of the temperature diffuse scattering is consequently based upon an erroneous interpretation of the observations and merits no further discussion.

The positions of the observed spots and streaks can be quantitatively explained if it is assumed that the additional disorder is characterized by strong correlation in directions parallel to the cube faces and particularly strong correlation along the cube edges. Lonsdale has suggested that the additional disorder represents internal strain. The available observations are compatible with this hypothesis.

LITERATURE

A. *Theory of X-Ray Diffraction in Mosaic Crystals*

C. G. Darwin, *Phil. Mag.*, **27**, 325, 675 (1914); **43**, 800 (1922).

B. *Theory of Lattice Vibrations*

M. Born and T. v. Karman, *Physik. Zeitschr.*, **13**, 297 (1912); **14**, 15 (1913).
M. Born, *Dynamik der Kristallgitter*, Leipzig, 1915.
I. Waller, *Dissertation*, Upsala, 1925.
M. Blackman, *Proc. Roy. Soc.*, **A148**, 384 (1935); **159**, 416 (1937).

C. Theory of the Temperature Effect

P. Debye, *Ann. der Phys.*, **43**, 49 (1914).
H. Faxén, *Zeitschr. f. Phys.*, **17**, 266 (1923).
I. Waller, *Zeitschr. f. Phys.*, **17**, 398 (1923); *Dissertation*, Upsala, 1925; *Ann. der Phys.*, **83**, 153 (1927).
M. v. Laue, *Ann. der Phys.*, **81**, 877 (1926).
H. Ott, *Ann. der Phys.*, **23**, 169 (1935).
W. H. Zachariasen, *Phys. Rev.*, **57**, 597 (1940); **59**, 860 (1941).
M. Born and K. Sarginson, *Proc. Roy. Soc.*, **A179**, 69 (1941).
H. A. Jahn, *Proc. Roy. Soc.*, **A179**, 320 (1942).
J. Weigle and C. S. Smith, *Phys. Rev.*, **61**, 23 (1942).

APPENDIX A

DYADICS

1. Fundamental Concepts

The concept of dyadics is used extensively in Chapter II. Since some readers may not be familiar with dyadic operators and their algebra, the more important properties of dyadics will be discussed in this appendix. The treatment follows closely that of J. Willard Gibbs.

Let $\bar{r}' = \bar{F}(\bar{r})$. The vector function $\bar{F}$ is said to be linear if

$$\bar{F}(\bar{r}_1 + \bar{r}_2) = \bar{F}(\bar{r}_1) + \bar{F}(\bar{r}_2) \qquad [A\cdot 1]$$

for all values of $\bar{r}_1$ and $\bar{r}_2$. When the condition A·1 is fulfilled, the following relation can be deduced

$$\bar{F}(k_1\bar{r}_1 + k_2\bar{r}_2 + \cdots) = k_1\bar{F}(\bar{r}_1) + k_2\bar{F}(\bar{r}_2) + \cdots \qquad [A\cdot 2]$$

where $k_1, k_2 \cdots$ are any positive or negative scalar quantities.

Let $\bar{C}_1, \bar{C}_2, \cdots$ be any set of given vectors and $\bar{D}_1, \bar{D}_2, \cdots$ another set equal in number. An expression of the form

$$\bar{r}' = \bar{r}\cdot\bar{C}_1\bar{D}_1 + \bar{r}\cdot\bar{C}_2\bar{D}_2 + \cdots \equiv \bar{r}\cdot(\bar{C}_1\bar{D}_1 + \bar{C}_2\bar{D}_2 + \cdots) \qquad [A\cdot 3]$$

is according to the definition A·1 a linear vector function. The linear relationship between the vectors $\bar{r}'$ and $\bar{r}$ will be written symbolically

$$\bar{r}' = \bar{r}\cdot\boldsymbol{\Phi}, \quad \boldsymbol{\Phi} \equiv \sum_j \bar{C}_j\bar{D}_j \qquad [A\cdot 4]$$

The quantity $\boldsymbol{\Phi}$ defined by Equations A·3 and A·4 is an operator, called a dyadic, by means of which the linear relationship between the two vectors $\bar{r}'$ and $\bar{r}$ can conveniently be expressed. At present no other meaning is to be attached to the operator $\boldsymbol{\Phi}$. The expression $\bar{r}\cdot\boldsymbol{\Phi}$, defined above, is called the scalar product of the vector $\bar{r}$ with the dyadic $\boldsymbol{\Phi}$. $\bar{r}$ is the prefactor and $\boldsymbol{\Phi}$ the postfactor. It is readily seen that the linear relationship between $\bar{r}'$ and $\bar{r}$ can be expressed in a similar manner as the scalar product of another dyadic $\boldsymbol{\Phi}_C$ with the vector $\bar{r}$, the dyadic this time being the prefactor of the product. We have

$$\begin{gathered}\bar{r}' = \bar{D}_1\bar{C}_1\cdot\bar{r} + \bar{D}_2\bar{C}_2\cdot\bar{r} + \cdots = (\bar{D}_1\bar{C}_1 + \bar{D}_2\bar{C}_2 + \cdots)\cdot\bar{r} \\ \bar{r}' = \boldsymbol{\Phi}_C\cdot\bar{r}, \quad \boldsymbol{\Phi}_C \equiv \sum_j \bar{D}_j\bar{C}_j\end{gathered} \qquad [A\cdot 5]$$

The operator $\boldsymbol{\Phi}_C$ is obtained from $\boldsymbol{\Phi}$ by interchanging the vector sets $\bar{C}_1, \bar{C}_2 \cdots$ and $\bar{D}_1, \bar{D}_2 \cdots$ and is called the dyadic conjugate to Φ. Hence, by definition

$$\bar{r} \cdot \Phi = \Phi_C \cdot \bar{r} \tag{A·6}$$

for every $\bar{r}$. The definitions A·3 and A·4 do not require $\bar{r} \cdot \Phi = \Phi \cdot \bar{r}$, i.e., the commutative law need not hold for the scalar product of a vector and an arbitrary dyadic.

The operator Φ is a sum of expressions of the type $\bar{C}\bar{D}$. Such a constellation of two vectors, with no symbol indicating scalar or vector multiplication between them, is called a dyad. The term dyadic, which we have introduced earlier, refers accordingly to a sum of dyads, i.e., to a dyadic polynomial. The first vector of a dyad is called the antecedent and the second vector the consequent.

Two dyadics Φ and Ψ are said to be equal if

$$\bar{r} \cdot \Phi = \bar{r} \cdot \Psi \qquad \text{for all values } \bar{r}$$

or

$$\Phi \cdot \bar{r} = \Psi \cdot \bar{r} \qquad \text{for all values } \bar{r} \tag{A·7}$$

or

$$\bar{s} \cdot \Phi \cdot \bar{r} = \bar{s} \cdot \Psi \cdot \bar{r} \qquad \text{for all values } \bar{s} \text{ and } \bar{r}$$

Utilizing this definition it is readily seen that

$$(\bar{C} + \bar{C}')\bar{D} = \bar{C}\bar{D} + \bar{C}'\bar{D}, \quad \bar{C}(\bar{D} + \bar{D}') = \bar{C}\bar{D} + \bar{C}\bar{D}' \tag{A·8}$$

Hence the associative law holds for the combination of vectors in dyads.

Let $\Phi = \sum_j \bar{C}_j\bar{D}_j$ and $\Psi = \sum_j \bar{C}_j'\bar{D}_j'$ be two dyadics. The sum $\Phi + \Psi$ is defined as follows.

$$\bar{r} \cdot \Phi + \bar{r} \cdot \Psi \equiv \bar{r} \cdot (\Phi + \Psi) \tag{A·9}$$

According to Equations A·7 we have thus the rather trivial result

$$\Phi + \Psi = \sum_j (\bar{C}_j\bar{D}_j + \bar{C}_j'\bar{D}_j') \tag{A·10}$$

It is easily seen that

$$(\Phi + \Psi)_C = \Phi_C + \Psi_C \tag{A·11}$$

Let us express the vector $\bar{r}$ in terms of a set of three given vectors $\bar{a}_1, \bar{a}_2, \bar{a}_3$ which do not all lie in a plane, i.e., we set $\bar{r} = x_1\bar{a}_1 + x_2\bar{a}_2 + x_2\bar{a}_3$. The relation A·4 may then be written in the form

$$\bar{r}' = x_1\bar{a}_1 \cdot \Phi + x_2\bar{a}_2 \cdot \Phi + x_3\bar{a}_3 \cdot \Phi \tag{A·12}$$

Since the operator Φ has significance only with reference to the linear relationship between $\bar{r}'$ and $\bar{r}$, it is evident from Equation A·12 that the three scalar products $\bar{a}_j \cdot \Phi$ completely define the operator. The three scalar products are, of course, vector quantities and may be called the vector components of Φ. The consideration just given permits the following restatement of the defintion A·7.

$$\Phi = \Psi \quad \text{if} \quad \begin{aligned} \bar{a}_1 \cdot \Phi &= \bar{a}_1 \cdot \Psi \\ \bar{a}_2 \cdot \Phi &= \bar{a}_2 \cdot \Psi \\ \bar{a}_3 \cdot \Phi &= \bar{a}_3 \cdot \Psi \end{aligned} \qquad [\text{A·13}]$$

where $\bar{a}_1$, $\bar{a}_2$, $\bar{a}_3$ are any three vectors which are not coplanar. We shall designate the vector set reciprocal to $\bar{a}_1$, $\bar{a}_2$, $\bar{a}_3$ by $\bar{b}_1$, $\bar{b}_2$, $\bar{b}_3$. (Reciprocal vectors are discussed in section 1·4.) The dyadic $\bar{b}_1(\bar{a}_1 \cdot \Phi) + \bar{b}_2(\bar{a}_2 \cdot \Phi) + \bar{b}_3(\bar{a}_3 \cdot \Phi)$ is, as a consequence of Equations A·13, identical with Φ, and the same statement evidently applies to the dyadic $(\Phi \cdot \bar{b}_1)\bar{a}_1 + (\Phi \cdot \bar{b}_2)\bar{a}_2 + (\Phi \cdot \bar{b}_3)\bar{a}_3$. Hence we may set

$$\begin{aligned} \Phi &= \bar{b}_1\bar{A}_1 + \bar{b}_2\bar{A}_2 + \bar{b}_3\bar{A}_3 = \bar{B}_1\bar{a}_1 + \bar{B}_2\bar{a}_2 + \bar{B}_3\bar{a}_3 \\ \bar{A}_j &= \bar{a}_j \cdot \Phi, \quad \bar{B}_j = \Phi \cdot \bar{b}_j \end{aligned} \qquad [\text{A·14}]$$

According to Equations A·14 any dyadic can be reduced to a sum of not more than three dyads. Any three vectors not all lying in a plane can be used as antecedents or as consequents of these three dyads. We shall refer to Equations A·14 as the trinomial form of the dyadic. The vectors $\bar{B}_1$, $\bar{B}_2$, $\bar{B}_3$ will be called the antecedent vector components and $\bar{A}_1$, $\bar{A}_2$, $\bar{A}_3$ the consequent vector components of the dyadic. A dyadic describes a linear relationship between two vectors $\bar{r}$ and $\bar{r}'$; we may say that the dyadic transforms vector $\bar{r}$ into vector $\bar{r}'$. Using this terminology there is a simple interpretation of the vector components of a dyadic: the antecedent vector components are the transformed vectors $\bar{b}_1$, $\bar{b}_2$, $\bar{b}_3$, whereas the consequent vector components are the transformed vectors $\bar{a}_1$, $\bar{a}_2$, $\bar{a}_3$.

It is of importance to note that the laws of algebra applicable to linear combinations of dyads also will be valid for the corresponding scalar and vector products. In other words, a linear equation satisfied by dyads will remain valid if each dyad is replaced by the scalar or by the vector product of its two vectors. Suppose that $\sum_j \bar{C}_j\bar{D}_j$ and $\sum_j \bar{C}'_j\bar{D}'_j$ are any two expressions for the same dyadic. Replacing all dyads by the corresponding scalar or vector products the following result is obtained.

If

$$\Phi = \sum_j \bar{C}_j\bar{D}_j = \sum_j \bar{C}'_j\bar{D}'_j$$

then

$$\Phi_V \equiv \sum_j \bar{C}_j \times \bar{D}_j = \sum_j \bar{C}'_j \times \bar{D}'_j = -(\Phi_C)_V \qquad [\text{A·15}]$$

and

$$\phi_S \equiv \sum_j \bar{C}_j \cdot \bar{D}_j = \sum_j \bar{C}_j' \cdot \bar{D}_j' = (\phi_C)_S$$

ϕ_V is called the vector and ϕ_S the scalar of the dyadic. As seen by Equations A·15 these quantities have values which are independent of the particular form in which the dyadic is expressed, i.e., they are invariant quantities.

A dyadic is said to be zero if $\bar{r} \cdot \phi = 0$ for every $\bar{r}$. It follows from Equation A·13 that the sufficient and necessary condition is $\bar{A}_1 = \bar{A}_2 = \bar{A}_3 = 0$. A dyadic which is zero can thus be reduced to a form which vanishes identically, i.e., $\phi = 0$. A dyadic is called an idemfactor if it transforms every vector $\bar{r}$ into $\bar{r}$ (whether $\bar{r}$ is used as prefactor or postfactor). An idemfactor, which will be denoted by the symbol $\mathbf{I}$, is hence defined by

$$\bar{r} \cdot \mathbf{I} = \mathbf{I} \cdot \bar{r} = \bar{r} \quad \text{for every } \bar{r} \qquad \text{[A·16]}$$

The trinomial form of an idemfactor is readily found. Using Equations A·14 and A·16 we have

$$\mathbf{I} = \bar{b}_1 \bar{a}_1 + \bar{b}_2 \bar{a}_2 + \bar{b}_3 \bar{a}_3 \qquad \text{[A·17]}$$

Let

$$\bar{r}' = \bar{r} \cdot \phi \quad \text{and} \quad \bar{r}'' = \bar{r}' \cdot \psi$$

where

$$\phi = \sum_j \bar{C}_j \bar{D}_j \quad \text{and} \quad \psi = \sum_j \bar{C}_j' \bar{D}_j'$$

The relationship between $\bar{r}''$ and $\bar{r}$ must then be linear and may accordingly be expressed by means of a dyadic which will be called the scalar product of ϕ by ψ and denoted by $\phi \cdot \psi$. The scalar product of two dyadics is thus defined by

$$\begin{aligned} \bar{r}' &= \bar{r} \cdot \phi \\ \bar{r}'' &= \bar{r}' \cdot \psi \\ \bar{r}'' &= \bar{r} \cdot (\phi \cdot \psi) \end{aligned} \qquad \text{[A·18]}$$

From the definition one finds

$$\phi \cdot \psi = \sum_j \sum_k (\bar{D}_j \cdot \bar{C}_k') \bar{C}_j \bar{D}_k' \qquad \text{[A·19]}$$

When both ϕ and ψ are reduced to trinomial form, ϕ being expressed in terms of the antecedent vector components and ψ in terms of the consequent vector components, the scalar product of ϕ by ψ assumes a simple form. If we have

$$\Phi = \sum_j \bar{B}_j \bar{a}_j \quad \text{and} \quad \Psi = \sum_j \bar{b}_j \bar{A}'_j$$

then

$$\Phi \cdot \Psi = \bar{B}_1 \bar{A}'_1 + \bar{B}_2 \bar{A}'_2 + \bar{B}_3 \bar{A}'_3 \qquad \text{[A·20]}$$

It is clear that the commutative law does not apply to scalar products of dyadics. One writes conveniently Φ^2 for the product $\Phi \cdot \Phi$, Φ^3 for the product $\Phi \cdot \Phi \cdot \Phi$, and so on. Suppose that $\Psi = \mathbf{I}$ in the product $\Phi \cdot \Psi$; then $\Phi \cdot \mathbf{I} = \bar{B}_1\bar{a}_1 + \bar{B}_2\bar{a}_2 + \bar{B}_3\bar{a}_3 = \Phi$, and similarly $\mathbf{I} \cdot \Phi = \Phi$. We may, in other words, replace the earlier definition of an idemfactor by

$$\Phi \cdot \mathbf{I} = \mathbf{I} \cdot \Phi = \Phi \qquad \text{[A·21]}$$

for every Φ.

The concept of the vector product of a vector and a dyadic may be introduced in the following manner. Let $\bar{r}$ and $\bar{r}_1$ be any two vectors and Φ a dyadic. The expression $\bar{r}' = (\bar{r} \times \bar{r}_1) \cdot \Phi$ describes a linear relationship between $\bar{r}'$ and $\bar{r} \times \bar{r}_1$; then the relationship between $\bar{r}'$ and $\bar{r}$ is also linear (since the vector product of two vectors is a linear vector function of either vector in the product). The dyadic describing the relationship between $\bar{r}'$ and $\bar{r}$ must, of course, change with $\bar{r}_1$. It will be denoted by $\bar{r}_1 \times \Phi$ and called the vector product of $\bar{r}_1$ by Φ. The defining equation is

$$(\bar{r} \times \bar{r}_1) \cdot \Phi \equiv \bar{r} \cdot (\bar{r}_1 \times \Phi) \qquad \text{[A·22]}$$

Let $\Phi = \sum_j \bar{C}_j \bar{D}_j$. From the definition it follows that

$$\bar{r}_1 \times \sum_j \bar{C}_j \bar{D}_j = \sum_j (\bar{r}_1 \times \bar{C}_j) \bar{D}_j \qquad \text{[A·23]}$$

It is readily shown that $(\bar{r}_1 \times \Phi)_C = -\Phi_C \times \bar{r}_1$ and hence that

$$\bar{r} \cdot (\bar{r}_1 \times \Phi) = (\bar{r} \times \bar{r}_1) \cdot \Phi = -(\Phi_C \times \bar{r}_1) \cdot \bar{r} = -\Phi_C \cdot (\bar{r}_1 \times \bar{r}) \qquad \text{[A·24]}$$

Setting $\Phi = \mathbf{I}$ one finds the particular result,

$$\bar{r} \times \bar{r}_1 = \bar{r} \cdot (\bar{r}_1 \times \mathbf{I}) = -(\mathbf{I} \times \bar{r}_1) \cdot \bar{r} \qquad \text{[A·25]}$$

showing that the vector product of two vectors can be written as the scalar product of either vector with a dyadic.

2. The Nonian Form of Dyadics

We have seen that any dyadic can be reduced to the trinomial form of Equations A·14 where either the antecedents or the consequents can be set equal to any three vectors which do not all lie in a plane. The three vectors $\bar{a}_1$, $\bar{a}_2$, $\bar{a}_3$ define a general oblique coordinate system. The vector components of the dyadic may, of course, be referred to this system or to the reciprocal system $\bar{b}_1$, $\bar{b}_2$, $\bar{b}_3$. For present purposes the latter alternative is more convenient. We set therefore $\mathbf{\Phi} = \sum_i \bar{B}_i \bar{a}_i$ and $\bar{B}_i = \sum_j \phi_{ij} \bar{b}_j$. Hence

$$\begin{aligned} &\phi_{11}\bar{b}_1\bar{a}_1 + \phi_{12}\bar{b}_2\bar{a}_1 + \phi_{13}\bar{b}_3\bar{a}_1 \\ \mathbf{\Phi} = &+\phi_{21}\bar{b}_1\bar{a}_2 + \phi_{22}\bar{b}_2\bar{a}_2 + \phi_{23}\bar{b}_3\bar{a}_2 \\ &+\phi_{31}\bar{b}_1\bar{a}_3 + \phi_{32}\bar{b}_2\bar{a}_3 + \phi_{33}\bar{b}_3\bar{a}_3 \end{aligned} \qquad \text{[A·26]}$$

When a dyadic is expressed in this manner, as a linear combination of the nine dyads $\bar{b}_j\bar{a}_i$, it is said to be given in nonian form and the nine coefficients ϕ_{ij} are called the scalar components of the dyadic. When all dyadics are referred to the same vector set $\bar{a}_1$, $\bar{a}_2$, $\bar{a}_3$ (and $\bar{b}_1$, $\bar{b}_2$, $\bar{b}_3$), i.e., when only one reference frame is used, it will naturally suffice to specify the scalar components of the dyadics and one obtains then the matrix representation

$$\mathbf{\Phi} = \begin{pmatrix} \phi_{11} & \phi_{12} & \phi_{13} \\ \phi_{21} & \phi_{22} & \phi_{23} \\ \phi_{31} & \phi_{32} & \phi_{33} \end{pmatrix} \qquad \text{[A·27]}$$

as a simplified form of Equation A·26. The matrix form of an idemfactor is clearly

$$\mathbf{I} = \begin{pmatrix} 1 & 0 & 0 \\ 0 & 1 & 0 \\ 0 & 0 & 1 \end{pmatrix} \qquad \text{[A·28]}$$

The results obtained in the preceding section are readily rewritten in terms of the nonian form. Let $\bar{r}' = \sum_i x_i' \bar{a}_i$, $\bar{r} = \sum_j x_j \bar{a}_j$, $\mathbf{\Phi} = \sum_i \sum_j \phi_{ij} \bar{b}_j \bar{a}_i$, and $\mathbf{\Psi} = \sum_i \sum_j \psi_{ij} \bar{b}_j \bar{a}_i$. The relation defining the dyadic $\mathbf{\Phi}$ is of the type $\bar{r}' = \bar{r} \cdot \mathbf{\Phi}$ and this may be written

$$x_i' = \sum_j \phi_{ij} x_j \qquad \text{[A·29]}$$

The definition A·13 gives

$$\mathbf{\Phi} = \mathbf{\Psi} \quad \text{when} \quad \phi_{ij} = \psi_{ij} \qquad \text{[A·30]}$$

for every set i, j. Similarly

$$k\mathbf{\Phi} = \sum_i \sum_j k\phi_{ij} \bar{b}_j \bar{a}_i \qquad \text{[A·31]}$$

$$\mathbf{\Phi} + \mathbf{\Psi} = \sum_i \sum_j (\phi_{ij} + \psi_{ij}) \bar{b}_j \bar{a}_i \qquad \text{[A·32]}$$

$$\Phi_V = \sum_i \sum_j \phi_{ij} \bar{b}_j \times \bar{a}_i \qquad [A\cdot33]$$

$$\Phi_S = \sum_i \sum_j \phi_{ij} \bar{b}_j \cdot \bar{a}_i = \sum_i \phi_{ii} \qquad [A\cdot34]$$

$$\Phi \cdot \Psi = \sum_i \sum_j \left(\sum_k \phi_{kj} \psi_{ik}\right) \bar{b}_j \bar{a}_i \neq \Psi \cdot \Phi = \sum_i \sum_j \left(\sum_k \psi_{kj} \phi_{ik}\right) \bar{b}_j \bar{a}_i \qquad [A\cdot35]$$

We note in particular that the scalar of a dyadic equals the sum of the diagonal components and that the matrix form of the product $\Phi \cdot \Psi$ has a structure analogous to the expression for the product of two corresponding determinants.

3. Complete and Incomplete Dyadics

Consider a dyadic $\Phi = \bar{B}_1\bar{a}_1 + \bar{B}_2\bar{a}_2 + \bar{B}_3\bar{a}_3 = \bar{b}_1\bar{A}_1 + \bar{b}_2\bar{A}_2 + \bar{b}_3\bar{A}_3$. The determinant of the dyadic, denoted by $|\Phi|$, is defined as the triple scalar product of the three antecedents times the triple scalar product of the three consequents, i.e.,

$$|\Phi| \equiv (\bar{B}_1\bar{B}_2\bar{B}_3)(\bar{a}_1\bar{a}_2\bar{a}_3) = (\bar{b}_1\bar{b}_2\bar{b}_3)(\bar{A}_1\bar{A}_2\bar{A}_3) \qquad [A\cdot36]$$

Now

$$(\bar{B}_1\bar{B}_2\bar{B}_3) = (\bar{b}_1\bar{b}_2\bar{b}_3) \begin{vmatrix} \phi_{11} & \phi_{12} & \phi_{13} \\ \phi_{21} & \phi_{22} & \phi_{23} \\ \phi_{31} & \phi_{32} & \phi_{33} \end{vmatrix}$$

Since $(\bar{b}_1\bar{b}_2\bar{b}_3)(\bar{a}_1\bar{a}_2\bar{a}_3) = 1$ we have therefore

$$|\Phi| = \begin{vmatrix} \phi_{11} & \phi_{12} & \phi_{13} \\ \phi_{21} & \phi_{22} & \phi_{23} \\ \phi_{31} & \phi_{32} & \phi_{33} \end{vmatrix} = |\Phi_C| \qquad [A\cdot37]$$

It follows from Equation A·35 that

$$|\Phi \cdot \Psi| = |\Phi|\,|\Psi| \qquad [A\cdot38]$$

A dyadic is said to be complete (or non-singular) if $|\Phi| \neq 0$ and incomplete (or singular) if $|\Phi| = 0$. Since $\bar{a}_1$, $\bar{a}_2$, $\bar{a}_3$ do not all lie in a plane, the vector components of an incomplete dyadic must be coplanar. One vector component can then be expressed as a linear combination of the two others, i.e., $\bar{A}_3 = k_1\bar{A}_1 + k_2\bar{A}$. If $|\Phi| = 0$ Φ may consequently be expressed as a sum of not more than two dyads.

$$\Phi = (\bar{b}_1 + k_1\bar{b}_3)\bar{A}_1 + (\bar{b}_2 + k_2\bar{b}_3)\bar{A}_2 = \bar{C}_1\bar{A}_1 + \bar{C}_2\bar{A}_2 \qquad [A\cdot39]$$

If $\bar{r} \cdot \Phi = 0$ for every $\bar{r}$, the dyadic Φ is said to be zero, and we write $\Phi = 0$. All the components ϕ_{ij} must then vanish. Hence, $|\Phi| = 0$, and we have a special case of a singular dyadic. If in Equation A·39 $\bar{A}_1$ and $\bar{A}_2$ or $\bar{C}_1$ and $\bar{C}_2$ are parallel vectors the incomplete dyadic can be reduced to a single dyad and the dyadic is then said to be linear. An incomplete dyadic which is neither zero nor linear is called planar. Clearly, linear dyadics can be considered special cases of planar dyadics.

Linear Dyadics. A linear dyadic is synonymous with a single dyad, i.e., $\boldsymbol{\Phi} \equiv \bar{C}\bar{D}$. It is evident that a linear dyadic transforms every vector $\bar{r}$ into a vector parallel to the consequent when $\bar{r}$ is used as prefactor and into a vector parallel to the antecedent if $\bar{r}$ is used as postfactor: $\bar{r} \cdot (\bar{C}\bar{D}) = (\bar{r} \cdot \bar{C})\bar{D}$ and $(\bar{C}\bar{D}) \cdot \bar{r} = (\bar{r} \cdot \bar{D})\bar{C}$. A linear dyadic is said to be unilinear, or uniaxial, if the antecedent and the consequent are parallel vectors. One sees that the equation $\bar{r} \cdot \boldsymbol{\Phi} = 0$, in addition to the trivial solutions $\bar{r} = 0$ and $\boldsymbol{\Phi} = 0$, has the following solution: $\boldsymbol{\Phi}$ is a linear dyadic and $\bar{r}$ is any vector normal to the antecedent. Similarly the equations $\bar{r} \cdot \boldsymbol{\Phi} = 0 = \boldsymbol{\Phi} \cdot \bar{r}$ are simultaneously satisfied if $\boldsymbol{\Phi}$ is a unilinear dyadic and $\bar{r}$ any vector normal to its axis.

Planar Dyadics. A planar dyadic has the general form $\boldsymbol{\Phi} \equiv \bar{C}_1\bar{D}_1 + \bar{C}_2\bar{D}_2$. The linear relationship $\bar{r}' = \bar{r} \cdot (\bar{C}_1\bar{D}_1 + \bar{C}_2\bar{D}_2)$ evidently corresponds to a transformation of a vector $\bar{r}$ into a vector $\bar{r}'$ lying in the plane of the consequents. Similarly $(\bar{C}_1\bar{D}_1 + \bar{C}_2\bar{D}_2) \cdot \bar{r}$ gives a vector in the plane of the antecedents. A planar dyadic is said to be uniplanar if antecedents and consequents all lie in a plane. The equations $\bar{r} \cdot \boldsymbol{\Phi} = 0 = \boldsymbol{\Phi} \cdot \bar{r}$ are obviously simultaneously satisfied if $\boldsymbol{\Phi}$ is uniplanar and $\bar{r}$ normal to the plane of $\boldsymbol{\Phi}$.

Equation A·38 shows that the scalar product of two complete dyadics is a complete dyadic, while the scalar product is incomplete if either or both factors are incomplete.

4. Symmetrical, Anti-Symmetrical, and Reciprocal Dyadics

A dyadic is said to be symmetrical if $\boldsymbol{\Phi} = \boldsymbol{\Phi}_C$ and anti-symmetrical if $\boldsymbol{\Phi} = -\boldsymbol{\Phi}_C$. In using Equations A·15 and A·38, if

$$\boldsymbol{\Phi} = \boldsymbol{\Phi}_C \quad \text{then} \quad \boldsymbol{\Phi}_V = 0$$

if

$$\boldsymbol{\Phi} = -\boldsymbol{\Phi}_C \quad \text{then} \quad \boldsymbol{\Phi}_S = |\boldsymbol{\Phi}| = 0$$

Thus no complete dyadic can be anti-symmetrical and it is easily seen that anti-symmetrical dyadics cannot be linear. Let $\boldsymbol{\Phi} = \bar{b}_1\bar{A}_1 + \bar{b}_2\bar{A}_2 + \bar{b}_3\bar{A}_3$ be anti-symmetrical. We may then set

$$\boldsymbol{\Phi} = \tfrac{1}{2}(\boldsymbol{\Phi} - \boldsymbol{\Phi}_C) = \tfrac{1}{2}(\bar{b}_1\bar{A}_1 - \bar{A}_1\bar{b}_1 + \bar{b}_2\bar{A}_2 - \bar{A}_2\bar{b}_2 + \bar{b}_3\bar{A}_3 - \bar{A}_3\bar{b}_3) \quad \text{[A·40]}$$

Consider next the linear relationship $\bar{r}' = \bar{r} \cdot \boldsymbol{\Phi}$. By using the representation A·40 and the identity $(\bar{r} \cdot \bar{b}_j)\bar{A}_j - (\bar{r} \cdot \bar{A}_j)\bar{b}_j = \bar{r} \times (\bar{A}_j \times \bar{b}_j)$, one finds readily

$$\bar{r} \cdot \Phi = -\tfrac{1}{2}\bar{r} \times \Phi_V \qquad \text{[A·41]}$$

This result shows that an anti-symmetrical dyadic is planar and completely defined by its vector. By comparing Equations A·25 and A·41 it will be noted that an anti-symmetrical dyadic can be expressed in the form

$$\Phi = -\tfrac{1}{2}\,\Phi_V \times \mathbf{I} = \tfrac{1}{2}\mathbf{I} \times \Phi_V \qquad \text{[A·42]}$$

Any dyadic can be written as a sum of a symmetrical and an anti-symmetrical part by means of the identity

$$\Phi \equiv \Phi^S + \Phi^A, \qquad \begin{aligned} \Phi^S &\equiv \tfrac{1}{2}(\Phi + \Phi_C) \\ \Phi^A &\equiv \tfrac{1}{2}(\Phi - \Phi_C) \end{aligned} \qquad \text{[A·43]}$$

The dyadic reciprocal to Φ is denoted by the symbol Φ^{-1} and defined by

$$\Phi \cdot \Phi^{-1} = \mathbf{I} = \Phi^{-1} \cdot \Phi \qquad \text{[A·44]}$$

Since $|\mathbf{I}| = 1$, it follows from Equation A·38 that Φ^{-1} exists only if Φ is complete. Clearly, if

$$\Phi = \bar{b}_1\bar{A}_1 + \bar{b}_2\bar{A}_2 + \bar{b}_3\bar{A}_3$$

then

$$\Phi^{-1} = \bar{A}_1^{-1}\bar{a}_1 + \bar{A}_2^{-1}\bar{a}_2 + \bar{A}_3^{-1}\bar{a}_3 \qquad \text{[A·45]}$$

where $\bar{A}_1^{-1}, \bar{A}_2^{-1}, \bar{A}_3^{-1}$ is the vector set reciprocal to $\bar{A}_1, \bar{A}_2, \bar{A}_3$. Suppose that the linear relationship $\bar{r}' = \bar{r} \cdot \Phi$ is given. The converse relationship is then expressed by $\bar{r} = \bar{r}' \cdot \Phi^{-1}$. The reciprocal of a product of dyadics is easily seen to be the product of the reciprocal dyadics taken in the reverse order, i.e.,

$$(\Phi \cdot \Psi \cdot \mathrm{X} \cdots)^{-1} = \cdots \mathrm{X}^{-1} \cdot \Psi^{-1} \cdot \Phi^{-1} \qquad \text{[A·46]}$$

The analogous statement applies to conjugate dyadics as a consequence of the definition A·6, i.e.,

$$(\Phi \cdot \Psi \cdot \mathrm{X} \cdots)_C = \cdots \mathrm{X}_C \quad \Psi_C \cdot \Phi_C \qquad \text{[A·47]}$$

Since $\Phi_C \cdot (\Phi^{-1})_C = (\Phi^{-1} \cdot \Phi)_C = \mathbf{I}$, one has $(\Phi^{-1})_C = (\Phi_C)^{-1}$, and one may thus write Φ_C^{-1} without ambiguity.

Let us next investigate how a dyadic transforms its own vector. It is seen from Equation A·41 that $\Phi_V \cdot \Phi^A = 0$ and hence

$$\Phi_V \cdot \Phi = \Phi_V \cdot \Phi^S = \tfrac{1}{2}\Phi_V \cdot (\Phi + \Phi_C) \qquad \text{[A·48]}$$

Setting $\Phi = \bar{b}_1\bar{A}_1 + \bar{b}_2\bar{A}_2 + \bar{b}_3\bar{A}_3$ and hence $\Phi_V = \bar{b}_1 \times \bar{A}_1 + \bar{b}_2 \times \bar{A}_2 +$

$\bar{b}_3 \times \bar{A}_3$ the right side of Equation A·48 is readily expanded and we find

$$\Phi_V \cdot \Phi = |\Phi|(\bar{a}_1 \times \bar{A}_1^{-1} + \bar{a}_2 \times \bar{A}_2^{-1} + \bar{a}_3 \times \bar{A}_3^{-1}) = |\Phi|(\Phi_C^{-1})_V \quad \text{[A·49]}$$

5. Some Properties of the Dyadics $\phi = \phi_C^{-1}$

In this section we shall discuss dyadics for which $\Phi = \Phi_C^{-1}$. We must then have $\Phi^{-1} = \Phi_C$. The trinomial form of Φ_C^{-1} is readily obtained from Equation A·45 and hence

$$\Phi = \bar{b}_1\bar{A}_1 + \bar{b}_2\bar{A}_2 + \bar{b}_3\bar{A}_3 = \bar{a}_1\bar{A}_1^{-1} + \bar{a}_2\bar{A}_2^{-1} + \bar{a}_3\bar{A}_3^{-1} = \Phi_C^{-1} \quad \text{[A·50]}$$

Since $\Phi \cdot \Phi^{-1} = \mathbf{I}$, it follows that $|\Phi^{-1}| = \frac{1}{|\Phi|}$. On the other hand $|\Phi_C| = |\Phi|$. Accordingly Equation A·50 demands that

$$|\Phi| = \frac{1}{|\Phi|}, \quad |\Phi| = \frac{(\bar{A}_1\bar{A}_2\bar{A}_3)}{(\bar{a}_1\bar{a}_2\bar{a}_3)} = \pm 1 \quad \text{[A·51]}$$

Since $\bar{A}_1$, $\bar{A}_2$, $\bar{A}_3$ are the transformed vectors $\bar{a}_1$, $\bar{a}_2$, $\bar{a}_3$ it follows that the transformation $\Phi = \Phi_C^{-1}$ preserves volumes.

Since $\Phi_C = \Phi^{-1}$, we may write $\bar{r}' = \bar{r} \cdot \Phi = \Phi^{-1} \cdot \bar{r}$. Taking the square of the vector $\bar{r}'$ we find

$$r'^2 = \bar{r} \cdot \Phi \cdot \Phi^{-1} \cdot \bar{r} = r^2 \quad \text{[A·52]}$$

showing that linear dimensions are preserved. (The preservation of volumes is obviously a necessary consequence of the preservation of all linear dimensions.)

A transformation leaving all linear dimensions unchanged is called a rotation. Any rotation is thus characterized by $\Phi = \Phi_C^{-1}$. The rotation is said to be proper if $|\Phi| = +1$ and improper if $|\Phi| = -1$.

If we change the algebraic sign for all nine scalar components of a proper dyadic Φ, we obtain the dyadic $-\Phi$ which is improper. There is accordingly an improper dyadic for every dyadic which is proper and a proper dyadic for every one that is improper. The simplest proper dyadic is the idemfactor. The corresponding improper dyadic is $-\mathbf{I}$ which transforms any vector $\bar{r}$ into $-\bar{r}$ and hence represents a simple inversion. Any improper dyadic can be considered as the scalar product of the corresponding proper dyadic with $-\mathbf{I}$ for we have

$$-\Phi = \Phi \cdot -\mathbf{I} = -\mathbf{I} \cdot \Phi \quad \text{[A·53]}$$

A solution $\bar{r}$ of the equation $\bar{r} \cdot \Phi = \bar{r}$ represents a point which is transformed into itself. The trivial solution of this equation is $\bar{r} = 0$. Let us investigate if there are other points which are invariant under transformations of the type $\Phi = \Phi_C^{-1}$. If $\bar{r} \cdot \Phi = \bar{r}$, then also $\bar{r} = \Phi \cdot \bar{r}$

(because $\boldsymbol{\phi}^{-1} = \boldsymbol{\phi}_C$), and we must accordingly look for simultaneous solutions of the equations

$$\bar{r} \cdot (\boldsymbol{\phi} - \mathbf{I}) = (\boldsymbol{\phi} - \mathbf{I}) \cdot \bar{r} = 0 \qquad \text{[A·54]}$$

These equations have a non-trivial solution $\bar{r} \neq 0$ only if $\boldsymbol{\phi} - \mathbf{I}$ is an incomplete dyadic. Setting $\boldsymbol{\phi} = \bar{b}_1\bar{A}_1 + \bar{b}_2\bar{A}_2 + \bar{b}_3\bar{A}_3$ we have $\boldsymbol{\phi} - \mathbf{I} = \bar{b}_1(\bar{A}_1 - \bar{a}_1) + \bar{b}_2(\bar{A}_2 - \bar{a}_2) + \bar{b}_3(\bar{A}_3 - \bar{a}_3)$. The condition to be imposed upon $\boldsymbol{\phi}$ is $|\boldsymbol{\phi} - \mathbf{I}| = 0$. This determinant is readily evaluated using Equation A·50 and one finds

$$|\boldsymbol{\phi} - \mathbf{I}| = (1 - \boldsymbol{\phi}_S)(|\boldsymbol{\phi}| - 1) = 0 \qquad \text{[A·55]}$$

This equation is satisfied by all proper dyadics and by the improper dyadic for which $\boldsymbol{\phi}_S = +1$. When $\boldsymbol{\phi} - \mathbf{I}$ is incomplete it is either zero, unilinear or uniplanar. Clearly, $\boldsymbol{\phi} - \mathbf{I}$ is zero if $\boldsymbol{\phi} = \mathbf{I}$ and Equations A·54 are then satisfied by any vector $\bar{r}$. It is easily seen that $\boldsymbol{\phi} - \mathbf{I}$ is unilinear if $\boldsymbol{\phi}$ is improper and $\boldsymbol{\phi}_S = +1$. In this case Equations A·54 are satisfied for any vector $\bar{r}$ which is normal to the axis $\bar{u}$ of $\boldsymbol{\phi} - \mathbf{I}$. This particular improper dyadic can be written in the form

$$\boldsymbol{\phi} = \mathbf{I} - 2\bar{u}\bar{u} \qquad \text{[A·56]}$$

The transformation represented by this dyadic is called a reflection and the invariant plane normal to $\bar{u}$ is the reflection plane.

The dyadic $\boldsymbol{\phi} - \mathbf{I}$ is uniplanar if $|\boldsymbol{\phi}| = +1$ and $\boldsymbol{\phi} \neq \mathbf{I}$. Equations A·54 are then satisfied by $\bar{r} = k\bar{u}$ where k is any scalar quantity and $\bar{u}$ the unit vector normal to the plane of $\boldsymbol{\phi} - \mathbf{I}$. This unique direction $\bar{u}$ is the proper rotation axis. If we define a proper rotation axis by the statement $k\bar{u} \cdot \boldsymbol{\phi} = \boldsymbol{\phi} \cdot k\bar{u} = k\bar{u}$, then every direction in a reflection plane is a proper rotation axis.

A direction $\bar{u}$ is said to be an improper rotation axis if

$$k\bar{u} \cdot \boldsymbol{\phi} = \boldsymbol{\phi} \cdot k\bar{u} = -k\bar{u} \qquad \text{[A·57]}$$

for every k. Since

$$|\boldsymbol{\phi} + \mathbf{I}| = (1 + \boldsymbol{\phi}_S)(|\boldsymbol{\phi}| + 1) \qquad \text{[A·58]}$$

Equations A·57 can be satisfied if $\boldsymbol{\phi}$ is improper or if $\boldsymbol{\phi}$ is proper with $\boldsymbol{\phi}_S = -1$. Equations A·57 are satisfied for any direction $\bar{u}$ if $\boldsymbol{\phi} = -\mathbf{I}$, for any direction $\bar{u}$ in a unique plane if $|\boldsymbol{\phi}| = +1$ with $\boldsymbol{\phi}_S = -1$, and by a unique direction $\bar{u}$ if $|\boldsymbol{\phi}| = -1$ and $\boldsymbol{\phi} \neq -\mathbf{I}$.

Equation A·49 shows that the vector $\boldsymbol{\phi}_V$ is parallel to the proper rotation axis of a proper dyadic and also parallel to the improper rotation axis of the corresponding improper dyadic.

Any dyadic $\mathbf{\Phi} = \mathbf{\Phi}_C^{-1}$ can be written in the form

$$\mathbf{\Phi} = \pm\{\bar{u}\bar{u} + (\mathbf{I} - \bar{u}\bar{u}) \cos \varphi + \mathbf{I} \times \bar{u} \sin \varphi\} \qquad [A \cdot 59]$$

where the upper sign corresponds to a proper and the lower sign to an improper character. $\bar{u}$ is the proper or improper rotation axis and φ is called the rotation angle. The scalar and the vector of the dyadic become

$$\mathbf{\Phi}_S = \pm(1 + 2 \cos \varphi), \quad \mathbf{\Phi}_V = \mp 2 \sin \varphi \, \bar{u} \qquad [A \cdot 60]$$

APPENDIX B

ELEMENTS OF GROUP THEORY

1. The Group Postulates

Suppose that a collection of elements

$$C_1, \ C_2, \ \cdots, \ C_j, \ \cdots \qquad [B\cdot 1]$$

is given. This collection, which may consist of a finite or an infinite number of elements, is said to be *closed* if there is given an associative law of combination such that with any two elements of the collection, taken in a definite order, is correlated a third element of the collection. Let C_j and C_k be two elements and let C_h be the element associated with the pair C_j, C_k taken in this order. The relationship is symbolically written

$$C_j \cdot C_k = C_h \qquad [B\cdot 2]$$

and C_h is called the product of C_j by C_k. The term product is used in an abstract sense and does not imply ordinary multiplication. In accordance with the postulate that the law of combination is associative we may write

$$C_h \cdot C_i = (C_j \cdot C_k) \cdot C_i = C_j \cdot C_k \cdot C_i = C_j \cdot (C_k \cdot C_i) \qquad [B\cdot 3]$$

The validity of the commutative law is neither assumed nor implied. Unless we have information to the opposite effect, it is therefore to be expected that the products $C_j \cdot C_k$ and $C_k \cdot C_j$ represent different elements of the collection. The commutative law may be valid as far as the product of certain elements is concerned, i.e.,

$$C_p \cdot C_q = C_q \cdot C_p \qquad [B\cdot 4]$$

and the elements C_p and C_q are then said to be commutative. If the relation B·4 holds for any two elements of the collection B·1, the collection is said to be commutative or Abelian with respect to the imposed law of combination.

Some examples of closed collections are:

I. The collection of all integers (positive, negative, and zero) with ordinary addition as law of combination.

II. The same collection as in example I, but with ordinary multiplication as the law of combination.

III. The collection of all elements $e^{j/n}$ where n is a given integer while $j = 0, 1, \cdots n - 1$ and with multiplication as law of combination.

IV. The collection of all vectors $L_1\bar{a}_1 + L_2\bar{a}_2 + L_3\bar{a}_3$ where L_1, L_2, L_3 are any three integers (positive, negative, and zero) and $\bar{a}_1, \bar{a}_2, \bar{a}_3$; the law of combination is vector addition.

Since the commutative law holds for scalar addition and multiplication as well as for vector addition, it follows that all four collections are Abelian. It is readily seen that the collection IV is no longer closed if the law of combination is changed to vector multiplication (unless we impose additional restrictions, for instance that $\bar{a}_1, \bar{a}_2, \bar{a}_3$ shall be orthogonal unit vectors).

We shall give a fifth example of a closed collection.

V. The collection of all dyadics of the type

$$\begin{aligned} & \phi_{11}\bar{b}_1\bar{a}_1 + \phi_{12}\bar{b}_2\bar{a}_1 + \phi_{13}\bar{b}_3\bar{a}_1 \\ \mathbf{\Phi} = & +\phi_{21}\bar{b}_1\bar{a}_2 + \phi_{22}\bar{b}_2\bar{a}_2 + \phi_{23}\bar{b}_3\bar{a}_2 \\ & +\phi_{31}\bar{b}_1\bar{a}_3 + \phi_{32}\bar{b}_2\bar{a}_3 + \phi_{33}\bar{b}_3\bar{a}_3 \end{aligned}$$

where $\bar{a}_1, \bar{a}_2, \bar{a}_3$ are given vectors, $\bar{b}_1, \bar{b}_2, \bar{b}_3$ the reciprocal vectors, and all ϕ_{jk} integers (positive, negative, or zero). The law of combination is scalar multiplication of dyadics (as defined in Equation A·35).

Since scalar products of dyadics do not obey the commutative law, the collection V is non-Abelian.

A closed collection is said to be a *group* if: for every element C_j there is an element E, called the identity element, such that $C_j \cdot E = E \cdot C_j = C_j$; and for every element C_j there is an element C_j^{-1}, called the inverse or reciprocal of C_j, such that $C_j \cdot C_j^{-1} = C_j^{-1} \cdot C_j = E$.

For the purpose of illustration let us find out if the collections given in the examples are groups. In the first example the integer zero is clearly the identity element and $-n$ is the inverse of the element n. The collection given in I is thus a group. In the second example the integer $+1$ satisfies the conditions imposed upon the identity element; but since the inverse of the element n, i.e., $1/n$, is not an element of the collection, it follows that the collection is not a group. The reader easily verifies that the collections given in examples III and IV are groups. The collection of example V has the idemfactor as identity element. However, the collection is not a group unless $|\mathbf{\Phi}| = \pm 1$, then otherwise the collection does not contain the reciprocal elements.

In the following we shall indicate the group nature of a collection by enclosing the collection (or the single symbol representing the collection) in parentheses. The number of different elements in a group (which may be finite or infinite) is called the order of the group. We shall write C_j^2 for $C_j \cdot C_j$, C_j^3 for $C_j \cdot C_j \cdot C_j$, and so on. Clearly, if C is an element of a group (G), all powers of C must be contained in (G). All powers of an element C need not be different, however, for there may exist a finite integer n such that

$$C^n = E \qquad \text{[B·5]}$$

Then $C^{n+1} = C$, $C^{n+2} = C^2$, and so forth. Hence, if n is the smallest integer for which the relation B·5 holds, there are only n different powers of C. Since $C^j \cdot C^{n-j} = C^{n-j} \cdot C^j = E$, $C^{n-j} \equiv C^{-j}$ is the element reciprocal to C^j. An element C which satisfies Equation B·5 is said to be of order n, and the collection of all powers of C evidently is a group of order n

$$(C) = (C, C^2, \cdots, C^{n-1}, C^n\ (= E)) \qquad \text{[B·6]}$$

A group of the type shown in B·6, in which all elements are powers of a single element, is called a cyclic group. All cyclic groups are Abelian, but the converse statement is not true.

2. Subgroups

If a collection consisting of some elements of a group (G) satisfies the group postulates, the collection is called a subgroup of (G). Every group has two trivial subgroups, namely, the group itself and the group consisting of the identity element alone.

We showed that the collection given in example I is a group and it is readily seen that the collection of all even integers (including zero) is a subgroup.

Suppose that $(H) = (E, H_1, H_2, \cdots)$ is a subgroup of (G) and let X be an element of (G). By the products $X \cdot (H)$ and $(H) \cdot X$ one understands the collections

$$\begin{aligned} X \cdot (H) &= X, X \cdot H_1, X \cdot H_2, \cdots \\ (H) \cdot X &= X, H_1 \cdot X, H_2 \cdot X, \cdots \end{aligned} \qquad \text{[B·7]}$$

All the elements of either collection are evidently different from one another, and they are all elements of (G). The two collections of B·7 are not in general identical.

If X lies in (H) all elements $X \cdot (H)$ (or $(H) \cdot X$) must also lie in (H), but since all are different $X \cdot (H)$ and (H) must be identical, i.e.,

$$X \cdot (H) = (H) \cdot X = (H) \qquad \text{[B·8]}$$

for any element X of any group (H).

Suppose now that the element X of Equation B·7 is an element of (G) which does not lie in the subgroup (H). The collection $X \cdot (H)$ is then called a right coset of (G) under the subgroup (H), whereas $(H) \cdot X$ is a left coset. It is easily shown that the subgroup (H) and the coset $X \cdot (H)$ (or the coset $(H) \cdot X$) can have no common element: if there were a common element one would have $H_j = X \cdot H_k$, hence $X = H_j \cdot H_k^{-1}$, and X would lie in (H) contradicting our assumption. Thus, if n_1 is the order of (H), the two collections (H) and $X \cdot (H)$ contain together $2n_1$ elements of (G). If Y is an element of (G) not lying in (H) nor in $X \cdot (H)$, there must be a coset $Y \cdot (H)$. Continuing this process all elements of (G) will eventually be used up; in other words, all elements of (G) will have been gathered into cosets as follows.

$$\begin{aligned} (G) &= (H), X \cdot (H), Y \cdot (H), \cdots \\ (G) &= (H), (H) \cdot X, (H) \cdot Y', \cdots \end{aligned} \qquad [B\cdot 9]$$

We shall refer to Equations B·9 as expansions of the group (G) in right or left cosets under the subgroup (H). Each coset contains n_1 elements, and it follows that the order of the group (G) is a multiple of the order of the subgroup (H). The ratio between the orders of (G) and (H) is called the index of (H) in (G). Hence the index is equal to the number of cosets in the expansion. The cosets in right and left expansion may be different, i.e., $X \cdot (H) \neq (H) \cdot X$, $Y \neq Y'$, and so on. The expansions of Equations B·9 will be conveniently written as follows.

$$\begin{aligned} (G) &= (H), X \cdot (H), Y \cdot (H) \cdots = (H) \cdot [E', X, Y, \cdots] \\ (G) &= (H), (H) \cdot X, (H) \cdot Y \cdots = [E', X, Y' \cdots] \cdot (H) \end{aligned} \qquad [B\cdot 10]$$

where the collections $E, X, Y, \cdots$ and $E, X, Y', \cdots$ need not be identical, nor are they necessarily groups.

When (H) is a subgroup of index two we have

$$(G) = (H), X \cdot (H) = (H), (H) \cdot X$$

and hence

$$X \cdot (H) = (H) \cdot X \quad \text{or} \quad (H) = X^{-1} \cdot (H) \cdot X \qquad [B\cdot 11]$$

Let X and Y be any two non-commuting elements of a group (G). The two products $X \cdot Y$ and $Y \cdot X$ are then two different elements of (G), i.e.,

$$A = X \cdot Y, \quad B = Y \cdot X \qquad [B\cdot 12]$$

The two elements A and B, i.e., the two products $X \cdot Y$ and $Y \cdot X$, are called conjugate elements. Eliminating Y we have

$$B = X^{-1} \cdot A \cdot X \quad \text{or} \quad X \cdot B = A \cdot X \qquad [B\cdot 13]$$

which can be used instead of Equations B·12 as definition of conjugate elements. Similarly if

$$(K) = X^{-1} \cdot (H) \cdot X \quad \text{or} \quad X \cdot (K) = (H) \cdot X \qquad [B\cdot 14]$$

(K) and (H) are called conjugate subgroups; (H) is assumed to be a subgroup of (G) and X any element of (G). It is readily proved that (K) actually is a subgroup of (G). Suppose that $H_i \cdot H_j = H_k$. Then $X^{-1} \cdot H_i \cdot X \cdot X^{-1} \cdot H_j \cdot X = X^{-1} \cdot H_k \cdot X$ and (K) consequently is a closed collection. Since $X^{-1} \cdot E \cdot X = E$ the collection (K) contains the identity element. Finally $X^{-1} \cdot H_j \cdot X \cdot X^{-1} \cdot H_j^{-1} \cdot X = E$ showing that (K) contains the inverse of any elements. Hence the collection (K) is a group, and since all elements of (K) evidently are elements of (G), (K) is a subgroup of (G).

Suppose that a subgroup (H) of (G) satisfies the condition

$$(H) = X^{-1} \cdot (H) \cdot X \qquad [B\cdot 15]$$

for every element X of (G). (H) is then said to be an invariant (or selfconjugate) subgroup of (G). It is shown by Equation B·11 that any subgroup of index two is an invariant subgroup.

Imagine a group (G) with an invariant subgroup (H) to be expanded in cosets. According to the definition B·15 we shall then have

$$\begin{aligned} (G) &= (H),\ X \cdot (H),\ Y \cdot (H), \cdots \\ &= (H),\ (H) \cdot X,\ (H) \cdot Y, \cdots \end{aligned} \qquad [B\cdot 16]$$

i.e., right and left cosets are identical. We shall next prove that the collection of cosets in the expansion B·16 is a group. It needs to be shown that the collection of cosets is closed, that it contains an identity element, and that it contains the inverse of any element. Let $X \cdot (H)$ and $Y \cdot (H)$ be any two cosets in the expansion. It is clear that the expansion also must contain the cosets $X \cdot Y \cdot (H)$, $X^{-1} \cdot (H)$, and $Y^{-1} \cdot (H)$ (these cosets need not be different from $X \cdot (H)$ or $Y \cdot (H)$ or from one another). Since $X \cdot (H) \cdot Y \cdot (H) = X \cdot (H) \cdot (H) \cdot Y = X \cdot (H) \cdot Y = X \cdot Y \cdot (H)$ (where we have made use of the assumption that (H) is an invariant subgroup) it follows that the collection of cosets is closed. Since $(H) \cdot (H) = (H)$ and $(H) \cdot X \cdot (H) = X \cdot (H) = (H) \cdot X$, the subgroup (H) itself is the identity element of the collection of cosets. Finally $X \cdot (H) \cdot X^{-1} \cdot (H) = (H)$ showing that $X \cdot (H)$ and $X^{-1} \cdot (H)$ are inverse elements. In accordance with B·10 we shall write

$$\begin{aligned} (G) &= (H) \cdot (E', X, Y, \cdots) \\ &= (E', X, Y, \cdots) \cdot (H) \end{aligned} \qquad [B\cdot 17]$$

where, as a consequence of the proof just given, $(E', X, Y, \cdots)$ is a group. We have here written E' instead of E to indicate that E' represents any element of (H). (We must have $E' \cdot (H) = (H)$, and this condition is satisfied if E' is any element of (H).) The group $(E', X, Y \cdots)$ is called the factor group of (H), and it is usually designated by the symbol (G/H), i.e.,

$$(H) \cdot (G/H) = (G/H) \cdot (H) = (G) \qquad \text{[B·18]}$$

Let (K) and (L) be two subgroups of a group (G) such that (K) and (L) have no other common element than the identity and such that the order of (G) is the product of the orders of (K) and (L). It can then be shown that

$$(G) = (K) \cdot (L) = (L) \cdot (K) \qquad \text{[B·19]}$$

and (G) is said to be the direct product of the subgroups (K) and (L). In accordance with this terminology the group (G) in Equations B·17 and B·18 is written as the direct product of the invariant subgroup (H) and the factor group (G/H). The statement in Equation B·19 is evidently proved if it can be shown that all elements in $(K) \cdot (L)$ (or in $(L) \cdot (K)$) are different from one another. Suppose then that two elements are equal, say $K_i \cdot L_j = K_p \cdot L_q$, where the pair of subscripts i, j is different from the pair p, q. It follows that $K_p^{-1} \cdot K_i = L_q \cdot L_j^{-1}$. The left side of this equation represents an element of (K) while the right side is an element of (L). Since, by postulate, the identity E is the only common element of (K) and (L), we must have $i = j$ and $p = q$. Hence all elements of the collection $(K) \cdot (L)$ are different and the collection $(K) \cdot (L)$ must be identical with the group (G).

Conversely: if (K) and (L) are known to be two groups having no other common element than the identity, then the product $(K) \cdot (L)$ is a group if

$$(K) \cdot (L) = (L) \cdot (K) \qquad \text{[B·20]}$$

This condition must be used in connection with the synthesis of new groups from a set of given groups.

3. Isomorphic Groups

A group (G) is said to have an $n:1$ isomorphism with a group (g) if the following conditions are fulfilled. To any one element X_j of (G) corresponds a unique element x of (g), but to any one element x of (g) correspond n elements $X_1, X_2, \cdots X_j \cdots X_n$ of (G). To the product $X_j \cdot Y_k$ in (G) corresponds the product $x \cdot y$ in (g) where x corresponds to X_j and y to Y_k. If (G) has a $1:1$ isomorphism with a group (g), the two groups (G) and (g) are said to be simply isomorphic.

The elements $H_1, H_2, \cdots H_j \cdots H_n$ in (G) which correspond to the identity element in (g) form an invariant subgroup (H) of (G).

This theorem is readily proved. Since both H_j and H_k correspond to the identity element e in (g) also $H_j \cdot H_k$ corresponds to e. Hence $H_1, H_2, \cdots H_n$ form a subgroup (H) of (G). If G_j is any element of (G) and g_j the corresponding element of (g), then the elements $G_j^{-1} \cdot (H) \cdot G_j$ of (G) correspond to the element $g_j^{-1} \cdot e \cdot g_j = e$ of (g). But the subgroup (H) of (G) corresponds to the identity element of (g). Consequently $(H) = G_j^{-1} \cdot (H) \cdot G_j$ and (H) is an invariant subgroup.

Clearly, a group (G) has an $n : 1$ isomorphism with the factor group (G/H) where n is the order of the invariant subgroup (H).

Suppose that (G) and (G') are simply isomorphic groups. If (H) is a subgroup of (G), it is obviously true that the collection (H') in (G') corresponding to (H) in (G) is a subgroup of (G'). Similarly, if (G) can be written as the direct product of two subgroups, the isomorphic group (G') can be written as the direct product of the two corresponding subgroups.

INDEX

A CATALOG OF SELECTED

DOVER BOOKS

IN SCIENCE AND MATHEMATICS

RELATIVITY, THERMODYNAMICS AND COSMOLOGY, Richard C. Tolman. Landmark study extends thermodynamics to special, general relativity; also applications of relativistic mechanics, thermodynamics to cosmological models. 501pp. 5⅜ × 8½. 65383-8 Pa. $12.95

APPLIED ANALYSIS, Cornelius Lanczos. Classic work on analysis and design of finite processes for approximating solution of analytical problems. Algebraic equations, matrices, harmonic analysis, quadrature methods, much more. 559pp. 5⅜ × 8½. 65656-X Pa. $13.95

SPECIAL RELATIVITY FOR PHYSICISTS, G. Stephenson and C.W. Kilmister. Concise elegant account for nonspecialists. Lorentz transformation, optical and dynamical applications, more. Bibliography. 108pp. 5⅜ × 8½. 65519-9 Pa. $4.95

INTRODUCTION TO ANALYSIS, Maxwell Rosenlicht. Unusually clear, accessible coverage of set theory, real number system, metric spaces, continuous functions, Riemann integration, multiple integrals, more. Wide range of problems. Undergraduate level. Bibliography. 254pp. 5⅜ × 8½. 65038-3 Pa. $7.95

INTRODUCTION TO QUANTUM MECHANICS With Applications to Chemistry, Linus Pauling & E. Bright Wilson, Jr. Classic undergraduate text by Nobel Prize winner applies quantum mechanics to chemical and physical problems. Numerous tables and figures enhance the text. Chapter bibliographies. Appendices. Index. 468pp. 5⅜ × 8½. 64871-0 Pa. $11.95

ASYMPTOTIC EXPANSIONS OF INTEGRALS, Norman Bleistein & Richard A. Handelsman. Best introduction to important field with applications in a variety of scientific disciplines. New preface. Problems. Diagrams. Tables. Bibliography. Index. 448pp. 5⅜ × 8½. 65082-0 Pa. $12.95

MATHEMATICS APPLIED TO CONTINUUM MECHANICS, Lee A. Segel. Analyzes models of fluid flow and solid deformation. For upper-level math, science and engineering students. 608pp. 5⅜ × 8½. 65369-2 Pa. $13.95

ELEMENTS OF REAL ANALYSIS, David A. Sprecher. Classic text covers fundamental concepts, real number system, point sets, functions of a real variable, Fourier series, much more. Over 500 exercises. 352pp. 5⅜ × 8½. 65385-4 Pa. $10.95

PHYSICAL PRINCIPLES OF THE QUANTUM THEORY, Werner Heisenberg. Nobel Laureate discusses quantum theory, uncertainty, wave mechanics, work of Dirac, Schroedinger, Compton, Wilson, Einstein, etc. 184pp. 5⅜ × 8½. 60113-7 Pa. $5.95

INTRODUCTORY REAL ANALYSIS, A.N. Kolmogorov, S.V. Fomin. Translated by Richard A. Silverman. Self-contained, evenly paced introduction to real and functional analysis. Some 350 problems. 403pp. 5⅜ × 8½. 61226-0 Pa. $9.95

PROBLEMS AND SOLUTIONS IN QUANTUM CHEMISTRY AND PHYSICS, Charles S. Johnson, Jr. and Lee G. Pedersen. Unusually varied problems, detailed solutions in coverage of quantum mechanics, wave mechanics, angular momentum, molecular spectroscopy, scattering theory, more. 280 problems plus 139 supplementary exercises. 430pp. 6½ × 9¼. 65236-X Pa. $12.95

GEOMETRY OF COMPLEX NUMBERS, Hans Schwerdtfeger. Illuminating, widely praised book on analytic geometry of circles, the Moebius transformation, and two-dimensional non-Euclidean geometries. 200pp. 5⅜ × 8¼.
63830-8 Pa. $8.95

MECHANICS, J.P. Den Hartog. A classic introductory text or refresher. Hundreds of applications and design problems illuminate fundamentals of trusses, loaded beams and cables, etc. 334 answered problems. 462pp. 5⅜ × 8½. 60754-2 Pa. $9.95

TOPOLOGY, John G. Hocking and Gail S. Young. Superb one-year course in classical topology. Topological spaces and functions, point-set topology, much more. Examples and problems. Bibliography. Index. 384pp. 5⅜ × 8¼.
65676-4 Pa. $9.95

STRENGTH OF MATERIALS, J.P. Den Hartog. Full, clear treatment of basic material (tension, torsion, bending, etc.) plus advanced material on engineering methods, applications. 350 answered problems. 323pp. 5⅜ × 8½. 60755-0 Pa. $8.95

ELEMENTARY CONCEPTS OF TOPOLOGY, Paul Alexandroff. Elegant, intuitive approach to topology from set-theoretic topology to Betti groups; how concepts of topology are useful in math and physics. 25 figures. 57pp. 5⅜ × 8½.
60747-X Pa. $3.50

ADVANCED STRENGTH OF MATERIALS, J.P. Den Hartog. Superbly written advanced text covers torsion, rotating disks, membrane stresses in shells, much more. Many problems and answers. 388pp. 5⅜ × 8½. 65407-9 Pa. $9.95

COMPUTABILITY AND UNSOLVABILITY, Martin Davis. Classic graduate-level introduction to theory of computability, usually referred to as theory of recurrent functions. New preface and appendix. 288pp. 5⅜ × 8½. 61471-9 Pa. $7.95

GENERAL CHEMISTRY, Linus Pauling. Revised 3rd edition of classic first-year text by Nobel laureate. Atomic and molecular structure, quantum mechanics, statistical mechanics, thermodynamics correlated with descriptive chemistry. Problems. 992pp. 5⅜ × 8½. 65622-5 Pa. $19.95

AN INTRODUCTION TO MATRICES, SETS AND GROUPS FOR SCIENCE STUDENTS, G. Stephenson. Concise, readable text introduces sets, groups, and most importantly, matrices to undergraduate students of physics, chemistry, and engineering. Problems. 164pp. 5⅜ × 8½. 65077-4 Pa. $6.95

THE HISTORICAL BACKGROUND OF CHEMISTRY, Henry M. Leicester. Evolution of ideas, not individual biography. Concentrates on formulation of a coherent set of chemical laws. 260pp. 5⅜ × 8½. 61053-5 Pa. $6.95

THE PHILOSOPHY OF MATHEMATICS: An Introductory Essay, Stephan Körner. Surveys the views of Plato, Aristotle, Leibniz & Kant concerning propositions and theories of applied and pure mathematics. Introduction. Two appendices. Index. 198pp. 5⅜ × 8½. 25048-2 Pa. $7.95

THE DEVELOPMENT OF MODERN CHEMISTRY, Aaron J. Ihde. Authoritative history of chemistry from ancient Greek theory to 20th-century innovation. Covers major chemists and their discoveries. 209 illustrations. 14 tables. Bibliographies. Indices. Appendices. 851pp. 5⅜ × 8½. 64235-6 Pa. $18.95

THE FOUR-COLOR PROBLEM: Assaults and Conquest, Thomas L. Saaty and Paul G. Kainen. Engrossing, comprehensive account of the century-old combinatorial topological problem, its history and solution. Bibliographies. Index. 110 figures. 228pp. 5⅜ × 8½. 65092-8 Pa. $6.95

CATALYSIS IN CHEMISTRY AND ENZYMOLOGY, William P. Jencks. Exceptionally clear coverage of mechanisms for catalysis, forces in aqueous solution, carbonyl- and acyl-group reactions, practical kinetics, more. 864pp. 5⅜ × 8½. 65460-5 Pa. $19.95

PROBABILITY: An Introduction, Samuel Goldberg. Excellent basic text covers set theory, probability theory for finite sample spaces, binomial theorem, much more. 360 problems. Bibliographies. 322pp. 5⅜ × 8½. 65252-1 Pa. $8.95

LIGHTNING, Martin A. Uman. Revised, updated edition of classic work on the physics of lightning. Phenomena, terminology, measurement, photography, spectroscopy, thunder, more. Reviews recent research. Bibliography. Indices. 320pp. 5⅜ × 8¼. 64575-4 Pa. $8.95

PROBABILITY THEORY: A Concise Course, Y.A. Rozanov. Highly readable, self-contained introduction covers combination of events, dependent events, Bernoulli trials, etc. Translation by Richard Silverman. 148pp. 5⅜ × 8¼. 63544-9 Pa. $5.95

AN INTRODUCTION TO HAMILTONIAN OPTICS, H. A. Buchdahl. Detailed account of the Hamiltonian treatment of aberration theory in geometrical optics. Many classes of optical systems defined in terms of the symmetries they possess. Problems with detailed solutions. 1970 edition. xv + 360pp. 5⅜ × 8½. 67597-1 Pa. $10.95

STATISTICS MANUAL, Edwin L. Crow, et al. Comprehensive, practical collection of classical and modern methods prepared by U.S. Naval Ordnance Test Station. Stress on use. Basics of statistics assumed. 288pp. 5⅜ × 8½. 60599-X Pa. $6.95

DICTIONARY/OUTLINE OF BASIC STATISTICS, John E. Freund and Frank J. Williams. A clear concise dictionary of over 1,000 statistical terms and an outline of statistical formulas covering probability, nonparametric tests, much more. 208pp. 5⅜ × 8½. 66796-0 Pa. $6.95

STATISTICAL METHOD FROM THE VIEWPOINT OF QUALITY CONTROL, Walter A. Shewhart. Important text explains regulation of variables, uses of statistical control to achieve quality control in industry, agriculture, other areas. 192pp. 5⅜ × 8½. 65232-7 Pa. $7.95

THE INTERPRETATION OF GEOLOGICAL PHASE DIAGRAMS, Ernest G. Ehlers. Clear, concise text emphasizes diagrams of systems under fluid or containing pressure; also coverage of complex binary systems, hydrothermal melting, more. 288pp. 6½ × 9¼. 65389-7 Pa. $10.95

STATISTICAL ADJUSTMENT OF DATA, W. Edwards Deming. Introduction to basic concepts of statistics, curve fitting, least squares solution, conditions without parameter, conditions containing parameters. 26 exercises worked out. 271pp. 5⅜ × 8½. 64685-8 Pa. $8.95